Love Unknown

Love Unknown

Women's Prayers and Poems Down the Ages

Compiled by
Monica Furlong

Hodder & Stoughton
LONDON SYDNEY AUCKLAND

First published in Great Britain in 2001, by arrangement with
SkyLight Paths Publishing, USA.

The right of Monica Furlong to be identified as the Author of
the Work has been asserted by her in accordance with the
Copyright, Designs and Patents Act 1988.

10 9 8 7 6 5 4 3 2 1

British Library Cataloguing in Publication Data
A record for this book is available from the British Library

ISBN 0 340 78526 8

Offest by Avon DataSet Ltd, Bidford on Avon, Warwickshire
Printed and bound in Great Britain by Clays Ltd, St Ives plc

Hodder & Stoughton
A Division of Hodder Headline Ltd
338 Euston Road
London NW1 3BH

Contents

Introduction

Prayer, to pray, are words that are so much part of our language that we rarely examine the idea and ask what it means. The obvious meaning, the one that a child would probably give if asked to define the word prayer, is "talking to God" or "asking God for something." Many of us, whether we believe in God or not, find ourselves blindly asking for help when our need is great enough — it is an aspect of our helplessness in the face of illness, death, bereavement, and other painful aspects of being human. The idea of talking to God opens up a vista. It beckons us out of a purely human perspective, and invites us to try to see the world, and ourselves within it, from a different angle. "It draws God who is great into a heart which is small" said Mechthild of Magdeburg. It is almost like the experience of the early astronauts, looking at earth from distant space instead of from a position on the earth itself. They found that first external vision astonishing, a source of wonder, and perhaps they experienced an impulse to reassess the human place within a much vaster context.

Mystics of all cultures have been similarly affected by a sense of wonder and vastness as they contemplated the presence of God. It is part of the human condition that we get stuck in our own local perspective. For example, I bring the limitations of my own perspective both to the selection of this material and to my understanding of it. How could it be otherwise? These are the limitations of a white Western Christian. To many from different cultures and from different religions, the emphases would be different. Geographically, nationally, intellectually, and emotionally, our natural tendency seems to be provincial, chauvinistic, lacking in imagination about, and sympathy for, what we do not directly know, though we can and should struggle against this blindness. But our personal experience, our joys, our loves, our worries, our labors, and our sorrows fill our consciousness until our personal concerns can block out all else. The great religions of the world, however, have always reminded us that we need release from that cramped perspective. We need stories, festivals,

Sabbaths, ceremonies, meditations to jolt us out of our pathetic narrowmindedness, our obsession with the internal village street. They remind us that we are bigger than our egos, that we belong to a larger enterprise altogether. And many of those stories, festivals, and ceremonies, though they differ from culture to culture and country to country, have centered on the idea of God.

God has been many things to many people—the sun, the moon, dancing energy, life force, creator, king, judge, lawgiver, father, mother, the earth itself, as well as being manifested in animal form. To the Jews, God has been a transforming presence who gave them a powerful identity and sustained them through centuries of dispersal. To them and to others suffering terrible forms of oppression, God has been a witness at a time when they had no other. To the saints, God has been a lover. The section "Love Unknown" in this collection shows what a poignant experience that has been. To women of our own time, to some of the medieval saints both male and female, and to some native peoples, God has been seen as mother, the source of earth's fertility. In classical Greek culture, the gods were a screen for preoccupations as old as human experience: love, sexual passion, war, art, domestic life, and the pleasures of reason.

Buddhism—on the whole avoiding the concept of God, though some Buddhists do retain it—is concerned with a somewhat different method of freeing its followers from their imprisonment in the "passing show" or "the chatter in the skull." The discipline of meditation can take many forms, but like the God-concept it helps to bring about a freeing, slow or immediate, to which the name *enlightenment* is usually given.

Prayer, then, which may take the form of meditation as well as the simpler forms of asking, or thanksgiving, or praying for others, is about a shift of consciousness, or at least an attempt at a shift of consciousness, to a new perspective. If we are less preoccupied with ourselves we are less likely to see others as competitive egos or deadly rivals. Many religions suggest that in some sense we *are* one another. The Anglican poet John Donne famously said that we are not islands—"No man is an island"—but all human beings are "part of the main." Rabbi Shmelke of Nikolsberg said that to strike another human being is like striking ourselves—it is bound to cause us suffering.

Prayer *for* other human beings involves us in their well-being, their health and happiness, and religion has often encouraged its adherents to carry their prayer forward into practical concern—to feed the hungry and house the homeless. Late in the twentieth century and on into the twenty-first, many have started praying also for the earth and its creatures, as the threat to *its* health and survival has become ever plainer. Tribal peoples have usually had an acute awareness of the welfare of the natural world, since their survival depended very directly on the animals and plants that they hunted and gathered. In more "sophisticated" and industrialized cultures, where for generations townspeople have had little to do with the growing or gathering of food, this knowledge is returning only slowly. Some of these prayers indicate a deep, and sometimes tragic, concern for human carelessness about nature. If people need to be cherished, healed, and sustained, then so does the natural world, Westerners are painfully learning. Having lost the old awe and wonder in the face of nature, modern civilizations have plundered the earth, destroying habitats, poisoning waters, hunting or fishing creatures to extinction. The only way back from this desperate situation is a new perspective, a collective turning away from the ego and its greed that all religions have taught.

So prayer is about a new perspective on the world about us, or perhaps the recovery of an earlier perspective. It is about a rediscovery of awe and wonder, of love and joy, of a transforming of grief and pain and loss, of a turning to one another and to the world in which we find ourselves. All this is its territory.

AN ATTITUDE OF MIND

You will notice that not all the contributions to this book are in the traditional forms that we associate with prayer—some are poems, some pieces of prose. Some are songs delighting in the earth and the pleasure of living upon it, some explore relationship with God, some are about daily life, others are about the huge adventures of birth and death. Some freely express joy, others grief. A few are very angry. All of them, however, without exception, are in my view about the perspective that prayer gives. As I made the collection I realized how blurred, at least in my mind, was the distinction between what is a prayer and what is not. It is not necessarily a piece of prose that begins by addressing God directly—in fact, some pieces of writing that do this feel anything but prayerful. A prayer, I came to feel, is always about an attitude of mind that lifts experience out of a narrow context and perceives the beauty, and sometimes the terror, with which all our lives are shot through. Some inkling of awe is perhaps the common ingredient. I invite you to approach these selections without expectations, as a way of discovering the attitude of prayer in both traditional and very unexpected places.

THE VOICE OF THE SILENT

And women's prayers? What is it about women's prayers that make them need a book to themselves? Are women's voices so different from men's?

It is the unanswerability of that last question that explains the need for a book like this.

For it is only in the last twenty to thirty years (a very short time in the long span of human culture) that women's voices have been raised—at least in large numbers—in public prayer.

In most religious cultures throughout history, for a complex variety of reasons, women have been silent. In Christianity, the advice of St. Paul to the Corinthian congregation in the middle of the first century—that "women should be silent in the churches"—was observed with an unquestioning precision so that up until the 1960s, and much later in some cases, women did not preach in churches, or, often enough, read or sing in choirs. (There were exceptions to this. The Shakers were led by a woman, Ann Lee; the early Methodists allowed women to speak in public and to take services; and the Society of Friends has always allowed an exceptional role to women.) The enforced silence of women was especially tragic, since increasing evidence shows that it was not like that at the beginning of Christianity. Women played a key part in establishing the early Christian churches and, as the story of Perpetua reveals, were prepared to suffer as martyrs alongside the men and to be vocal about their reasons. But as so often happens, a sense of propriety killed the early liberation; the early churches, eager to acquire adherents, worried about "what people might think."

In Judaism, too—from which, of course, the Christians borrowed extensively—women had a very limited public role, partly because, as in so many older cultures, women seemed somehow subsumed in the family as daughter, wife, or widow. Scholars point out how often women in ancient scriptures are not named—even poor Jephtha's daughter, required to give up her life for her people, is not allowed an individual identity beyond being her father's child.

It is not easy for us now to get into the mind-set that saw women simply as adjuncts of men—one that very often deprived women of education and denied many of their gifts. But I do not think it helps for modern women to view the past as a kind of male conspiracy to keep women down, because the blindness around the assumptions were so universal, among women as well as men, that almost no one, women or men, saw through them before the Enlightenment brought them into question. Perhaps this was because women were so demonstrably constrained by the huge burden of childbearing. Until very recent times it was common for married women to give birth as many as ten times, and even if they survived the constant experience of pregnancy and childbirth (and many did not), that, and the laborious running of a home, left them little time for a public role. Nor were unmarried women notably freer, except in remote instances where they owned private wealth. The life of Christina Rossetti shows the domestic labor that was expected of a daughter, even if, as in Christina's case, she was more gifted than her brother — from whom, of course, no domestic labor was expected.

There *were* women who survived or overcame their multiple handicaps — Christina Rossetti is one of them — and wrote prayers and poems that achieved publication, but many must have been lost, since women's writing was not prized, and many women lacked the contacts enjoyed by Christina in her search for a publisher.

Christina is part of the long procession of women, a kind of underground stream, who from early in history had tried to express themselves in writing, very often on religious themes, but whose work only broke surface very occasionally.

EARLY WRITING BY WOMEN

Among the earliest prayers and poems by women that we have are those of Sappho. They are fragments of astonishing beauty and simplicity; religion and secular concerns are meshed together, as in so much early writing. The next rising of the spring was not until the Middle Ages, hundreds of years later, when a formidable group of religious women began to express themselves in prose and poetry. It is not surprising that quite a lot of this writing emerged either from convents, or from convent-educated women. Convents, which often had excellent libraries, were among the few places where women could obtain a good education, and nuns were some of the few women who had the leisure as well as the skills to be able to read. Heloise and Beatrijs of Nazareth were, because of convent education, able to read and write in Latin. Hildegard of Bingen, who was brought up by her hermit aunt from the age of about eight, was painfully aware that her Latin was not good. Many medieval women could not read and write at all, while some could read but not write (the more difficult skill of the two). The fourteenth-century

Margery Kempe, the mother of fourteen children, minded bitterly that she could not read and write, and was obliged to employ an amanuensis to write down her religious thoughts.

Most of those who could read and write were unlike Heloise or Hildegard in knowing Latin, and could only write in the vernacular: the local dialect of their country. This excluded them from public religious discourse, which traditionally took place in Latin. Suddenly, however, in the early medieval period, there was a kind of democratic movement in the world of religion—an uprush of writing in the vernacular by men as well as women—and many women were at last liberated to write. Angela of Foligno, Hadewijch of Brabrant, Mechthild of Magdeburg, Catherine of Siena, Beatrijs of Nazareth (who chose the Flemish dialect as her medium although she was a Latin scholar), and perhaps the most important, Julian of Norwich, were among them, to our lasting gain. The Beguines, the lay movement for women in Northern Europe, which included as members women who lived alone and others who lived together in small communities, not only performed good works among the poor, but also ran schools and probably taught adults to read and write. The Beguines produced many distinguished writers.

Many of these women writers were widely read across Europe, by men as well as women, perhaps because they often wrote powerfully about their experiences rather than expounding arguments and doctrines. One of the Beguines, Marguerite Porete, wrote a book so influential that it got her burned by the Inquisition, and in the wake of this disaster one or two Beguines joined more conventional religious orders, probably as a form of protection. What is remarkable—what perhaps clinched the women's literary success—was both the personal note with which they often wrote, as well as the passion with which they wrote of their love for God.

At about the same time, in other parts of the world, other women—a very few—were also emerging from obscurity, the Sufi mystic Rabi'a and the Hindu mystic Mirabai among them. The religious passion that they express is interestingly similar to that of their European counterparts.

Women's religious and other writing then went underground again, though there were moments when it reappeared with distinction—in particular in the work of Teresa of Ávila.

THE MODERN ERA

In the nineteenth century, Western women were slowly beginning to formulate their resentment at exclusion from the field of religion (and, of course, from other areas), putting down roots of dissent that were to flower in the twentieth century. The American Elizabeth Cady Stanton criticized the way in which the Bible was used to keep women subordinate. In England, the attempt to forbid women to stand as candidates for the new lay church councils in England brought about what a historian calls "the first clear statement of Christian feminism." There was a flowering of women's religious writing, particularly as far as hymn writing was concerned. Anna Laetitia Waring, Cecil Frances Alexander, Frances Ridley Havergal, Maria Willis, and Christina Rossetti herself all wrote excellent hymns that generations of Christians have sung, and I was delighted to include some of them in this book. If we find in them what, for the modern woman's taste, seems an excessive emphasis on self-surrender, on the speaker's extreme sinfulness and general unworthiness, nevertheless the passion of the work and the skill of the writing still make them very appealing—an important milestone on women's long journey to be treated as fully equal and human.

But the acceptance of women as full participants on the religious scene had a long journey ahead of it and is still not complete. Examining books of prayers edited by male clergy as late as the 1960s and 1970s, it is still possible to find women's voices almost entirely absent, as if none of the great medieval writers or the nineteenth-century hymn writers had existed.

But change was coming, and coming fast. It came partly because, throughout the twentieth century, women were becoming emancipated, moving from obtaining the franchise to full secondary and tertiary education, and thence to professional status, economic parity, control of their fertility, and the other changes we now, in the West, take for granted. One of the results of this was that women at last had the confidence to contest their lowly status in church and synagogue. Spreading through Presbyterian, Baptist, and Methodist churches was a demand that women should be ordained as ministers, and this was taken up by Episcopal churches in the United States, Britain, and other parts of the world. This change did not come easily, at least in the Episcopal churches, and as the struggle continued, women, and sometimes women and men together, banded into prayer groups, house churches, and small movements designed to advance women's ministry.

This produced a flowering of liturgy, written not by clergy but by ordinary worshipers who wanted religious services to express *their* concerns, and who were exasperated at the way language of the "Dearly beloved brethren" type had excluded women.

Judaism too moved to ordain women as rabbis, though in Judaism as in Christianity, the more conservative groups felt unable to support such a change. In Judaism too there was a flowering of women's prayers. At about the same time, Western Buddhism also began to offer women more leadership roles. But perhaps in all religions there have always been some women, like the Hindu Mirabai, who broke the mold, though word of them has not always been preserved.

Moving toward a new sense of identity in religions that had kept them silent and subordinate, Christian and Jewish women alike had to struggle with scriptures in which women were excluded from much of the action. For this reason, certain passages of the Bible—the song of Miriam, the story of Ruth and Naomi (a very moving account of solidarity between women), and the Wisdom literature in which wisdom, an aspect of God, is given a feminine persona—all became very important to women urging change. Christians relished these passages as well as the significance of the fact—often obscured in liturgy and teaching—that it was a woman, Mary Magdalene, who made the first momentous announcement of the Resurrection.

The new thinking about women produced predictable upheavals. Many women in synagogues and churches, who had unthinkingly gone along with their silent and lowly status in the past, began to raise difficult questions. (Other women, it must be said, were equally indignant that the issues had been raised at all.) Some left institutional religion for small prayer groups or for religious bodies like the Quakers, whose attitudes to women had been more exemplary. Many left organized religion altogether. Others sought religious expression by seeking out ancient forms of worship from far-distant periods of history, when, supposedly, matriarchy had ruled. But something significant had happened. Women were no longer prepared to be silent in churches and synagogues. They had found their voices after the centuries of suppression, and discovered that they were strong and often lyrical. Just as, in singing, women's voices complement men's voices in choirs, so in their perceptions, their understanding, and their particular wisdoms they could add something of value to religious discourse. It is not, probably, that women are so very different from men—it is rather that their life experience often has been, and still is, a very different one.

So are women's prayers turning out to be significantly different from men's prayers? It is perhaps too soon to know, though this collection of prayers and poems may go a little way to suggest a conclusion.

FINDING OUR ROOTS

One striking feature is that modern women's prayers and perspective are often taken up with "roots," with reestablishing a partially lost identity, as well as self-esteem, as they seek to restore some of what has been suppressed and to put themselves in a landscape in which there is continuity with a female past that has been largely obliterated: the generations of women who had no names, could not read or write, and were excluded from public discourse.

Many contemporary women's prayers also are very taken up with themes of justice and of poverty (injustice and poverty have affected the lives of a good many women, though men too suffer in this regard, of course). Ecological issues too come up a good deal, in my experience, in prayer groups. Whether women worry or care more about these issues than men, I would not like to say. Movingly, in Oodgeroo of the Noonuccal's poem "We Are Going," the destruction of the earth and its creatures is linked to the destruction of Australian Aboriginal communities.

Bearing children and caring for them were issues rarely thought to be of much spiritual interest before women began to write out of their experiences of childbirth. Until modern times, men often had little to do with either and were unlikely to pray about it, except, sometimes with desperation, that their wives might survive the ordeal. There is less writing on the subject by women than you might expect, considering its huge importance in many women's lives. Perhaps women still need to convince themselves that issues that primarily affect them have spiritual depth.

One of the things I have enjoyed most about compiling this collection has been the ability to draw from a pool of women's writing that covers a huge span of history. It is wonderful to get a glimpse of women's ceremonies in ancient Greece — ceremonies that were about Aphrodite, Hestia, or the moon. It is moving to contemplate the religious passion of the Sufi Rabi'a or the Hindu *bhakta* Mirabai, whose words and feelings are strikingly similar to those of their medieval Christian contemporaries. I love the metrical mastery of the nineteenth-century women hymn writers, and if there are undertones of masochism here and there in their work, it echoes the way women have dealt for centuries with powerlessness, a kind of "making the best of a bad job." The amazing voice of forgiveness from a concentration camp, and Irina Ratushinskaya's clear, moral voice

from a KGB prison, are wonderful evocations of good-
ness and love in situations where it seems unimaginable that both would not be destroyed. And I also
found a sense of hope in the fact that many distinguished contemporary women poets — Denise
Levertov, Judith Wright — have such a profound
sense of the wonder and awe of human existence and
of the natural world.

It has been good, too, to look at life through the
window of different religious viewpoints: Buddhism,
Judaism, Christianity, Native American spirituality,
and others. I enjoyed the Buddhist insistence on "getting free," the ritual grace of both Judaism and
Christianity, the ecstatic Native American delight in the
world of trees and mountains and creatures. I liked the
humor, conscious and unconscious, of one or two of the
pieces: of the little girl who asked God to try to be fair
to girls even though he was male himself, and, more
darkly, Betsy Sholl sternly asking God, in the persona
of Job's wife, what he thought he was up to in dispos-
ing of *her* ten children just to teach Job a lesson.

Virtually every poem or prayer in the book has been
written by a woman, but there are one or two important exceptions. In describing Simone Weil's profound
religious experience brought on by reading George
Herbert's poem "Love," I have quoted Herbert's poem

in full so the reader may recall the words that so profoundly moved Simone Weil. Since Homer is wonderful at describing women's ceremonies, of which otherwise we know little, I have used some of his descriptions, beautifully translated by Charles Boer.

THE VOICE OF "ANONYMOUS"

More controversially, I have used some anonymous pieces of writing: one from Africa, others by American Indians, and some from Gaelic-speaking Scotland. Attributing songs and poems to individuals is a relatively late phenomenon, and in cultures that still do not attribute authorship, it is usually the case that some at least are written, or anyhow spoken, by women. So rather than exclude such material altogether, it seemed better to include material that concerned itself with what had traditionally been women's concerns, such as children and cleaning house. One or two prayers, particularly in the first section, cannot even be said to have this shaky justification, but they have such a joyful sense of the wonder of life that I have included them anyway. Some of them were probably written by women, and if the others were not, I am using the excuse that for centuries women were obliged to hide behind "anonymous," and now I am shamelessly claiming some "anonymous" territory back on their behalf.

This book has a practical purpose. The prayers and poems are intended not only to be read at home, as one reads any other book, but also to be used in the quiet of prayer groups or in the public discourse of worshiping communities — indeed, wherever such insights are valued and used. It is for those who love God, or wish they did; for those who love humanity, and wish they loved it better; and those who love the natural world, but feel at a loss to halt its damage and decline. Prayer may spur us to better and wiser efforts.

Finally, I would like to make two personal acknowledgments: to the St. Hilda Community of London, a prayer group of women and men that has worked for fourteen years to bring about a new attitude to women in the Christian churches. I have loved being a member, and I owe them a debt of gratitude, love and laughter for some marvelous evenings spent in their company. And I would also like to thank David O'Neal, my editor at SkyLight Paths, whose idea the book was. I have very much valued his appreciation and encouragement, and his many good suggestions and helpful comments.

MONICA FURLONG
London

1

EARTH OUR MOTHER

Joy and gratitude for the natural world can unite writers from a wide variety of different cultural backgrounds and religions. It is something all human beings have in common—the experience of the earth they share and upon which they depend for their existence. Tribal peoples say this more unselfconsciously than the rest of us; like the writer of the Navajo chant, they know themselves to be part of what they describe.

Earth, our mother, breathe forth life
all night sleeping
now awaking
in the east
now see the dawn

Earth, our mother, breathe and waken
leaves are stirring
all things moving
new day coming
life renewing

Eagle soaring, see the morning
see the new mysterious morning
something marvelous and sacred
though it happens every day
Dawn the child of God and Darkness.

Pawnee prayer

For all things bright and beautiful,
For all things dark and mysterious and lovely,
For all things green and growing and strong,
For all things weak and struggling to push life up
    through rocky earth,
For all human faces, hearts, minds, and hands
    which surround us,
And for all nonhuman minds and hearts, paws
    and claws, fins and wings,
For this Life and the life of this world,
For all that you have laid before us, O God,
We lay our thankful hearts before you.

Gail A. Riccuiti

The mountains, I become part of it . . .
The herbs, the fir tree, I become part of it.
The morning mists, the clouds, the gathering
    waters,
I become part of it.
The wilderness, the dew drops, the pollen . . .
I become part of it.

Navajo chant

Birds nest in my arms,
on my shoulders, behind my knees,
between my breasts there are quails,
they must think I'm a tree.
The swans think I'm a fountain,
they all come down and drink when I talk.
When sheep pass, they pass over me,
and perched on my fingers, the sparrows eat,
the ants think I'm the earth,
and men think I'm nothing.

Gloria Fuertes

O beautiful for spacious skies,
For amber waves of grain,
For purple mountains' majesty,
Above the fruited plain.
America, America,
God shed his grace on thee,
And crown thy good with brotherhood
From sea to shining sea.

Katharine Lee Bates

I believe God is everything. . . . Everything that is or ever was or ever will be. And when you can feel that, and be happy to feel that, you've found It. . . . My first step from the old white man was the trees. Then air. Then birds. Then other people. But one day when I was sitting quiet and feeling like a motherless child, which I was, it come to me: that feeling of being part of everything, not separate at all. I knew that if I cut a tree, my arm would bleed. And I laughed and I cried and I run all round the house. I knew just what it was. In fact, when it happen, you can't miss it.

Alice Walker, The Color Purple

This is what I want to happen: that our earth
    mother
may be clothed in ground corn four times over,
that frost flowers cover her over entirely,
that the mountain pines far away over there
may stand close to each other in the cold,
that the weight of snow crack some branches!
In order that the country may be this way
I have made my prayer sticks into something
    alive.

Zuni prayer

THE NEW MOON

She of my love is the new moon,
The King of all creatures blessing her;
Be mine a good purpose
Towards each creature of creation.

Holy be each thing
Which she illumines;
Kindly be each deed
Which she reveals.

Be her guidance on land
With all beset ones;
Be her guidance on the sea
With all distressed ones.

May the moon of moons
Be coming through thick clouds
On me and on every mortal
Who is coming through affliction.

May the virgin of my love
Be coming through dense dark clouds
To me and to each one
Who is in tribulation.

May the King of grace
Be helping my hand
Now and for ever
Till my resurrection day.

Gaelic, Anonymous

Father our Creator,
You created all things, seen and unseen,
Listen to my silent prayer as I stand before you.

As my weary eyes look back over distant
    horizons,
Back to those days where my people walked,
The foot prints of my grandfathers are imprinted
    on the earth
And their images become real to me.

I see my Grandfathers standing tall and strong,
warriors of long ago
I hear them singing
I hear them dancing
And my spirit moves within me.

They told me of the emus fighting
And the kangaroos picking up the scent of our
    hunters
The images fade away as I feel the hurt of my
    people.

I can hear the cries of my Grandmothers as
    they cry
for their children.

Grandfather, you can see me as I stand here and
    feel this hurt.
Father, Creator, is this the purpose of my being
    here
Or is it your plan to reshape my people
To be once again the proud race it once was?

Let me walk with you and my Grandfathers
Towards the dawning of a proud and new nation.
I thank you for my Sacred Being.
Amen.

Aboriginal Jubilee Prayer

2

THE VALLEY OF LOVE AND DELIGHT

This section is about the joy of being human — the sheer pleasure of being alive, the wonder of loving another human being or of loving God. These experiences are often seen as separate from one another. I do not believe that the mystics quoted here believe that to be the case. For them, all love is inseparable, although it finds its purpose and fulfilment in God. To quote Beatrijs of Nazareth, "she feels her spirit roams free through the depths and the heights and the immensity of love."

'Tis the gift to be simple, 'tis the gift to be free,
'Tis the gift to come down where you ought to be
And when you find yourself in the place just right
'Twill be in the valley of love and delight.

Shaker song

May it be delightful my house,
From my head may it be delightful,
To my feet may it be delightful,
Where I lie may it be delightful,
All above me may it be delightful,
All around me may it be delightful.

Navajo chant

YERUSHALAYIM SHEL ZAHAV

The mountain air is as clear as wine, and the
    smell of the pine tree
is carried on the evening breeze with the sound
    of bells.
The city is imprisoned in a sleep of tree and
    stone,
the city which dwells alone and in its heart
    a wall.
Jerusalem of gold, of copper and of light,
I am a harp for all your songs.

We have returned to the water cisterns, to the
    market and the squares.
A *shofar* is heard on the Temple Mount in the
    Old City.
In the caves in the rocks a thousand windows
    gleam.
Let us once again descend to the Dead Sea by
    way of Jericho.

Jerusalem of gold, of copper and of light,
I am a harp for all your songs.

But when I come today to sing to you and to
    crown you,
I am less than the least of your children and the
    last of your poets,
for your name burns the lips like the kiss of a
    seraph.
If I forget you, O Jerusalem, which is all gold.
Jerusalem of gold, of copper and of light,
I am a harp for all your songs.

Naomi Shemer

THE SOUL IN LOVE

And so as the fish swims in the vastness of the oceans and rests in the deeps, and as the bird boldly soars in the heights and the vastness of the air, in the same way she feels her spirit roam free through the depths and the heights and the immensity of love.

Beatrijs of Nazareth

THE BIRTHDAY

My heart is like a singing bird
Whose nest is in a water'd shoot;
My heart is like an apple-tree
Whose boughs are bent with thick-set fruit;
My heart is like a rainbow shell
That paddles in a halcyon sea;
My heart is gladder than all these,
Because my love is come to me.

Raise me a dais of silk and down;
Hang it with vair and purple dyes;
Carve it in doves and pomegranates,
And peacocks with a hundred eyes;
Work it in gold and silver grapes,
In leaves and silver fleurs-de-lys;
Because the birthday of my life
Is come, my love is come to me.

Christina Rossetti

BLISS

My beloved came,
I watched the road,
and I, the solitary,
attained Him.

I decorated the plate
for *puja,*
I gave my jewels
to Him.

And finally,
He sent messages,
He came.

Bliss adorns me,
Hari is a sea
of love.

My eyes are linked
to his,
in Love,

Mira, a sea of bliss,
admits
the Dark-one.

Mirabai

Puja is an offering in worship; the "Dark-one" is the god
Krishna.

THE VISITING SEA

As the inhastening tide doth roll,
Home from the deep, along the whole
   Wide shining strand, and floods the caves,
   —Your love comes filling with happy waves
The open sea-shore of my soul.

But inland from the seaward spaces,
None knows, not even you, the places
   Brimmed, at your coming, out of sight
   —The little solitudes of delight
This tide constrains in dim embraces.

You see the happy shore, wave-rimmed,
But know not of the quiet dimmed
   Rivers your coming floods and fills,
   The little pools 'mid happier hills,
My silent rivulets, over-brimmed.

What! I have secrets from you? Yes.
But, visiting Sea, your love doth press
    And reach in further than you know
    And fills all these, and, when you go,
There's loneliness in loneliness.

Alice Meynell

Nada te turbe,
nada te espante.
Quien a Dios tiene
nada le falta.
Nada te turbe,
nade te espante.
Solo Dios basta.

No need for fear
Or deep despair
Seekers of God
Receive his care.
No need for fear
Or deep despair
We are at home
And God is there.

Prayer of St. Teresa of Ávila

In this good world
The sun burns on puddles
Clouds mass in the sky above the cooling-towers
Snow lies on slag heaps
And detergent floats on rivers limpid as silk.
In this good world
Praise bursts from our lips
Like diamonds
Like jewels from the kind princess's mouth.
In this good world
Our curses turn to praise
Perversity perverted;
Even on the rack
We're held by joy.

Monica Furlong

I am the rose of Sharon, and the lily of the valleys.

As the lily among thorns, so is my love among the
daughters.

As the apple tree among the trees of the wood, so
is my beloved among the sons.

I sat down under his shadow with great delight,
and his fruit was sweet to my taste.

He brought me to the banqueting house, and his
banner over me was love.

Stay me with flagons, comfort me with apples, for
I am sick of love.

His left hand is under my head, and his right
hand doth embrace me.

I charge you, O ye daughters of Jerusalem, by
the roes, and by the hinds of the field, that ye
stir not up, nor awake my love, till he please.

The voice of my beloved! Behold, he cometh
leaping upon the mountains, skipping upon
the hills.

My beloved is like a roe or a young hart; behold,
he standeth behind our wall, he looketh forth
at the windows, shewing himself through the
lattice.

My beloved spake, and said unto me, Rise up, my
love, my fair one, and come away.

For, lo, the winter is past, the rain is over and
gone;

The flowers appear on the earth; the time of the
singing of birds is come, and the voice of the
turtle is heard in our land.

The fig putteth forth her green figs, and the vines
with the tender grape give a good smell.
Arise, my love, my fair one, and come away.

My dove, that art in the clefts of the rock, in the
secret places of the stairs, let me see thy
countenance, let me hear thy voice; for sweet
is thy voice, and thy countenance is comely.

Take us the foxes, the little foxes, that spoil the
vines: for our vines have tender grapes.

My beloved is mine, and I am his: he feedeth
among the lilies.

Until the day break, and the shadows flee away,
turn, my beloved, and be thou like a roe or a
young hart upon the mountains.

Song of Solomon 2:1–17

Love penetrates the senses and storms the soul with all its power. When love grows in the soul, then it rises up with great longing to God and flowingly expands to receive the miracle that breaks in upon it. Love melts through the soul and into the senses. And so the body too gains its part and conforms in all ways to love.

Mechthild of Magdeburg

And God said to the soul:
I desired you before the world began.
I desire you now
As you desire me.
And where the desires of two come together
There love is perfected.

Lord, you are my lover,
My longing,
My flowing stream,
My sun,
And I am your reflection.

It is a rare
And a high way,
Which the soul follows,
Drawing the senses after,
Just as the person with sight leads the blind.
In this way the soul is free
And lives without the heart's grief,
Desiring nothing but her Lord,
Who works all things well.

Mechthild of Magdeburg

I learned that love was our Lord's meaning.
And I saw for certain, both here and elsewhere,
that before he ever made us, God loved us;
and that his love has never slackened,
     nor ever shall.
In this love all his works have been done,
and in this love he has made everything serve us;
and in this love our life is everlasting.
Our beginning was when we were made,
but the love in which he made us
     never had beginning.
In this we have our beginning.
All this we shall see in God for ever.
May Jesus grant this.

                                        Julian of Norwich

O to continue to drink deep of the streams of the great salvation, until I wholly lose the thirst for the passing things of earth; to live watching for my Lord, to be wide awake when he comes, to open to him quickly and enjoy his likeness to the full.

Ann Griffiths

3

LOVE UNKNOWN

If the last section described the joy of love, this one describes its more baffling aspects: the searching, the uncertainty, the fear of loss, as evident in some of these mystical writers as in the writers of courtly love by whom many of them were influenced. There is pain — "burning," as Hildegard calls it — in love, though this may be part of our growth into understanding. For the religious writer, it is part of trust, the coming to rely upon God even in moments of darkness. "He knows the way he taketh" says the nineteenth-century Anna Laetitia Waring, and "I will walk with him." Rabi'a is ready to accept what God gives her, even if it is the loss of God himself. What matters, says Hadewijch, is to "commit all your being to love."

Love unknown. Why, why, why?

Angela di Foligno

I slept for a moment,
the Beloved appeared,
when I rose to greet him,
he was
gone.

Some lose him
sleeping,
I lost him,
awake,

Mira's lord, *Girðhara,*
brings happiness to
the
home.

Mirabai

Girðhara means "immovable mountain."

ANTIPHON FOR GOD THE FATHER

Burn, everlasting one, in love
as you loved when you first were
father in the burning
dawn before the world's day!

Loving your son you loved
us all into being; let us
all be his limbs.

See the need that befalls us!
Lift it away from us
and for your child's sake lead us
into safety, into bliss.

Hildegard of Bingen

God! If I worship Thee in fear of Hell, burn me in Hell; and if I worship Thee in hope of Paradise, exclude me from Paradise; but if I worship Thee for Thine own sake, withhold not Thine everlasting beauty.

My Lord, whatever share of this world Thou dost bestow on me, bestow it on Thine enemies, and whatever share of the next world Thou dost give to me, give it to Thy friends — Thou art enough for me.

Rabi'a the Mystic

Like a silkworm weaving
her house with love
from her marrow,

and dying
in her body's threads
winding tight, round
and round.

I burn
desiring what the heart desires.

Cut through, O Lord,
my heart's greed,
and show me
your way out,
lord white as jasmine.

Mahadeviyakka

Passionate, with longing in my eyes,
Searching wide, and seeking nights and days,
Lo! I beheld the Truthful One, the Wise,
Here in my own house to fill my gaze.

Just for a moment a flower grows,
Bright and brilliant on a green-clad tree
Just for a moment a cold wind blows
Through the bare thorns of a thicket free.

Lalleswari, or Lal Diddi, of Kashmir

O love, set your whole mind
On God's love who made you.
Commit all your being to love;
And then you shall heal all your wounds,
Neither fearing pain nor
Fleeing from sorrow in anything.
You should rely on love
And then you shall know what to love and what
    to hate.
Be content with all things:
For that is the sign of love's presence,
And that you are so easily oppressed
Denies you many a beautiful gift.
If you love you wish to trust yourself in God
And keep yourself in charity
Then all shall be yours:
And you shall win your love.

Hadewijch of Brabant

And he showed me more, a little thing, the size
of a hazel-nut, on the palm of my hand, round
like a ball. I looked at it thoughtfully and won-
dered 'What is this?' And the answer came, 'It
is all that is made.' I marvelled that it continued to exist and did not suddenly disintegrate;
it was so small. And again my mind supplied
the answer, 'It exists, both now and for ever,
because God loves it.' In short, everything
owes its existence to the love of God.

Julian of Norwich

In heav'nly love abiding,
no change my heart shall fear;
and safe is such confiding,
for nothing changes here.
The storm may roar without me,
my heart may low be laid,
but God is round about me,
and can I be dismayed?

Wherever he may guide me,
no want shall turn me back;
my Shepherd is beside me,
and nothing can I lack.
His wisdom ever waketh,
his sight is never dim,
he knows the way he taketh,
and I will walk with him.

Green pastures are before me,
which yet I have not seen;
bright skies will soon be o'er me,

where the dark clouds have been.
My hope I cannot measure,
my path to life is free,
my Saviour has my treasure,
and he will walk with me.

Anna Laetitia Waring

Lord, I rack my brains to find ways of loving you and I don't succeed.

Lord, I am here before You like the dry ground upon which the prophet called down the dew.

Lord, I have loved You so long, but don't know how to love You.

Most tender Lord, give me Your arms. I am returning to our home with the tiny steps of a small child.

Gabrielle Bossis

God, the night has passed and the day has dawned. How I long to know if Thou hast accepted my prayers or if Thou hast rejected them. Therefore console me, for it is Thine to console this state of mine. Thou hast given me life and cared for me, and Thine is the glory. If Thou wantst to drive me from Thy door, yet I would not forsake it, for the love that I bear in my heart towards Thee.

Rabi'a the Mystic

Under vaults of cathedrals eternal,
Barefoot where dusty roads wind,
With nakedly trembling candles
People seek a God who is kind.

That He'll understand and take pity
Through the murders, the raving and lies,
That He'll put his hands on temples
As on cruel injuries.

That He'll see the shouting faces,
Dark of souls, eyes that light never knew,
That the fool and the whore He will pardon,
And the priest, and the poet, too.

That He'll save the fleer from pursuers,
That He'll give to the hungry bread . . .
Perhaps God is a cross in a hand's palm?
Perhaps God is a sky as dark as lead?

The road to Him, how discover?
With what measure the hope, pain and grief?
People seek God, a kind one.
God grant they may find and believe.

Irina Ratushinskaya, Odessa, 1970

In 1938 I spent ten days at Solesmes, from Palm Sunday to Easter Tuesday, following all the liturgical services. I was suffering from splitting headaches; each sound hurt me like a blow; by an extreme effort of concentration I was able to rise above this wretched flesh, to leave it to suffer by itself, heaped up in a corner, and to find a pure and perfect joy in the unimaginable beauty of the chanting and the words. . . . It goes without saying that in the course of these services the thought of the Passion of Christ entered into my being once and for all.

[At Solesmes I learned by chance] of the existence of those English poets of the seventeenth century who are named metaphysical. In reading them later on, I discovered the poem called "Love" [by George Herbert]. Often, at the culminating point of a violent headache, I make myself say it over, concentrating all my attention upon it and clinging

with all my soul to the tenderness it enshrines.
I used to think I was merely reciting it as a
beautiful poem, but without my knowing it the
recitation had the virtue of a prayer. It was
during one of these recitations that . . . Christ
himself came down and took possession of me.

> *Simone Weil, in a letter to Fr. Henri Perrin,*
> *from Marseilles, May 15, 1942*

Love

Love bade me welcome; yet my soul drew back,
Guilty of dust and sin.
But quick-eyed Love, observing me grow slack
From my first entrance in,
Drew nearer to me, sweetly questioning
If I lack'd anything.
"A guest," I answer'd, "worthy to be here:"
Love said, "You shall be he."
"I the unkind, ungrateful? Ah, my dear,
I cannot look on Thee."
Love took my hand and smiling did reply,
"Who made the eyes but I?"

"Truth, Lord; but I have marr'd them: let my
    shame
Go where it doth deserve."
"And know you not," says Love, 'Who bore the
    blame?'
"My dear, then I will serve."
"You must sit down," says Love, "and taste my
    meat."
So I did sit and eat.

George Herbert

I
looked for the Dark One
I
found his image
in my heart

I
stood in his court,
my life in his hands,
only his medicine healed.

Mira sold to *Girdhara,*
the world calls her
wayward.

Mirabai

Girdhara means "immovable mountain."

4

JOIN YOUR
HANDS GENTLY

Prayer, say these writers, is not simply a matter of muttering words. It is a state of mind for which you need to prepare yourself. You need to set aside other concerns, quieten what Jean Watt calls the "itch always to be doing," sit still, still your mind, let go. Denise Levertov describes it as a sort of settling and uses the image of grains of sand settling in a well until the water becomes completely clear. Sometimes what follows is distractions, boredom, disquieting thoughts no longer held down by busyness. Sometimes there is a kind of flash—what Ann Lewin compares to the sudden sighting of a kingfisher.

Join your hands gently;
Let the world be placed
Beyond their reach,
Beyond their itch
Always to be doing;
Exempt from speech
This little space thus formed
Between your folded fingers,
Between your going
And your slow return —
This still enclosure
With its own high walls:
Join your hands gently, so,
No lovelier way than this of letting go.

Jean M. Watt

Prayer is like watching for the
Kingfisher. All you can do is
Be where he is likely to appear, and
Wait.
Often, nothing much happens;
There is space, silence and
Expectancy.
No visible sign, only the
Knowledge that he's been there,
And may come again.
Seeing or not seeing cease to matter,
You have been prepared.
But sometimes, when you've almost
Stopped expecting it,
A flash of brightness
Gives encouragement.

Ann Lewin

SANDS OF THE WELL

The golden particles
descend, descend,
traverse the water's
depth and come to rest
on the level bed
of the well until,
the full descent
accomplished, water's
absolute transparence
is complete, unclouded
by constellations
of bright sand.
Is this
the place where you
are brought in meditation?
Transparency
seen for itself—
as if its quality
were not, after all,
to enable
perception *not* of itself?

With a wand
of willow I again
trouble the envisioned pool,
the cloudy nebulae
form and disperse,
the separate
grains again
slowly, slowly
perform their descent,
and again
stillness ensues.

Denise Levertov

Let silence be placed around us,
like a mantle,
Let us enter into it,
as through a small secret door;
stooping,
to emerge into
an acre of peace,
where stillness reigns,
and the voice of God
is ever present.

The voice of God,
in the startled cry
of a refugee child,
waking
in unfamiliar surroundings.
The voice of God,
in the mother,
fleeing with
her treasure
in her arms, who says
"I am here."

The voice of God
in the father
who points to the stars
and says:
"there is our signpost
there is our lantern. Be of good courage."

O Lord, may the mantle of silence
become a cloak of understanding
to warm our hearts in prayer.

Kate McIlhagga

The prayer has great power
Which we pray with all our strength.
It makes an embittered heart mellow,
A sad heart joyful,
A foolish heart wise,
A timid heart bold,
A weak heart strong,
A blind heart clear-seeing,
A cold heart ardent.
It draws God who is great into a heart which is
    small.
It drives the hungry soul up to the fullness of
    God.
It unites the two lovers, God and soul, in a place
    of bliss,
Where they converse long of love.

Mechthild of Magdeburg

IN WHOM WE LIVE AND MOVE AND HAVE OUR BEING

Birds afloat in air's current,
sacred breath? No, not breath of God,
it seems, but God
the air enveloping the whole
globe of being.
It's we who breathe, in, out, in, the sacred,
leaves astir, our wings
rising, ruffled — but only the saints
take flight. We cower
in cliff-crevice or edge out gingerly
on branches close to the nest. The wind
marks the passage of holy ones riding
that ocean of air. Slowly their wake
reaches us, rocks us.
But storm or still,
numb or poised in attention,
we inhale, exhale, inhale,
encompassed, encompassed.

Denise Levertov

BECOMING DIFFERENT

There can be all the difference in the world between beginning a prayer with 'O Almighty God' and beginning it with 'Thou' breathed to Someone—*there*. We need to practise that, until the Presence becomes so real that He is in deed and truth possessing the very centre where for us the important 'I' stands supreme. . . .

Why is it so difficult to grasp and hold until it possesses you, is right in the centre of you, so that it is integrated in all you do? We must think and wrestle with a thought like this as Jacob did with the Angel. How to receive and pray, grasp and pray, hold on and pray, until I find myself, suddenly, with great surprise, different. Though I am still full of pride and fear and lovelessness—I am different. Not that I have at last conquered my fear only . . . but that at the centre I am different. Like Herschel, the great conductor, who comes into the concert hall and notices all the little irrelevant details that flash before his eyes—a woman's hat, the lights, the small violins—and then the music starts and suddenly he is possessed of something beyond himself, and says: 'I watch my moving hands and they grow strange—what is it moves the body: what am I?'

FINDING WHAT IS

We have to find our way into that rhythm in which God has swung the world—and the moment is always the same. God's calling—my response. His love—my obedience. The greatest good we can set ourselves, with all the passion that is within us, is to see God and give in to what Is.

Florence Allshorn

5

TALKING TO GOD

This is the very heart of what this collection is all about: trying to catch the moment of prayer as prayer—not the experience of thinking about prayer, or trying to ease oneself into doing it, but the timeless instant of self-forgetfulness that oddly leaves us more ourselves than we were before. For most modern people, prayer does not seem an easy or natural activity. Perhaps we are too beset by activity and determined busyness, and perhaps some of us dread prayer, "the silences we strain to fill," or fear that we are simply talking to ourselves. Emily Dickinson complains bitterly that although she is "knocking everywhere," she cannot seem to find the right address. But others have a lovely confidence that they are heard, some of them in the most appalling of circumstances—an unknown writer in Ravensbruck concentration camp, Irina

Ratushinskaya in a KGB prison. Some, like Jane Austen, fasten on safe, sensible words, requests to be helped through the "dailiness" of life; others, like Anne Brontë, suffer the strongest of doubts. "Talking to God" covers a huge range of thoughts and emotions, the whole gamut of human longing and struggle and hope.

PRAYER

At least — to pray — is left — is left —
Oh Jesus — in the Air —
I know not which thy chamber is —
I'm knocking — everywhere —
Thou settest Earthquake in the South —
And Maelstrom in the Sea —
Say, Jesus Christ of Nazareth —
Hast thou no Arm for Me?

Emily Dickinson

God of listening, God of peace,
In our hearts may you increase,
Till our flow of words shall cease,
And we hear you.

Listening is the hardest skill,
Silences we strain to fill,
Far too restless to be still
And just hear you.

If our well-planned words defeat
Words of others that we meet,
Hesitant and incomplete,
Father, hear them.

If the insights that we seek
Come from someone tired and weak,
Looking for a chance to speak,
Help us hear them.

Janet Shepperson

God, the stars are shining:
All eyes have closed in sleep;
The kings have locked their doors.
Each lover is alone, in secret, with the one he
     loves.
And I am here too: alone, hidden from all of
     them —
With You.

Rabi'a the Mystic

We adore the glory and the truth that is God.
Everything within us utters praise.
Our being is formed for this purpose and no other.
All our loves and works find meaning in you.

Jesus, who shows us what God is like,
forgive us our failure to understand
but keep us in your dazzling presence.

For there we learn the nature of holiness
and partake with you in the secret of the godhead.

St. Hilda Community

Dear God,
Are boys really better than girls? I know you
are one, but try to be fair.

From Children's Letters to God

O Lord, remember not only the men and women of goodwill but also those of ill will. But do not remember the suffering they have inflicted upon us; remember the fruits we brought thanks to this suffering, our comradeship, our loyalty, our humility, the courage, the generosity, the greatness of heart which has grown out of this; and when they come to judgment, let all the fruits that we have borne be their forgiveness.

The prayer of an unknown woman,
found on a piece of wrapping paper in
Ravensbruck concentration camp

Take my life, and let it be
consecrated, Lord, to thee;
take my moments and my days,
let them flow in ceaseless praise.

Take my hands, and let them move
at the impulse of thy love;
take my feet, and let them be
swift and beautiful for thee.

Take my voice, and let me sing
always, only, for my King;
take my lips, and let them be
filled with messages for thee.

Take my silver and my gold;
not a mite would I withhold;
take my intellect, and use
ev'ry power as thou shalt choose.

Take my will, and make it thine:
it shall be no longer mine;

take my heart: it is thine own;
it shall be thy royal throne.

Take my love; my Lord, I pour
at thy feet its treasure-store;
take myself, and I will be
ever, only, all for thee.

Frances Ridley Havergal

Lord, hear; Lord, forgive; Lord, do.

Hear what I speak not; forgive what I speak amiss; do what I leave undone; that, not according to my word or my deed, but according to thy mercy and truth, all may issue to thy glory and the good of thy kingdom.

Maria Hare

Think through me, thoughts of God,
My Father, quiet me,
Till in thy holy presence, hushed,
I think my thoughts with thee.

Think through me, thoughts of God,
That always, everywhere,
The stream that through my being flows
May homeward pass in prayer.

Think through me, thoughts of God,
And let my own thoughts be
Lost like the sand-pools on the shore
Of the eternal sea.

Amy Carmichael

While faith is with me, I am blest;
It turns my darkest night to day;
But, while I clasp it to my breast,
I often feel it slide away.

What shall I do if all my love,
My hopes, my toil, are cast away?
And if there be no God above
To hear and bless me when I pray?

Oh, help me, God! For thou alone
Canst my distracted soul relieve.
Forsake it not: it is thine own,
Though weak, yet longing to believe.

Anne Brontë

OFFERING

We hold up our smallness to your greatness,
our fear to your love.
Our tiny act of giving to your great generosity
Ourselves to you.

St. Hilða Community

All as I asked:
There will be for me, will be
(O Lord, thank you!)
A far road
And new people.
There will be for me, will be
A homeless song
And a proud memory.
There will be for me a heaven
Won by honour,
And a cloak beneath my feet.
There will be for me —
Sometimes —
A happy story
Made of wormwood and mint,
A dress, a semi-mask,
A lace dance . . .
And no one will say:
"She saw life and that was it!"

Irina Ratushinskaya, KGB Prison, Kiev,
January 1983

Give us grace, almighty Father, to address thee with all our hearts as well as with our lips. Thou art everywhere present: from thee no secrets can be hidden. Teach us to fix our thoughts on thee, reverently and with love, so that our prayers are not in vain, but are acceptable to thee, now and always. Amen.

Incline us O God to think humbly of ourselves, to be saved only in the examination of our own conduct, to consider our fellow-creatures with kindness, and to judge of all they say and do with the charity which we would desire from them ourselves.

Grant us grace, almighty Father, so to pray as to deserve to be heard.

Jane Austen

At your back,
At your feet,
We shall sit down beside you.
Desiring your waters,
Your seeds,
Your riches,
Your long life,
Your old age,
Desiring these, I set you down quietly.
As you sit here quietly
As I wish, according to my words,
You will take us to be your children.
So that all my children
May be saved.
All will be happy.
Safely they will bring forth their young.
So that all my children may finish their roads
So that they may grow old,
So that you may bless us with life,
So that none of my spring children
May be left standing outside.
So that you may protect us (I have done this).

May our roads be fulfilled;
May we grow old;
May our roads reach to dawn lake;
May we grow old;
May you bless us with life.

Zuni prayer

Father, we thank thee for our happiness, for our great gift of life: for the wonder and bloom of the world. We bless thee that it takes a very little thing to make us happy, yet so great a thing to satisfy us that only thyself canst do it, for thou alone art greater than our hearts. We bless thee for thy calling which is so high that no man can perfectly attain unto it, and for thy grace which stoops so low that none of us can ever fall too low for it. Above all we bless thee that thou didst send thy Son, Jesus Christ our Lord, for having seen him we have seen thee, whose truth doth ever warm and whose grace doth ever keep.

Helen Waddell

All this day, O Lord,
let me touch as many lives as possible for thee;
and every life I touch, do thou by thy Spirit
    quicken,
whether through the word I speak,
the prayer I breathe, or the life I live.

Mary Sumner

Spirit of God, that moved of old
Upon the waters' darkened face,
Come, when our faithless hearts are cold,
And stir them with an inward grace.

Thou that art power and peace combined,
All highest strength, all purest love,
The rushing of the mighty wind,
The brooding of the gentle dove.

Come give us still thy powerful aid,
And urge us on, and keep us thine;
Nor leave the hearts that once were made
Fit temples for thy grace divine;

Nor let us quench thy sevenfold light;
But still with softest breathings stir
Our wayward souls, and lead us right,
O Holy Ghost, the comforter.

Cecil Frances Alexander

Let us make our way together, Lord, wherever you go I must go, and through whatever you pass, there too will I pass.

St. Teresa of Ávila

How lovely are thy holy groves
God of heaven and earth
My soul longs and faints
for the circle of thy trees.
My heart and my flesh
sing with joy to thee
O God of life.

May all things move and be moved in me
all know and be known in me
May all creation
dance for joy within me.

Chinook prayer

Lord, thou knowest what I want,
if it be thy will that I have it,
and if it be not thy will,
good Lord, do not be displeased,
for I want nothing which you do not want.

Julian of Norwich

6

RITUALS, CEREMONIES, AND SEASONS

If prayer can be difficult as a lonely exercise, it can be very different when shared with a community of other believers. The experience of worshiping in a synagogue, church, or temple can sweep the individual along in ritual, music, and prayer. Sitting in zazen in a Zen monastery can bring the sitter to a depth of meditation hard to achieve alone. Rituals performed at home, such as the lighting of the Sabbath candles, also have profound meaning. Doing something, as opposed to saying something, feels helpful, as Roman Catholics with their rosaries and Tibetans with their prayer wheels also discover. Most religions, if not all, also have a sense of the times of day and the seasons of the year, of particular prayers said and rituals associated with the rising or setting of the sun, with changes in the climate, and with growth or decline in the natural world. Festivals, too, are intimately caught up in our sense of climate, as Christmas, at the heart of winter in the cold Northern hemisphere with its emphasis on light and fire, reminds many Westerners. Festivals are sometimes mixed with bits of paganism, which hint at the older festivals that preceded them, fertility rites, and earth religions. Perhaps this makes them more rather than less effective, as they touch ancestral responses in the worshipers. Cooking, too, is as important a ritual as any in many religious festivals, with classic dishes associated with particular meanings. I have included a Jewish recipe to remind us of this. Food, so often prepared by women, itself demonstrates transformation as raw materials are changed into something very different. In Judaism, meals are intimately part of religious practice; they are symbolic, in the case of charoseth and other foods, of the stories that give meaning.

Alongside traditional religious practices, however, there has been in some women's groups a conscious return to the cult of primitive goddesses — of the "Great Goddess," as some prefer to say — along with rituals of invocation. "The Charge of the Goddess" in this section is a moving hymn to neopaganism.

At Candlelighting
May this Sabbath
lift our spirits
lighten our hearts.

Sanctification over Wine
Let us bless the source of life
that ripens fruit on the vine
as we hallow the Sabbath day
in remembrance of creation.

Washing the Hands
Washing the hands, we call to mind
the holiness of the body.

Blessing over Bread
Let us bless the source of life
that brings forth bread from the earth.

Blessing after the Meal
Let us acknowledge the source of life
for the earth and for nourishment.
May we protect the earth
that it may sustain us,
and let us seek sustenance
for all who inherit the world.

Marcia Falk

CHANUKAH

We come to drive away darkness,
in our hands are light and fire.
Each one is a small light,
and all of us are a mighty light.
Away with darkness, away with blackness!
Away before the light.

Sarah Levy

CHRISTMAS

We stand at the turning of the year, the time of death and birth, of darkness and light, of sadness and joy, and we remember the baby born in a stable who pours glory upon our lives. As we give presents to one another we recognise the love present in our world, a love that redeems the cruelty, pain and fear.

Monica Furlong

AN ASH WEDNESDAY PRAYER

O God,
you have made us for yourself,
and against your longing there is no defence.
Mark us with your love,
and release in us a passion for your justice
in our disfigured world;
that we may turn from our guilt and face you,
our heart's desire. Amen.

Janet Morley

LENT

Dragons lurk in desert spaces
penetrating the mind with evil claw.
Serpents' teeth seek out the chinks
insidiously, relentlessly gnawing on the bone;
searching out the interstices of muscle and sinew.

Such is the pain of the wilderness.
Alone, alone, alone,
Christ sits
in the waste place of abandoned pleas and
    questions
until exhausted
finally
at last
the realisation
comes
that in the end
there is only
God.

In the nighttime of our fears,
and in our time of questioning,
Be present, ever present God.
Be present with those
camped out in the fields of hopelessness,
with refugees and homeless,
those who live lives of quiet desperation.
Be present until the desert places
blossom like the rose
and hope is born again.

Kate McIlhagga

THE CHARGE OF THE GODDESS

I who am the beauty of the green earth and the white moon among the stars and the mysteries of the waters, I call upon your soul to arise and come unto me. For I am the soul of nature that gives life to the universe. From Me all things proceed and unto Me they must return. Let My worship be in the heart that rejoices, for behold—all acts of love and pleasure are My rituals. Let there be beauty and strength, power and compassion, honor and humility, mirth and reverence within you. And you who seek to know Me, know that your seeking and yearning will avail you not, unless you know the Mystery: for if that which you seek, you find not within yourself, you will never find it without. For behold, I have been with you from the beginning, and I am that which is attained at the end of desire.

Doreen Valiente, adapted by Starhawk

THE BAPTISM BLESSING

Thou Being who inhabitest the heights
Imprint thy blessing betimes,
Remember Thou the child of my body,
In Name of the Father of peace;
When the priest of the King
On him put the water of meaning,
Grant him the blessing of the Three
Who fill the heights.
The blessing of the Three
Who fill the heights.

Sprinkle down upon him Thy grace,
Give Thou to him virtue and growth,
Give Thou to him flocks and possessions,
Sense and reason void of guile,
Angel wisdom in his day,
That he may stand without reproach
In Thy presence.
He may stand without reproach
In Thy presence.

Gaelic, Anonymous

HARVEST

We dare not ask you bless our harvest feast
Till it is spread for poorest and for least.
We dare not bring our harvest gifts to you
Unless our hungry brothers share them too.

Not only at this time, Lord, every day
Those whom you love are dying while we pray.
Teach us to do with less, and so to share
From our abundance more than we can spare.

Now with this harvest plenty round us piled,
Show us the Christ in every starving child;
Speak, as you spoke of old in Galilee,
'You feed, or you refuse, not them but me!'

Lilian Cox

CHAROSETH

Apples, ½ pound
Raisins, 2 ounces
Almonds, 2 ounces
Cinnamon

Peel and core the apples and chop finely, together with the almonds and raisins. Mix together, adding cinnamon to taste. Then form into a neat block and place in a glass dish, or roll into tiny balls and coat with chopped nuts.

Florence Greenberg

At the Passover meal, Charoseth represents the mortar with which the children of Israel built the slave cities for Pharaoh. The bitter memory has been transformed into a sweet.

7

LIVING IS DAILINESS

Dailiness, say many of the holy men and women of the world, is the vehicle through which God expresses himself in our world. The routines of work, travel, family, and friendship are the places where, if anywhere, we shall find God. Judith Wright speaks of the astonishing moment, known perhaps to everyone, where, unlooked for, an extraordinary awareness suddenly "slants a sudden laser through the common day." It is the small as well as the great actions of our everyday life that make us, for good or ill, the people that we are. Today, as St. Thérèse of Lisieux observes, is in a sense the only day we have, or may have, to love God and our neighbor. Work, which so often for women has meant domestic work, is an instrument of giving and a tool of hospitality. The stranger whom we house or feed may turn out to be the Divine. For the

Gaelic peoples of the Scottish isles, everyday work—kindling the fire, milking the cow, working the loom—was full of religious meaning. Angels and archangels watched over it all. Although many of the prayers here come from the Christian tradition, they speak to us all as examples of the strong sense of the importance of the everyday that is shared by so many religious traditions.

Living is dailiness, a simple bread
that's worth the eating. But I have known a wine,
a drunkenness that can't be spoken or sung
without betraying it. Far past Yours or Mine,
even past Ours, it has nothing at all to say;
it slants a sudden laser through the common day.
It seems to have nothing to do with things at all,
requires another element or dimension.
Not contemplation brings it; it merely happens,
past expectation and beyond intention;
takes over the depth of flesh, the inward eye,
is there, then vanishes. Does not live or die,
because it occurs beyond the here and now,
positives, negatives, what we hope and are.
Not even being in love, or making love,
brings it. It lunges a sword from a dark star.
Maybe there was once a word for it. Call it grace.
I have seen it, once or twice, through a human face.

Judith Wright

Now, into the keeping of God I put
All doings of today.
All disappointments,
hindrances,
forgotten things,
negligences.
All gladness and beauty,
love,
delight,
achievement.
All that people have done for me,
All that I have done for them,
my work and my prayers.

And I commit all the people whom I love
to his shepherding,
to his healing and restoring,
to his calling and making;
Through Jesus Christ our Lord.

Margaret Cropper

My life is an instant,
An hour which passes by;
My life is a moment
Which I have no power to stay.
You know, O my God,
That to love you here on earth —
I have only today.

St. Thérèse of Lisieux

God give me work
Till my life shall end
And life
Till my work is done.

On the grave of the writer Winifred Holtby

BLESSING OF THE KINDLING

I will kindle my fire this morning
In presence of the holy angels of heaven,
In presence of Ariel of the loveliest form,
In presence of Uriel of the myriad charms,
Without malice, without jealousy, without envy,
Without fear, without terror of any one under
 the sun,
But the Holy Son of God to shield me.

God, kindle Thou in my heart within
A flame of love to my neighbour,
To my foe, to my friend, to my kindred all,
To the brave, to the knave, to the thrall,
On Son of the loveliest Mary,
From the lowliest thing that liveth,
To the Name that is highest of all.

Gaelic, Anonymous

Every day is a fresh beginning,
Listen my soul to the glad refrain.
    And, spite of old sorrows
    And older sinning,
    Troubles forecasted
    And possible pain,
Take heart with the day and begin again.

Susan Coolidge

FOLDING THE SHEETS

You and I will fold the sheets
Advancing towards each other
From Burma, from Lapland.

From India where the sheets have been washed
    in the river
And pounded upon stones:
Together we will match the corners.

From China where women on either side of the
    river
Have washed their pale cloth in the White Stone
    Shallows
'Under the shining moon.'

We meet as though in the formal steps of a dance
To fold the sheets together, put them to air
In wind, in sun over bushes, or by the fire.

We stretch and pull from one side and then the
    other—
Your turn. Now mine.
We fold them and put them away until they are
    needed.

A wish for all people when they lie down in
    bed—
Smooth linen, cool cotton, the fragrance and stir
    of herbs
And the faint but perceptible scent of sweet clear
    water.

Rosemary Dobson

I should like a great lake of finest ale
For the King of Kings
I should like a table of the choicest food
For the family of heaven
Let the ale be made from the fruits of faith
And the food be forgiving love.

I should welcome the poor to my feast
For they are God's children
I should welcome the sick to my feast
For they are God's joy.
Let the poor sit with Jesus at the highest place
And the sick dance with the angels.

God bless the poor
God bless the sick
And bless the human race.
God bless our food.
God bless our drink.
All homes, O God, embrace.

St. Bridget of Kildare

Make us worthy, Lord, to serve our fellow-men throughout the world who live and die in poverty and hunger.

Give them, through our hands, this day their daily bread, and by our understanding love, give peace and joy.

Prayer of Mother Teresa

A RUNE OF HOSPITALITY

I saw a stranger today.
I put food for him in the eating-place
And drink in the drinking-place
And music in the listening-place.
In the Holy Name of the Trinity
He blessed myself and my house
My goods and my family.
And the lark said in her warble
Often, often, often
Goes Christ in the stranger's guise.
O, oft and oft and oft,
Goes Christ in the stranger's guise.

Christ has no body now on earth but yours;
yours are the only hands with which he can do
      his work,
yours are the only feet with which he can go
      about the world,

yours are the only eyes through which his
    compassion
can shine forth upon a troubled world.
Christ has no body now on earth but yours.

St. Teresa of Ávila

8

MOTHERS AND FOREBEARS

The number of named women in history until modern times is very few. The ones who are named tend to be divine, or semidevine. As such, they are a source of inspiration like many of the women named in this section, or they were associated with, or relatives of, famous men, like Miriam, the sister of Moses. A very few, like Sappho, or Naomi and Ruth, or Hatshepsut, have found their own way into history, achieving in some cases a kind of iconic status. Since they are relatively few they are treasured as part of women's history, often connected with religion, and, like the other named women, they lift a curtain, however briefly, on the lost world of women's experience.

THE SONG OF MIRIAM

For when the horses of Pharaoh with his chariots and his horsemen went into the sea, the Lord brought back the waters of the sea upon them; but the people of Israel walked on dry ground in the midst of the sea. Then Miriam, the prophetess, the sister of Aaron, took a timbrel in her hand; and all the women went out after her with timbrels and dancing. And Miriam sang to them:

"Sing to the Lord, for he has triumphed gloriously;
the horse and rider he has thrown into the sea."

Exodus 15:19–21

RUTH AND NAOMI

And Ruth said, Intreat me not to leave thee, or to return from following after thee: for whither thou goest, I will go; and where thou lodgest, I will lodge: thy people shall be my people, and thy God my God:

Where thou diest, will I die, and there will I be buried: the Lord do so to me, and more also, if aught but death part thee and me.

Ruth 1:16–17

QUEEN HATSHEPSUT

By my life, by the love of Ra and the favour of my father Amen. . . . I bear the white crown, I am diademed with the red crown. . . . I rule over this land like the son of Isis, I am mighty like the son of Nu. . . . I shall be for ever like the star which changeth not. He gave me my royal power over Egypt and the red country, all the foreign lands are under my feet . . . all the marvels and all the precious things of this land, they are presented to my palace altogether . . . turquoise of the land of Reshut — they bring to me the choicest things from the oasis of Testesu, acacia, juniper, merwood . . . all the good woods of the divine land. . . . Tribute is brought to me from the land of the Tahennu in ivory, seven hundred tusks. . . . She lives, she is stable, she is in good health, she is joyous as well as her double on the throne of Horus of the living like the sun, for ever and ever.

Hatshepsut

HYMN TO APHRODITE

I sing of Aphrodite, the lover's goddess,
beautiful, gold-crowned, a blossom
riding the seafoam, resting on the wind.
She comes ashore, and women
in gold bracelets meet her, bearing
silken garments for her lovely body,
copper rings for her shell ears,
chains of gold for her silver breasts.

They lead her from the seashore.
Do not look upon her! Your eyes
would dazzle from such beauty.
But you do not need to see her.
You already know her. It is she
who moves you in your dance.
She is the music of your life.
Do you need to ask her name?
Call her Love. Call her Joy.
Call her golden Aphrodite.

She is the moment when body
knits to body and the world flowers.
She enlivens everything: plants
in the meadow, the ocean's fish,
animals hidden in the forest,
birds tumbling on the wind.
She is our darling, who under
the wheeling stars makes all
things blossom and bear fruit.
At her approach storms clear,
dark clouds dissolve to blue,
sweet earth and all the oceans
smile, and her light dances brilliant
through the flourishing world.

Homer, adapted by Patricia Monaghan

WISDOM

Doth not wisdom cry? and understanding put
    forth her voice?
She standeth in the top of high places, by the
    way in the places of the paths.
She crieth at the gates, at the entry of the city, at
    the coming in at the doors.
Unto you, O men, I call; and my voice is to the
    sons of men.
O ye simple, understand wisdom: and ye fools, be
    of an understanding heart.
Hear; for I will speak of excellent things; and the
    opening of my lips shall be right things. . . .
Receive my instruction, and not silver; and
    knowledge rather than choice gold.
For wisdom is better than rubies; and all the
    things that may be desired are not to be
    compared to it.
I wisdom dwell with prudence, and find out
    knowledge of witty inventions. . . .
Counsel is mine, and sound wisdom: I am
    understanding; I have strength.

By me kings reign, and princes decree justice.

By me princes rule, and nobles, even all the
   judges of the earth.

I love them that love me, and those that seek me
   early shall find me.

Riches and honour are with me; yea, durable
   riches and righteousness.

My fruit is better than gold, yea, than fine gold;
   and my revenue than choice silver. . . .

The Lord possessed me in the beginning of his
   way, before his works of old.

I was set up from everlasting, from the
   beginning, or ever the earth was.

When there were no depths, I was brought forth;
   when there were no fountains abounding with
   water.

Before the mountains were settled, before the
   hills was I brought forth:

While as yet he had not made the earth, nor the
   fields, nor the highest part of the dust of the
   world.

When he prepared the heavens, I was there:
   when he set a compass upon the face of the
   depth:

When he established the clouds above: when he
   strengthened the fountains of the deep:

When he gave to the sea his decree, that the
   waters should not pass his commandment:
when he appointed the foundations of the earth:
Then I was by him, as one brought up with him:
   and I was daily his delight, rejoicing always
   before him;
Rejoicing in the habitable part of his earth; and
   my delights were with the sons of men. . . .
Blessed is the man that heareth me, watching
   daily at my gates, waiting at the posts of my
   doors.
For whoso findeth me findeth life, and shall
   obtain favour of the Lord.
But he that sinneth against me, wrongeth his own
   soul.

Proverbs 8

GREETING SHEKINAH

Two figures face each other,
Sitting close to the earth in the old way;
Outside in the early morn
The women face each other,
Eye to eye, smile to smile,
Squatting over the earth,
Backs curved like earthen pots.
So gracefully they sit,
Pouring water over each other's hands.
Fire pales as the sun rises;
The spice of dew consecrates the hour.
"Shekinah of the sun, Shekinah of the moon,
We greet You with our morning song,
We greet You with the washing of hands,
We greet you with our dawn fire.
Shekinah of the morning star, Shekinah of
    the dew,
We welcome You as the running deer,
Our feet swift in dancing.
We welcome You as the golden eagle,

Our hands spread in prayer.
We welcome You as the shimmering stream,
Our spirit flowing to the sea of Your delight.
We bless the day with our rising smoke.
Let our prayers ascend to the skies.
Let our prayers touch the earth.
Shalom Achoti, shalom Sister,
All life sings Your song."

Lynn Gottlieb

THE HYMN TO HESTIA

Hestia,
you who received the highest honor,
to have your seat forever
in the enormous houses of all the gods
and all the men who walk on the earth,
it is a beautiful gift you have received,
it is a beautiful honor.
Without you, mankind would have no feasts,
since no one could begin the first and last drink
of honey-like wine without an offering
to Hestia.

Homer, translated by Charles Boer

KALI

Kali
queen of fatality, she
determines the destiny
of things, nemesis.
the permanent guest
within ourselves.
woman of warfare,
of the chase, bitch
of blood sacrifice and death.
dread mother, the mystery
ever present in us and
outside us, the
terrible hindu woman God
Kali
who is black.

Lucille Clifton

IN THE YOUNG SPRING EVENING

In the young spring evening
The moon is shining full
Girls form a circle
As though round an altar

And their feet perform
Rhythmical steps
Like the soft feet of Cretan girls
Must once have danced.

Round and round an altar of love
Designing a circle
In the delicate flowering grass

The stars that are shining
Around the beautiful moon
Hide their own bright faces
When She, at Her fullest

Paints the earth with Her
Silvery light.

Now, while we are dancing
Come! Join us!
Sweet joy, revelry,
Bright light!

Inspire us, muses
Oh, you with the beautiful hair.

Sappho, translated by Charoula

THE MARTYRDOM OF PERPETUA AND FELICITY IN THE ROMAN CIRCUS

Now dawned the day of their victory, and they [the group of Christians] went forth from the prison into the amphitheatre as it were into heaven, cheerful and bright of countenance; if they trembled at all, it was for joy, not for fear. Perpetua followed behind, glorious of presence, as a true spouse of Christ and darling of God; at whose piercing look all cast down their eyes. Felicity likewise, rejoicing that she had [now] borne her child in safety, that she might fight with the beasts, came now from blood to blood, from the midwife to the gladiator, to wash after her travail in a second baptism. And when they had been brought to the gate and were being compelled to put on, the men the dress of the priests of Saturn, the women the dress of the priestesses of Ceres, the noble Perpetua remained of like firmness to the end, and would not. For she said: For this cause

came we willingly unto this, that our liberty
might not be obscured. For this cause we have
devoted our lives, that we might do not such
thing as this; this we agreed with you. Injustice
acknowledged justice; the tribune suffered that
they should be brought forth as they were,
without more ado. Perpetua began to sing. . . .
When they came into Hilarion's sight, they
began to say to Hilarion . . . 'Thou judgest us,
and God thee.'

For the women the devil had made ready a
most savage cow, prepared for this purpose
against all custom; for even in this beast he
would mock their sex. They were stripped
therefore and made to put on nets; and so they
were brought forth. The people shuddered,
seeing one a tender girl, the other her breasts
yet dropping from her late childbearing. So
they were called back and dressed in loose
robes. Perpetua was first thrown, and fell upon
her loins. And when she had sat upright, her
robe being rent at the side, she drew it over to
cover her thigh, mindful rather of modesty
than of pain. Next, looking for a pin, she likewise pinned up her dishevelled hair; for it was
not meet that a martyr should suffer with hair

dishevelled, lest she should seem to grieve in her glory. So she stood up, and when she saw Felicity smitten down, she went up and gave her her hand and raised her up. And both of them stood up together. . . . Perpetua called to her brother, and another catechumen and spoke to them saying 'Stand fast in the faith, and love ye all one another, and be not offended because of our passion.' [The people called that the Christians, a number of them mauled by beasts, should be despatched by a swordsman]. . . . Perpetua was pierced between the bones and shrieked out; and when the swordman's hand wandered still (for he was a novice), herself set it upon her own neck. Perchance so great a woman could not else have been slain . . . had she not herself so willed it.

The Passion of Perpetua and Felicity, c. 202 A.D.,
Acta Sanctorum 1688

Hilarion was the Procurator who had condemned Perpetua and the other Christians.

THE TWO SISTERS—THE DREAMING

On the Island of the Spirits of the Dead,
one of two sisters talks.
"We must make a canoe and follow the way
the sun walks."
They've filled the canoe with sacred 'rannga'
    things,
and paddled away into the night
singing ritual songs.

"Sister, look back!" the first sister calls.
"Do you see the morning star?"
Her sister looks out along their wake.
"Nothing. Nothing's there."

The little sister has fallen asleep.
Again her sister calls,
"Sister, look back for the morning star."
"Nothing. Nothing at all."

A spear of light is thrown across
the sea and lies far
ahead of the sisters' course.
"Sister, the morning star."

The sun comes up and walks the sky.
A fish with whiskers swims
ahead, and leaps out of the sea,
while the sisters sing.

Day and night, and day and night,
the sisters are gone
with the morning star and the leaping fish
and the sky-walking sun.

The sisters, hoar with dried salt spray,
the semen of the sea,
make landfall where the parrots scream
From paperbark trees.
The sisters beach the bark canoe,
unload the 'rannga' things.
They thrust one in the earth. From there
the first goanna comes.
They've gone inland. Their digging sticks
make sacred springs.
They leave behind them 'rannga' forms
for all living things.

Out gathering food, the sisters have hung
their dilly-bags in a tree.
While they're away, men come and steal
their sacred ceremonies.
The sisters hear men singing and
song-sticks' "tjong-tjong."
"Cover your ears. We cannot hear
the sacred song.

O, all our sacred ceremonies
belong now to the men.
We must gather food, and bear
and rear children."

Manoowa

LET WISDOM WEAR THE CROWN:
HYMN TO GAIA

When the Wise Woman wears the crown
Marvels innumerable come to pass:
The sun rises in the East:
Seeds, well sown, swell,
Bring forth grass,
Oaks, lilies.

Earth's children moan
In grief; laugh when they are glad.
Wonders and marvels come to pass
When the Wise Woman wears the crown.

Water flows down hill,
Finds its level on the plain
When the Wise Woman is queen
Tigers and wolves kill
And none is moved to complain
If mild nourish fierce

As frost is chill
And fire burns, babes grow into women,
Sage and Child laugh, fear no bane
And find no thing to be ill.

The heart untaught, moves the blood;
Sap of love quickens male flower
To seek female rose, rose to receive.
Unguided, the new-born knows its food.
The eye sees. Brain feels its particular power
As bare stalk knows when to bud
And death to come in its time.
Marvels, marvels, miraculous dower
And plenitude of incalculable good.
We know these to be ours,
We sing, dance on the green,
When Wisdom wears the crown,
When the Wise Woman is queen.

Elsa Gidlow

MAGNIFICAT

And Mary said, My soul doth magnify the Lord,
And my spirit hath rejoiced in God my Saviour.
For he hath regarded the low estate of his
    handmaiden:
for, behold, from henceforth all generations shall
    call me blessed.
For he that is mighty hath done to me great
    things; and holy is his name.
And his mercy is upon them that fear him from
    generation to generation.
He hath shewed strength with his arm; he hath
    scattered the proud in the imagination of their
    hearts.
He hath put down the mighty from their seats,
    and exalted them of low degree.
He hath filled the hungry with good things; and
    the rich he hath sent empty away.
He hath holpen his servant Israel, in
    remembrance of his mercy;
As he spake to our fathers, to Abraham and to his
    seed forever.

Luke 1:46–55

JOB'S WIFE

Then his wife said to him, "Do you still hold fast your integrity?
Curse God and die." Job 2:9.

Yes, I said it.
And I told him to pull out his hair,
scream till his eyes turned black.

Some integrity,
scraping himself with broken pots.
An expert on God.
I'm an expert on mustard plaster,
bad breath.

On ten children —
their shoulders, their eyes,
the curve of their buttocks
I knew better than my own hands.

So you're God.
Tell me I'm straw, chaff, mist.

Tell me the sea has springs
deep and cold as dreams
that make me wake exhausted.

Enough thunder.
What have you done
with my children?

Betsy Sholl

9

THE PLACE OF
SELF-DISCOVERY

These moving poems and prayers describe the lives of women who have struggled and have felt pain and despair — in one case to the point of suicide, in another possibly to the point of madness — and have found a way through. Oodgeroo of Noonuccal (the fine Australian poet more usually known as Kath Walker) notes the way that love and pain are inextricable: "light and sister shade." For the Buddhist women Mutta, Nanduttara, and Siha, there has been the cutting away of lives that degraded and destroyed them, and the extraordinary discovery that they are free. The themes are familiar ones: the constriction of guilt in women's lives, the desperate attempt to cling to love, and the consequent release at the moment of letting go. It is an unfamiliar but very convincing study of salvation, which perhaps is something like what Dawna Markova suggests is "the lived life."

The desert waits,
ready for those who come,
who come obedient to the Spirit's leading;
or who are driven,
because they will not come any other way.

The desert always waits,
ready to let us know who we are —
the place of self-discovery.
And whilst we fear, and rightly,
the loneliness and emptiness and harshness,
we forget the angels,
whom we cannot see for our blindness,
but who come when God decides
that we need their help;
when we are ready
for what they can give us.

Ruth Burgess

I will not die an unlived life,
I will not go in fear
Of falling or catching fire,
I choose to inhabit my days,
To allow my living to open to me,
To make me less afraid,
More accessible,
To loosen my heart
Until it becomes a wing,
A torch, a promise.
I chose to risk my significance:
To live.
So that which comes to me as seed,
Goes to the next as blossom,
And that which comes to me as blossom,
Goes on as fruit.

Dawna Markova

MUTTA SPEAKS

I'm free. Ecstatically free
I'm free from three crooked things:
the mortar,
the pestle
and my hunchbacked husband
All that drags me back is cut-cut!

Mutta, a Therigata nun

SONG

Life is ours in vain
Lacking love, which never
Counts the loss or gain.
But remember, ever
Love is linked with pain.

Light and sister shade
Shape each mortal morrow
Seek not to evade
Love's companion, Sorrow,
And be not dismayed.

Grief is not in vain,
It's for our completeness.
If the fates ordain
Love to bring life sweetness'
Welcome too its pain.

Oodgeroo of the Noonuccal (Kath Walker)

I used to worship
fire, the moon, sun,
all the gods
I used to go down
to the riverbanks
for the bathing rites
I took holy vows
shaved half my head
slept on the ground
wouldn't eat food after sundown
Then I decked myself
out with many ornaments
baths, unguents, massage —
you name it —
Tried everything
to stave off death
I was a slave to my body
Then I really "got" it
saw my body as it really is
went homeless
Lust? Sex?

Forget it
All that binds me head and foot
is loosened.

Nanduttara, a Therigata nun

THE FORMER COURTESAN VIMALA

I used to be puffed up
high on good looks
intoxicated by a rosy complexion
voluptuous figure
I was haughty, vain,
looked down on other women
I was young
All painted up
I stood at the brothel door
like a hunter laying snares,
showing my wares —
Here are my breasts, a thigh
(lifts a skirt)
I conjured, mocked, seduced —
Today I'm bald
Clad in the outer robe, I go begging
Sitting at the foot of a tree,

I no longer discriminate
All ties have been cut
I said, cut.

Vimala

Vimala was converted by one of the Buddha's disciples, whom
she had tried in vain to seduce. She became a lay believer.

SIHA
WHO THOUGHT OF SUICIDE,
BUT GAVE IT UP

Distracted
too passionate
dumb about
the way things work
I was stung and tossed
by memories
Haunted, you could say
I went on like this,
wandering for seven years
Thin, pale, desperate
Nothing to hold me
Taking a rope
I went to the woods
Hanging is better
than this low life.
The noose was strong
I tied it to the branch of a tree
flung it round my neck
when suddenly — look —
it snapped!
Not my neck
my *heart* was free.

Siha, a Therigata nun

THE EDGE

Three times to the world's end I went,
Three times returned as one who brings
Tidings of light beyond the dark
But voiceless stays, still marvelling.

After great pain I had great joy
Three times that never else I knew;
The last reflection of its light
Fades from the pupils of my eyes.

Webbed by the world again I walk
The mazy paths that women tread
Watchful lest any harm should come
To those who journeyed back with me.

But still, as Lazarus who was born
Again beyond the edge of death,
I see the world half otherwise
And tremble at its mysteries.

Rosemary Dobson

10

THE SONG IS GONE

This section is full of the sense of grieving and loss—grieving for the lost way of life of Aboriginal peoples and for the tragedy of lost animal and plant species, which in turn has affected vulnerable peoples. "If the earth is spoiled," says the Yoruba poem, "it cannot be repaired." There is also anger about the way greed for profit has destroyed much that was precious.

BORA RING

The song is gone; the dance
is secret with the dancers in the earth,
the ritual useless, and the tribal story
lost in an alien tale.

Only the grass stands up
to mark the dancing-ring: the apple gums
posture and mime a past corroboree,
murmur a broken chant.

The hunter is gone: the spear
is splintered underground; the painted bodies
a dream the world breathed sleeping and forgot.
The nomad feet are still.

Only the rider's heart
halts at a sightless shadow, an unsaid word

that fastens in the blood the ancient curse,
the fear as old as Cain.

Judith Wright

The bora ring is the ceremonial space in which ritual
Aboriginal dances were performed.

WE ARE GOING

For Grannie Coolwell

They came in to the little town
A semi-naked band subdued and silent,
All that remained of their tribe.
They came to the place of their old bora ground
Where now the many white men hurry about
    like ants.
Notice of estate agent reads: 'Rubbish May Be
    Tipped Here'.
Now it half covers the traces of the old bora ring.
They sit and are confused, they cannot say their
    thoughts:
'We are as strangers here now, but the white
    tribe are the strangers.
We belong here, we are of the old ways.
We are the corroboree and the bora ground,
We are the old sacred ceremonies, the laws of the
    elders.

We are the wonder tales of Dream Time, the
    tribal legends told.
We are the past, the hunts and the laughing
    games, the wandering camp fires.
We are the lightning bolt over Gaphembah Hill
Quick and terrible,
And the Thunder after him, that loud fellow.
We are the quiet daybreak paling the dark
    lagoon.
We are the shadow-ghosts creeping back as the
    camp fires burn low.
We are nature and the past, all the old ways
Gone now and scattered.
The scrubs are gone, the hunting and the
    laughter.
The eagle is gone, the emu and the kangaroo are
    gone from this place.
The bora ring is gone.
The corroboree is gone.
And we are going.

Oodgeroo of the Noonuccal (Kath Walker)

Show us, O God, how to love not only animals, birds and all green and growing things, but the soil, air and water by which we live, so that we may not exploit or pollute them for our own profit or convenience.

Help us to cherish these necessities for our survival; and guide those in authority to ensure that the human spirit may not be starved in pursuit of material comfort and wealth.

Phoebe Hesketh

Lord, purge our eyes to see
Within the seed a tree,
within the glowing egg a bird,
Within the shroud a butterfly.
Till, taught by such we see
Beyond all creatures, thee
And hearken to thy tender word
And hear its "Fear not; it is I."

Christina Rossetti

AFTER EDEN

We ate not flesh in Eden, but afterwards,
when things got hard, we forgot
the peaceful kinship of that ancient kingdom.
As our teeth sank into their flesh
we had to deny them. So we said
they had no souls, no reason, no thumbs,
no speech. We were so different. We made
a chain of things to protect us—fire, medicine,
our locking houses, many kinds of clothes.
And we renamed them—farm product, fur crop,
renewable resource. Pray that we will see
their faces again in the mirror of creation,
the miracle of animals, their clear eyes
meaning more than profit to our own!

Jean Pearson

Enjoy the earth gently
For if the earth is spoiled
It cannot be repaired
Enjoy the earth gently.

Yoruba prayer

Helper of all who are helpless,
we call on you in times of stress
and in times of devastation.
Pick up the broken pieces
of our hearts, our homes, our history
and restore them to the way they were,
or give us the means of starting over
when everything seems lost.
O God, our help in ages past,
we place all our hope in you.

Miriam Therese Winter

11

BIRTH AND DEATH

At Maes Howe, on mainland Orkney in the Northern Isles of Scotland, there is an ancient tomb, probably built to take the bodies of chieftains and nobles. It is entered through a long narrow tunnel, which one has to bend double to walk through. Only when you reach the inner space, and can stand up, do you realize that the whole is constructed rather like a womb. The dead chieftain who once, like all the rest of us, left the peace of the womb and made his passage out into the daylight has now made his journey in reverse. Before visiting Maes Howe I had never thought to link birth and death in that way, but I found it a welcome idea. Death is a kind of second birth, only we do not know where it will take us, any more than the baby in the womb knows where it is going. So I decided to combine birth and death in this section.

For most women until recent times, giving birth was a journey through the valley of the shadow of death, in which they knew they might easily lose their lives. The passionate Gaelic prayer to the much-loved saint Bride must have been a comfort. There is another heartfelt invocation to a baby who, with the infinite pathos of the very young, was not going to live to discover the world. The two bitter Aboriginal mourning songs, while painful to read, catch the anger and helplessness of bereavement with a force and clarity that many of us will recognize.

A BIRTHING PRAYER TO ST. BRIDE

There came to me assistance,
Mary fair and Bride;
As Anna bore Mary,
As Mary bore Christ,
As Eile bore John the Baptist
Without flaw in him,
Aid thou me in mind unbearing,
    Aid me, O Bride!

As Christ was conceived of Mary
Full perfect on every hand,
Assist thou me, foster-mother,
The conception to bring from the bone;
As thou didst aid the Virgin of joy,
Without gold, without corn, without kine,
Aid thou me, great is my sickness,
    Aid me, O Bride.

Gaelic, Anonymous

TO BE SUNG BY THE ONE
WHO FIRST TAKES THE CHILD
FROM ITS MOTHER

Newborn, on the naked sand
Nakedly lay it.
Next to the earth mother,
That it may know her,
Having good thoughts of her, the food giver.

Newborn, we tenderly
In our arms take it,
Making good thoughts.
House-god, be entreated,
That it may grow from childhood to manhood,
Happy, contented,
Beautifully walking
The trail to old age.
Having good thoughts of the earth its mother,
That she may give it the fruits of her being.
Newborn, on the naked sand
Nakedly lay it.

Pueblo song

THE NEWBORN

My little son, I have cast you out
To hang heels upward, wailing over a world
With walls too wide.
My faith till now, and now my love:
No walls too wide for that to fill, no depth
Too great for all you hide.

I love, not knowing what I love,
I give, though ignorant for whom
The history and power of a name.
I conjure with it, like a novice
Summoning unknown spirits: answering me
You take the word and tame it.

Even as the gift of life
You take the famous name you did not choose
And make it new.
You and the name exchange a power:
Its history is changed, becoming yours,
And yours by this: who calls this, calls you.

Strong vessel of peace, and plenty promised,
Into whose unsounding depths I pour
This alien power;
Frail vessel launched with a shawl for sail,
Whose guiding spirit keeps his needle-quivering
Poise between trust and terror,
And stares amazed to find himself alive;
This is the means by which you say *I am,*
Not to be lost till all is lost,
When at the sight of God you say *I am nothing,*
And find, forgetting name and speech at last,
A home not mine, dear outcast.

Anne Ridler

ELEGY

I am going home with thee
To thy home! to thy home!
I am going home with thee
To thy home of winter.

I am going home with thee
To thy home! to thy home!
I am going home with thee
To thy home of autumn,
of spring and of summer.

I am going home with thee,
Thou child of my love,
To thine eternal bed
To thy perpetual sleep.

I am going home with thee,
Thou child of my love,
To the dear Son of blessings,
To the Father of grace.

Anonymous

There, in that other world, what waits for me?
What shall I find after that other birth?
No stormy, tossing, foaming, smiling sea,
But a new earth.

No sun to mark the changing of the days,
No slow, soft falling of the alternate night,
No moon, no star, no light upon my ways,
Only the Light.

No gray cathedral, wide and wondrous fair,
That I may tread where all my fathers trod.
Nay, nay, my soul, no house of God is there,
But only God.

Mary Coleridge

TWO ABORIGINAL WOMEN'S MOURNING SONGS

The blowflies buzz . . .

Ah, the blowfly is whining there, its maggots are
    eating the flesh.
The blowflies buzz, their feet stray over the
    corpse . . .
The buzzing goes on and on . . .
Who is it, eating there, whose flesh are they
    eating? . . .
Ah my daughter, come back here to me!
Ah, our daughter was taken ill—
You didn't sing for her, as a father should!
You are foolish and silly, you sing only to please
    the ears of women!
You like to lie close to a young girl, a virgin, and
    give her a child!
You will not stay in one place;
Here and there, all over the place, you go among
    the camps,

You go walking hither and thither, looking for
    sweethearts.
Ah, before it was here that you used to stay.
You should be ashamed to do that before all these
    strangers!
Presently I will take up a knife and cut you!
(B says: 'This is all that I do: I get food to eat,
    and tobacco to smoke!')
No, you go to sit down beside some woman,
You sit close, close beside her . . .
Ah, my lost, sick child—ah, the blowflies!
Soon I will hit that woman of yours, that Y! She
    is rubbish, that woman of yours, her face is
    ugly, she smells like an evil spirit! Presently,
    when she is pregnant, I won't look after her!
You, B, you, her husband, you indeed, all by
    yourself, you can help her in childbirth!
All you others, eat . . .

Ah my daughter, my grandchild!
Ah, the snake with its tongue flickering, at
    Dagalbawei . . .
Ah, my daughter, ah, the mound of the snake!
Ah my grandchild! My grandchild!

At Bumbiwalwalyun, and far away, the snake
  scatters its young,
At Waidja and Dirmalangan, Ganal and Ngoiwul.
My daughter, my grandchild! My daughter is
  sick and hungry!
All you others, you eat till your bellies burst!
You used to be jealous before, when your
  husband called her.
All you lot are alive still—ah, my daughter, my
  grandchild!
Ah, your father has cried and cried, while mucus
  flowed into his mouth!
My daughter, my husband! My daughter, sick
  and hungry!
Ah, my daughter, my husband!
Presently your child will grow, and you won't be
  looking after him,
because you will be dead! Presently other
  children will hit him, other
women will not look after him properly . . . !
Ah, my daughter, my grandchild!

These songs come from North Eastern Arnhenland, Australia.

I am no longer afraid of death
I know well
Its dark and cold corridors
leading to life.

I am afraid rather of that life
which does not come out of death
which cramps our hands
and retards our march.

I am afraid of my fear
and even more of the fear of others,
who do not know where they are going,
who continue clinging
to what they consider to be life
which we know to be death!

Julia Esquivel

12

BLESSINGS

As the anonymous mother's blessing translated from the Gaelic shows, blessings, though they can be used in many different ways, are particularly moving as a parting prayer, a commending of another or of a group to safety, happiness, and good actions until those who part have the pleasure of meeting once more. Blessings leave a good taste on the palate, a sense of harmony and peace.

BLESSING

The blessing of God,
The eternal goodwill of God,
The shalom of God,
the wildness and the warmth of God,
be among us and between us
Now and always. Amen.

Anonymous

When people turn
from the table
where bread is broken
and candles glow,
be sure you have invited them
not to your house
but to their own,
and offered not your wisdom
but your love.

Anonymous

May the power and the mystery go before us, to
    show us the way,
shine above us to lighten our world,
lie beneath us to bear us up,

walk with us and give us companionship,

and glow and flow within us to bring us joy.
    Amen.

Judith Walker-Riggs

THE MOTHER'S BLESSING

Be the great God between thy two shoulders
To protect thee in thy going and in thy coming,
Be the Son of Mary Virgin near thine heart,
And be the perfect Spirit upon thee pouring —
Oh, the perfect Spirit upon thee pouring!

Gaelic, Anonymous

May the God who dances in creation,
and embraces us with human love,
who shakes our lives like thunder,
bless us and drive us out with power
to fill the world with her justice. Amen.

Janet Morley

About the Contributors

Alexander, Cecil Frances (1818–1895) An Irish poet and hymn-writer, she grew up in County Wicklow, Ireland. Her book *Hymns for Little Children* (1848) included three favorite hymns that are still widely sung today: "All Things Bright and Beautiful," "Once in Royal David's City," and "There Is a Green Hill Far Away." She also wrote Irish ballads. She was married to Bishop William Alexander.

Allshorn, Florence (1887–1950) A missionary in Uganda with the Church Missionary Society, she returned to Britain just before the Second World War with her health undermined. When she recovered, she set up the experiment of a lay community in Sussex, known as St. Julian's, which for forty years was a resource for people needing rest, a place of calm and beauty where they could recuperate and refind themselves.

She had original and practical insights about leading the spiritual life.

Austen, Jane (1775–1817) The daughter of a clergyman, she spent much of her life living in a rectory at Steventon, later at Chawton, both in the Hampshire countryside, in the south of England. Lack of money made it impossible for her to marry the man she loved. She was the author of *Pride and Prejudice* and other classic novels that placed her among the most famous of writers in the English language.

Bates, Katherine Lee (1859–1929) An American poet, she was born in Falmouth, Massachusetts, but spent much of her life in nearby Wellesley, where she became a professor of English at Wellesley College. She wrote or edited several scholarly books, but is most widely known as composer of the song "America the Beautiful."

Beatrijs of Nazareth (c.1200–c.1268) Beatrijs was born into a wealthy merchant family in the Brabant in Flanders, and was educated at first by the Beguines, then later by the Cistercians at Florival, where she received the same education a boy of the period would have had—the trivium and the quadrivium, a study of arts and sciences. She later learned calligraphy and manuscript illumination, and took vows as a

Cistercian nun. She became prioress of the convent of Our Lady of Nazareth at Lier. She was a scholar, writer, and poet, very much influenced, like some of her contemporaries, by the poetry of courtly love, which she applied to her relationship with God. Despite her skill in Latin, she chose to write in the Flemish dialect.

The Beguines This order of women was founded in the Netherlands in the twelfth century. They were a religious group and did not take vows; some lived in community, and some lived a lay life in their own homes. Their influence spread to other parts of northern Europe. They offered unique support and companionship to single women without insisting on the vows and austerities of convent life. They performed works of charity, which included caring for the sick and running schools. They included some fine women poets. They fell under papal disapproval at the Council of Vienne in 1311 when they, and their male counterparts, the Beghards, were accused of heresy and condemned. At least one Beguine was burned. Some of the women, like Mechthild of Magdeburg, joined convents for protection.

Bossis, Gabrielle (1874–1950) French author of *He and I*, a diary-style account of her discussions with Jesus.

Brontë, Anne (1820–1849) **Born in Yorkshire, England,** she was the youngest of the renowned Brontë literary family. Occasionally employed as governesses, she and her sisters Emily and Charlotte joined together in 1846 to pseudonymously publish *Poems* by *Currer, Ellis, and Acton Bell.* All three eventually publicly admitted their gender, continuing to write prolifically and publish some of the best-known novels and poems in the English language. Her two novels, *Agnes Grey* and *The Tenant of Wildfeld Hall* were published in 1847 and 1848, immediately before her death of tuberculosis in 1849.

Burgess, Ruth (1948–) **She grew up in Birmingham,** England, and South Wales and now lives in Sunderland, England. She is a member of the Iona Community, a Christian group attached to the island of Iona in western Scotland, who have produced some outstanding writing on Christian themes, in particular prayers and liturgical writing.

Carmichael, Amy (1867–1951) A Christian missionary in south India who wrote prolifically and well. She was an advocate for women and was especially concerned about the fate of children who were given to temples by their parents and sometimes neglected.

Clifton, Lucille (1936–) Born in Depew, New York, to a working class family of book lovers with no formal education, she attended Howard University as a drama major. An award-winning African-American poet of family history, relationships, community, and racial history, she has also published many books for children and young adults. Her published poems can be found in many books, including *Quilting: Poems 1987–1990* and *Good Woman: Poems and a Memoir: 1969–1980*. She has been the Distinguished Professor of Humanities at St. Mary's College of Maryland since 1991.

Coleridge, Mary (1861–1907) Born into a literary family in London, England, she was a descendant of Samuel Taylor Coleridge, and her parents entertained Tennyson, Browning, Ruskin, and several of the Pre-Raphaelite painters. She was a novelist, literary critic, and a rather shy poet, for a long time refusing to offer her poetry for publication.

Coolidge, Susan (1835–1905) Her real name was Sarah Chauncy Woolsey. She grew up in Cleveland, Ohio. She was the author of *What Katy Did* (1872) and two other much-loved Katy books, as well as other books for girls. Katy was a strong and rather rebellious heroine, which made her a novelty among the well-behaved children in many nineteenth-century children's books.

Cropper, Margaret (1886–1980) A poet who spent her life in Westmorland, England, she took much of her inspiration from its life and speech. Much of her poetry used Christian themes.

Dickinson, Emily (1830–1886) Born and lived all her life in Amherst, Massachusetts, she was educated at the Amherst Academy and Mount Holyoke Seminary. She lived as a recluse from the age of about thirty, and wrote over 2,000 poems, only seven of which were published in her lifetime. This was partly because of the advice of her mentor, Thomas Higginson, who, while recognizing her genius, felt that her work was too unconventional for publication. In 1890, however, Higginson and her Amherst friend Mabel Loomis Todd published a selection, which they called *Poems*. In 1960 a complete edition of her poems was published using the original typography and spellings, which her editors had changed.

Dobson, Rosemary (1920–) New South Wales, Australia-born poet. Winner of the Patrick White Award in 1984, her many books include her *Collected Poems* (1991).

Esquivel, Julia (1930–) An exile of her native Guatemala, she has spent much of her life working for the poor and the oppressed. Poet and theologian, she served on the staff of the World Council of Churches in Geneva. More recently, she taught at the Methodist Seminary in Mexico City, where she also worked with women's groups, Guatemalan refugees, the Jewish community, and international groups seeking justice for Latin America.

Falk, Marcia Born and raised in New York, she graduated from Brandeis University and Stanford University, where she earned a Ph.D. in English and comparative literature. She was a Fulbright Scholar in Bible and Hebrew literature at the Hebrew University in Jerusalem, eventually returning as a Postdoctoral Fellow. Along with writing her own poetry, she works to discover and translate old and new voices of other women poets, especially those writing in Hebrew and Yiddish. Her most recent work, *The Book of Blessings* (1997), is a prayer book that recreates Hebrew and English liturgy from a contemporary, nonhierarchical, gender-inclusive perspective. She is currently the Rabbi Sally Priesand Visiting Professor of Jewish Women's Studies at Hebrew Union College in Cincinnati.

Fuertes, Gloria (1918–1998) Born in Madrid into a poor family, she was the youngest of nine children and one of only three who survived childhood. She attended the Instituto de Educación Profesional de la Mujer, where she received the education that was then considered necessary for a future housewife. The Civil War and the loss of her fiancé changed her life, transforming her into a pacifist. In 1939 she wrote her first story for children. In 1950, her first poem, *Isla Ignorada,* was published, and she established *Versos con Faldas,* a group of female poets. A founder of *Arquero* magazine and a librarian at the International Institute of Madrid, she wrote many children's books and volumes of poetry. She received many awards for her work, including the Guipúzcoa Prize and the International Hans Christian Andersen award.

Foligno, Angela di (c.1248–c.1309) She was born of well-to-do parents in Umbria and married at twenty into a life of fashion and luxury. She was deeply influenced by St. Francis, and perhaps imitating the saint, she stood in front of the altar of the church of San Francesco and removed all her clothes as a sign of giving herself to God. Dramatically, her mother, husband, and children suddenly died — presumably in an epidemic — and Angela sold her country estate, gave away all her possessions, and joined the Third Order of Franciscans in order to care for lepers and the poor. It is not certain whether she could write, but her *Book of the Experience of the Truly Faithful,* which described thirty steps toward God, was dictated by her in the Umbrian dialect.

Gidlow, Elsa (1898–1986) She was one of the first openly lesbian writers in America and was indicted by

Senator Joseph McCarthy in the 1950s. She helped found the Druid Heights community in the California redwoods, of which Alan Watts and other writers and artists were members.

Gottlieb, Lynn (1949–) American, born in Bethlehem, Pennsylvania. She travelled to Israel as a high school exchange student and this experience kindled in her the desire to become a rabbi. There were no women rabbis at that time. Ordained in 1981, she is active in creating new, contemporary forms of Judaism, as reflected in her book, *She Who Dwells Within: A Feminist Vision of a Renewed Judaism* (1995). She once said: "God has a female presence but that presence is in exile. It is not until we redeem Her and bring Her home to rest in us that the entire world will be redeemed."

Greenberg, Florence (1882–1980) London-born cookery expert, journalist, and writer.

Griffiths, Ann (1776–1805) She grew up on a farm in Montgomeryshire, Wales, and had a deeply mystical temperament. She joined the Methodists in 1797. She married in 1804 and died the next year in childbirth. She was an outstandingly gifted writer of hymns, none of which were published until after her death.

Hadewijch of Brabant (mid-thirteenth century) An educated woman who knew French and Latin but who chose to write in the Brabantine dialect, she used the tradition of the *minnesänger,* the poetry of courtly love, to write about her passion for God. She was a leader in the Beguine community, but for some unknown reason was disgraced.

Hare, Maria (1798–1870) British. She was a religious writer and diarist, who was born at Knutsford in Cheshire and educated mainly at home. She traveled widely in Europe and married the Reverend Augustus Hare. She designed an education program for home-bound mothers.

Hatshepsut, Queen of Egypt (1500 BCE) She was the daughter of Thutmose I and the half-sister of his successor, Thutmose II. When he died young, and his heir, Thutmose III, was still a child, Hatshepsut had herself made Pharaoh, a distinction unique for a woman, and ruled for many years before Thutmose III took his revenge and Hatshepsut disappeared. She built a magnificent temple at Deir el-Bahri near Thebes.

Havergal, Frances Ridley (1836–1879) A well-known British hymn-writer, she was born in Worcestershire, England, and educated at home. She published poetry, hymns, and a book called *Havergal's Psalmody,* and gave the proceeds to the Church Missionary Society. She refused all offers of marriage. She disapproved of women's rights and of "strong-minded women" in general.

Hildegard of Bingen (1098–1179) Born in the Rhineland, she was the tenth child in an aristocratic family and was given to her aunt Jutta, a hermit, at the age of eight, apparently as a form of tithing to show the devoutness of her family—a practice she was to deplore in her adult writing. She suffered acutely from appalling migraine headaches throughout her life. She took vows as a Benedictine nun at the age of fifteen. At the age of thirty-eight she followed her aunt as abbess of the monastery. She was multigifted as musician, poet, and biologist, and was deeply interested also in medicine. She had visions, many of which are detailed in her book *Scivias*. Toward the end of her life she embarked on preaching tours all over the countryside, an extraordinary project for a woman of her period.

Holtby, Winifred (1898–1935) She was born in Yorkshire, England, and had a deep love of the Yorkshire countryside, something very obvious in her novels, particularly in the most famous of them, *South Riding*. She served in France during the First World War as a WAAC, a member of the Women's Auxiliary Army Corps. She met the writer Vera Brittain at Oxford

University, and they shared a commitment to pacifism and to feminist principles. After Winifred Holtby's early death, Vera Brittain wrote a book about her: *Testament of Friendship* (1940).

Julian of Norwich (c.1342–c.1413) An English mystic, she lived as an anchoress outside the walls of St. Julian's Church, Norwich. (Unfortunately her cell was destroyed by bombing during the Second World War.) She received a series of visions on May 8, 1373, which she later wrote down, and these are known as *The Showings* or *Revelations of Divine Love*. Her theology placed a strong emphasis on the love of God—she believed that this would redeem all the souls in hell, an unusual and near-heretical belief at the time—and she used the image of mother love to illustrate the tenderness and forgiveness of God.

Lalleswari (fourteenth century) Born in Kashmir of an upper class Hindu family, she became a mystical poet. She left her husband and joined a sect called the Saivites, who believed that the human soul is one with God.

Levertov, Denise (1923–1997) She grew up in Ilford, Essex, and was educated at home by her Welsh mother and by her father, a Russian Jew, who settled in

England after the First World War and became an Anglican priest. She worked as a nurse in England but left for the United States in 1948 and lived in New York City. She had already published a volume of poetry in England. In America, under the mentorship of Kenneth Rexroth and later James Laughlin of New Directions, she was to publish much more poetry that would be greatly admired by literary critics and others. She was a very gifted poet, mystical yet down to earth. She campaigned for civil rights and against the Vietnam War, the Bomb, and U.S.-backed regimes in Latin America. She converted to Roman Catholicism.

Levy-Tanai, Sarah (1911–1975) A contemporary Israeli teacher and composer of children's songs, she was born in Jerusalem to Yemenite parents and then orphaned at a young age. Her song compositions include the popular "Kol Dodi" (My Love's Voice). In 1949, she founded the Inbal Dance Troupe and in 1973 she received the Israel Prize for her contribution to dance in Israel.

Lewin, Ann (1936–) She lives in Southampton, Hampshire, England. She worked for twenty-seven years as a teacher, and then as a student welfare adviser at Southampton University. She writes poetry and prayers. Her latest volume of poetry is *Candles and Kingfishers* (2000). She gives retreats and quiet days.

Mechthild of Magdeburg (c.1210–1280) Born into a noble Saxon family, at fifteen she joined the Beguines and remained a member for forty years. She was a mystic and spiritual writer and wrote *The Flowing Light of the Godhead*. Like other Beguines, she was interested in the poetry of courtly love. In old age she joined the Cistercian convent at Helfta, possibly as protection from the Inquisition.

Markova, Dawna Internationally known for her ground-breaking work in helping people learn with passion and live on purpose. She is the CEO of Professional Thinking Partners, Inc., in Utah, co-founder of the Worldwide Women's Web, and former research affiliate of the Organizational Learning Center at Massachusetts Institute of Technology. Her books include *I Will Not Die an Unlived Life, The Open Mind*, and *No Enemies Within; An Unused Intelligence*, co-authored with her husband and business partner, Andy Bryner; and *How Your Child Is Smart* and *Learning Unlimited*, co-authored with Anne R. Powell. She also co-edited *Random Acts of Kindness*, has been a frequent guest on National Public Radio, and was featured on a PBS special.

McIlhagga, Kate (1938–) She grew up in Glasgow, Scotland, and would have liked to have been ordained in the Church of Scotland when she left the University of St. Andrew's in the 1960s, but women could not be ordained in the Church of Scotland at the time, so she trained as a youth and community worker. She married and had three sons. In 1981 she was ordained as a United Reformed minister, and in the same year she became a member of the Iona Community. At present she is a minister of three rural parishes in North Northumberland and is beginning to prepare for retirement.

Meynell, Alice (1847–1922) Born of a well-to-do and artistic family in London, she spent her childhood mostly in Italy and Switzerland where she was privately educated by her father. She converted to Roman Catholicism in 1872. In 1875 she published a volume of poetry, *Preludes,* which was much admired by Ruskin, W. M. Rossetti and George Eliot. She married the distinguished journalist and editor Wilfred Meynell, and they co-edited a number of journals. She was a supporter of women's suffrage, and was concerned about the social status of women. She disliked sentimental mentions of "the feminine," saying that it was a force, not a grace.

Mirabai (c.1498–c.1550) She was born in Rajasthan and raised as a princess. She was married at eighteen to the Rajput heir apparent but was widowed before he ascended the throne. Mirabai, who all her life had a devotion to Krishna, gave herself up to religious practices and left the court for a series of journeys. She was an adept of the medieval yogic tradition of the north of India, a *bhakta*—a devoted one—searching for and submitting to the supreme reality, Krishna. Aesthetics and enlightenment were combined in this tradition, and Mirabai was an accomplished musician and sang her compositions.

Morley, Janet (1951–) She wrote some of the first inclusive prayers used in Britain, which were then widely used and admired both for their use of language and for their theological excellence. She went on to work as adult education adviser for Christian Aid, where she continued to write and edit material for use by Christian groups. She is now working for the Methodist Church as secretary for adult learning.

Oodgeroo of the Noonuccal (Kath Walker) (1920–1993) A well-known Australian poet from the Noonuccal tribe of Stradbroke Island, near Brisbane, she reverted to her tribal name as a protest against the bicentennial celebrations of 1988. She has published several books of poetry. Under the name of Kath Walker she had been made a Member of the British Empire in 1971.

Rabi'a the Mystic (ninth century) A Sufi saint born of poor parents in Basra and orphaned as a child, she was sold into slavery but later freed. She devoted much of her life to prayer.

Ratushinskaya, Irina (1954–) Born in Russia, she was arrested in Kiev at the age of twenty-eight and sentenced to seven years hard labor and five years internal exile, accused of anti-Soviet agitation and propaganda, on account of her poetry. In a labor camp in Mordovia, she was held in a special unit for women political prisoners where she suffered beatings, force-feeding, and solitary confinement at temperatures so cold that the KGB told her she would never be able to bear children. She continued to write poetry in the prison, and the poems were smuggled out and published, arousing interest in her plight around the world. In 1986, on the eve of the Reykjavik summit, she was released. She came to London and eventually settled with her husband in Britain, where six years later she gave birth to twin sons. She has continued to write.

Riccuiti, Gail Reverend and Associate Professor of Homiletics, Colgate Rochester Divinity School, she has served churches in Massillon, Ohio, and in Byron and Rochester, New York, and she was Vice Moderator of the 189th General Assembly (UPCUSA). She is co-author of the two-volume *Birthings and Blessings*.

Ridler, Anne (1912–) She grew up in Warwickshire, England, and was educated at King's College, London. She worked as secretary and editorial assistant to T.S. Eliot, and later in publishing. She married and had four children. She wrote poetry, plays, and an opera libretto; made translations of opera libretti; and edited several well-known poets.

Rossetti, Christina (1830–1894) She lived in London, where she was closely associated with the group of religious painters known as the Pre-Raphaelite Brotherhood, of which her brother, Dante Gabriel Rossetti, was a member. She was a poet and the author of many poems on themes of love or religion, as well as the longer, very sensual poem "Goblin Market."

St. Bridget of Kildare (fifth century) Irish holy woman. She is often called St. Brigid, St. Bride, or St. Bridget of Kildare. Little is known about her, but she did found a great monastery at Kildare. She is buried at Downpatrick with St. Patrick and St. Columba, and with them she is patron of Ireland; hence her nickname Mary of the Gael. St. Bridget is associated notably with charity and justice. Devotion to her was widespread in Great Britain before the Protestant Reformation, as witnessed in many names, e.g., Bridewell, Kilbride, Kirkbride, and McBride. Her Feast Day is celebrated February 1.

St. Hilda Community This community, founded in 1987, is a prayer group of women and men, which began meeting in the East End of London, at first as a form of protest at the Church of England's refusal to allow women ordained in other countries to celebrate Holy Communion in its churches. The Community openly invited visiting women priests to celebrate in the university chapel where they held their meetings, from which the Community was eventually expelled on the orders of the then Bishop of London. (This was at a time when the Church of England was still undecided about whether to ordain women.) The group wrote many prayers and liturgies using inclusive language, and went on to publish two books of prayers: *Women Included* (1991) and *New Women Included* (1996). The Community still meets regularly.

Sappho (c. 610–c. 580 BCE) She was born on Lesbos but later lived at Mytilene, though for a while she was exiled from there to Sicily. Only two complete examples of her odes remain, though there are beautiful fragments of other poems. Her use of the four-line stanza, which Catullus and Horace went on to use, gave the name *Sapphic* to this literary form. Because Sappho wrote with admiration and affection of a group of women and girls to whom she seems to have been a leader, or possibly teacher, the island Lesbos has given the word *lesbian* for women who are sexually attracted to other women. It is not known whether Sappho herself actually was lesbian. She married and had a daughter, Cleis.

Shakers Popular name for the Millennial Church, an eighteenth-century body, which, because of persecution in England, left for America in 1774. They settled near Albany, New York, and later had other settlements in different parts of the country. They were led by Mother Ann Lee, whom they regarded as the "female principle in Christ" as Jesus had been the "male principle." They practiced celibacy and renewed their numbers by conversion. They were famous for their music and dancing and for the simple beauty of the furniture, houses, and farm implements that they made.

Shemer, Naomi (1931–) Israeli composer, known as "the First Lady of Israeli Song." Her popular songs include "Yerushalayim shel Zahav" (Jerusalem of Gold) and "Lu Yehi" (Let It Be), which was inspired by The

Beatles' tune of the same name. She won the Israel Prize in 1983.

Shepperson, Janet She is a member of the Corrymeela Community in Northern Ireland and wrote *The Furthest North You Can Go.*

Sholl, Betsy Winner of the 1997 Felix Pollak Prize in Poetry for her fifth book of poetry *Don't Explain,* she grew up on the New Jersey shore and holds degrees from Bucknell University, the University of Rochester, and Vermont College. She has published five books of poetry, including *Changing Faces, Appalachian Winter,* and *Rooms Overhead.* The fourth, *The Red Line,* won the 1991 Associated Writing Programs Award for Poetry. She teaches at the University of Southern Maine and at Vermont College.

Starhawk (1951–) American, she is one of the primary voices of the ecofeminism and Goddess movements. She is the author or coauthor of eight books, including *The Spiral Dance* and *The Twelve Wild Swans* (2000).

Sumner, Mary (1828–1921) As the wife of the Rector of Old Alresford in Hampshire, she felt a need to bring together country women of different backgrounds — "cottage women and elegant and aristocratic women," as she put it—in the common enterprise of giving their children a spiritual upbringing. She founded the Mothers' Union in 1876, an Anglican organization, which now has 750,000 members concerned with the well-being of families worldwide.

St. Teresa of Ávila (1515–1582) She entered a Carmelite convent as a young woman, but it was very casually run, with the nuns entertaining young men from the town. After some years of boredom and discontent and an unexplained severe illness, Teresa underwent a spiritual change. She began to pray at great depth and to have unusual spiritual experiences of levitation and ecstasy. She was later to found her own stricter form of the Carmelite life, the Discalced (i.e., without shoes) Carmelites, and set up houses for friars and nuns all over Spain. She was a friend of St. John of the Cross. She wrote what was almost a scientific study of the stages of prayer, and combined mystical experiences with an extremely busy and practical life.

Teresa, Mother (1910–1997) Born in Yugoslavia, of Albanian parents, she grew up in Macedonia. She went to India in 1928 to join an order of nuns, the Sisters of Loretto, and she taught in their school and eventually became the headmistress of it. In 1948, however, she felt a call to work in the slums of Calcutta, and by 1950 she had started her own order, the Order of the Missionaries of Charity. In 1952 she established the House for the Dying, where her work became famous. It spread widely both in India and in other parts of the world. She was awarded the Nobel Peace Prize in 1979.

St. Thérèse of Lisieux (1873–1897) Born in a deeply devout family, Thérèse followed her two older sisters into the Carmelite convent in Lisieux at the age of fifteen. A spoiled child at home, she suffered a good deal under a harsh superior. She worked out what she called her "Little Way," a spiritual method in which whatever happened could be accepted as a way of loving God, described by her in her moving autobiography *The History of a Soul.* She died of tuberculosis at the age of twenty-four. She was much loved and admired in France, and many village churches there still have statues of Thérèse. During the First World War, many French soldiers went into battle carrying medallions of Thérèse. She was canonized in 1925.

Therigata nuns (c.500–400 BC) These were female disciples of the Buddha (their male equivalent were known as Theragata) who had given up worldly preoccupations to live a nomadic and contemplative life with minimal possessions in the forests and parks of India. *Therigata* means "songs of the nuns." They were accomplished poets, encouraged by the Buddha to use local dialect in their poem/prayers, rather than the formal scholarly language of Sanskrit.

Underhill, Evelyn (1875–1941) She came from a well-to-do background and was privately educated before taking her degree at King's College, London. She taught the philosophy of religion for a while at Manchester College, Oxford. She married Hubert Stuart Moore and lived for many years in Campden Hill Square in London. She was interested in mystical experience and wrote a classic book about it: *Mysticism* (1911). She underwent a conversion experience and became an Anglican. She was very much influenced by the Catholic theologian Friedrich von Hugel (1852–1925), but she never became a Catholic. She continued to write and became well-known as a giver of retreats and as a spiritual director, which was unusual for women in the early twentieth century.

Waddell, Helen (1889–1965) Of Irish descent, she was born in Tokyo, of a Presbyterian missionary and Chinese scholar, Hugh Waddell. She returned to Ireland to go to school and university in Belfast where her studies in

Latin later helped with her translations of medieval Latin poetry. Her books about the Middle Ages introduced many readers to the period. Her novel about the medieval Scholastic Peter Abelard, *Peter Abelard* (1933), was a huge success, selling thirty editions. She also published some translations from the Chinese.

Walker, Alice (1944–) American novelist from Georgia. She studied at Sarah Lawrence College, and went on to work as teacher and social worker in New York City. She was active in the Civil Rights movement. *The Color Purple* (1982) won the Pulitzer Prize, and was made into a film by Steven Spielberg.

Walker, Kath (See Oodgeroo of the Noonuccal)

Walker-Riggs, Judith American, she is currently Interim Minister of the Main Line Unitarian Church in Devon, Pennsylvania. She earned a Doctor of Divinity degree from Meadville/Lombard Theological School in Chicago, and is a frequent guest speaker and preacher.

Waring, Anna Laetitia (1823–1910) Born in Glamorgan, Wales, and brought up as a Quaker, she converted to Anglicanism in 1842 and became a well-known hymn writer. Her *Hymns and Meditations* (1850) went into twenty editions. In addition to writing, she was a constant visitor to Bristol prison and worked for the Prisoners' Aid Society. She never married, but lived with her three sisters.

Watt, Jean Macdonald (1915–) Born in Reading, England, of Scottish and Welsh parentage, she has lived in Scotland since 1933. She is a mother and grandmother, and has been a social worker. Her interests are music, painting, and writing. She has published poetry and prose translations from French and German.

Weil, Simone (1909–1943) A Parisian, Simone Weil was a contemporary of Simone de Beauvoir and Jean-Paul Sartre at the Ecole Normale Supérieure. She taught philosophy but also worked in the Renault car factory as a way of sharing the life of the working class. She went to Spain to serve in the Civil War but was soon invalided home after an accident. She was attracted by Christianity but repelled by the way it was practiced. She wrote several books on religious themes and had a strong mystical sense. She died in an English hospital during the Second World War, partly of tuberculosis, partly from starving herself so as not to eat more than her contemporaries under the Nazi occupation of France.

Winter, Miriam Thérèse Medical Mission Sister and Professor of Liturgy, Worship, Spirituality, and Feminist Studies at Hartford Seminary, Hartford, Connecticut, she is also a musician and writer. She has worked with the hungry and the homeless on four continents. Her many books include *The Singer and the Song* (a memoir), *Woman Wisdom*, and *The Gospel According to Mary*. She earned a Ph.D. in Liturgical Studies at Princeton Theological Seminary.

Wright, Judith (1915–2000) An Australian from Armidale, New South Wales, born into a prominent farming family, she had a distinguished literary career as a poet, publishing eleven books of poetry. She also worked on issues of human rights, conservation and Aboriginal land rights.

I regret that there are some women whose works are included in this collection whose life and work, despite research, I still know very little about. If they or their friends read this book, I would be glad to learn more. —M. F.

Credits

The author is grateful to the following authors and publishers for permission to reproduce the material listed below. This page constitutes a continuation of the copyright page.

The late Florence Allshorn and the St. Julian's Trust, Coolham, Sussex, England, for excerpts from *The Notebooks of Florence Allshorn* selected and arranged by a member of St. Julian's Community. Published by St. Julian's, 1990.

National Aboriginal and Torres Strait Islander Catholic Council, Australia, for "Aboriginal Jubilee Prayer."

SPCK for the poem by Beatrijs of Nazareth from *Beguine Spirituality: An Anthology* by Fiona Bowie. Translations by Oliver Davies (London: SPCK, 1989).

Gabrielle Bossis and Brother Steven Prizzo of Librairie Mediaspaul of Sherbrooke, Quebec, Canada, for quotations from *He and I* (Editions Paulines).

Ruth Burgess for *The Desert.*

E. Richard Brodhag for "Think through Me" and "It Is Not Far to Go" by Amy Carmichael from *Mountain Breezes,* published by CLC Books, Fort Washington, Pa.

SPCK for *Harvest Prayer* by Lilian Cox from *Little Book of Prayers* (London: SPCK, 1988).

Curtis Brown Pty. Ltd., Sydney, Australia, for "The Edge" and "Folding the Sheets" by Rosemary Dobson.

Julia Esquivel for "I Am No Longer Afraid of Death."

Hardie St. Martin for "Bird's Nest" by Gloria Fuertes.

Monica Furlong for "In This Good World" from *God's a Good Man* (London: Mowbray, 1974).

Celeste West and Booklegger Publishing, P.O. Box 460654, San Francisco, CA 94146, (415) 642-7569, for Elsa Gidlow's work.

Lynn Gottlieb and HarperCollins for "Greeting Shekinah" from *She Who Dwells Within,* © 1995 by Lynn Gottieb. Reprinted with permission.

Hamlyn Publishers for the charoseth recipe from *Jewish Cookery* by Florence Greenberg (London: Hamlyn, 1958.).

SPCK for the poem by Hadewijch of Brabant from *Beguine Spirituality: An Anthology* by Fiona Bowie. Translations by Oliver Davies (London: SPCK, 1989).

Cornell University Press for "Antiphon for God the Father" by Hildegard of Bingen, translated by Barbara Newman from *Saint Hildegard of Bingen: Symphonia* (Ithaca, N.Y.: Cornell University Press, 1988).

SPCK for passages from Julian of Norwich from *The SPCK Book of Christian Prayer* (London: SPCK, 1995).

Methodist Publishing House, Peterborough, England, for selection from *Candles and Kingfishers*, copyright Ann Lewin. Used by permission.

Bloodaxe Books, Northumberland, England, and New Directions Publishing, New York, for "In Whom We Live and Move and Have Our Being" and "Sands of the Well" from *Sands of the Well* by Denise Levertov.

Sarah Levy and Reform Synagogues of Great Britain for the Chanukah prayer from *Forms of Prayer for Jewish Worship, Volume I: Daily and Sabbath Prayer Book* (London: Reform Synagogues of Great Britain, 1977).

Manoowa and Oxford University Press, Australia, for "The Two Sisters," from *Anthology of Australian Poetry 1986*, edited by Les Murray, told by Manoowa, translated by Robert Robins.

Kate McIlhagga and the Iona Community for "Let Silence Be Placed around Us" and "Dragons Lurk in Desert Places."

SPCK for poems and prose by Mechthild of Magdeburg from *Beguine Spirituality* by Fiona Bowie, translated by Oliver Davies (London: SPCK, 1989).

Cool Grove Press, Brooklyn, New York, for poems from *Sweet on My Lips: The Love Poems of Mirabai.* Translated by Louise Landes Levi and P. Tej Hazeinika.

Janet Morley and SPCK for "Ash Wednesday Prayer" and "May the God who dances in creation" from *All Desires Known* (London: SPCK, 1989).

SPCK for the prayer by Mother Teresa from *The Silence of the Heart* edited by Kathryn Spink (London: SPCK, 1989).

John Wiley & Sons Australia for "Song" and "We Are Going" by Oodgeroo of the tribe Noonuccal (formerly known as Kath Walker) from *My People,* third edition (Jacaranda Press, 1990). Reprinted by permission of John Wiley & Sons Australia.

Andrew Nurnberg Associates, London, for poems by Irina Ratushinskaya from *Dance with a Shadow* translated by David McDuff (Newcastle, England: Bloodaxe Books, 1992).

Carcanet Press for "Choosing a Name" by Anne Ridler from *Collected Poems* (Manchester, England: Carcanet Press, 1988).

The St. Hilda Community, London, and SPCK for "We adore," "We stand at the turning of the year," and "We hold up our smallness to your greatness" from *Women Included* (London: SPCK, 1991).

Betsy Sholl for an excerpt from "Job's Wife" from *Rooms Overhead,* Alice James Books (Farmington, Maine: Alice James Books, 1986).

SPCK for the prayer by Thérèse of Lisieux from *The SPCK Book of Christian Prayer* (London: SPCK, 1995).

Shambhala Publications, Inc., for poems of the Therigata nuns from *Songs of the Sons and Daughters of the Buddha,* translated by Andrew

Index of First Lines

Master Tables

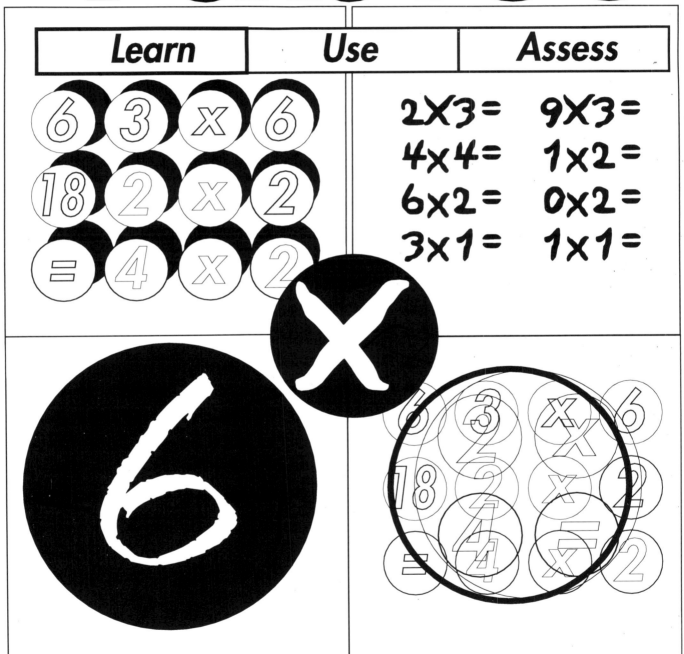

Learn	Use	Assess

6 3 x 6
18 2 x 2
= 4 x 2

2X3 =   9X3 =
4x4 =   1x2 =
6x2 =   0x2 =
3x1 =   1x1 =

6

Written by Murray Brennan
Published by Prim-Ed Publishing
www.prim-ed.com

0572UK

OXFORD HOUSE SC
COLCHE

Foreword

Mastering Tables *is a comprehensive programme for teachers to assist pupils in learning, practising, assessing and extending their knowledge and recall of multiplication tables through challenging, fun activities.*

Research shows that children's instant recall of basic number facts will only progress from short-term memory (easily forgotten) to the long-term memory through constant practice and reinforcement of the same table facts. Mastering Tables *provides teachers with a variety of activities and techniques to help pupils achieve instant recall and understanding of related times table facts.*

Pupils will enjoy the self-competition aspect of these activities while at the same time reinforcing their knowledge of essential facts.

An ideal mathematical support programme, Mastering Tables *provides a framework to:*

- *encourage and develop mental calculation skills;*
- *develop problem-solving strategies and skills;*
- *develop and maintain speed of recall;*
- *provide support to the overall daily mathematics programme.*

Contents

Mastering your tables

Reviewing your tables

Teachers notes

Mastering Tables *provides a variety of activities to facilitate remediation, practice and extension of basic times table facts.*

Covering the basic tables, 2 – 10, Mastering Tables *also extends pupils to consider the 12, 15, 20, 25 and 50 times tables. Derivatives for each table are covered throughout the related activities. For example, as the three times table facts and patterns are studied, so too are the 30 times table facts; four times table studies the 40 times table and so on.*

Teachers can use Mastering Tables *for formal classroom lessons, revision and reinforcement, extension or homework activities.*

Calculators may be a useful mathematical tool for pupils when tackling more difficult stages of these multiplication tables.

The activities are divided into four main learning areas.

(A) Learning your tables

Nominated Set A or B can be used in separate lessons to reinforce simple table facts.

For those pupils having difficulty or wanting to improve their accuracy scores, this activity page can be used for homework or revision activities.

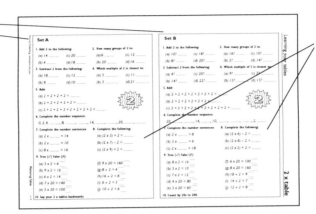

Provides two sets of mathematical activities using the four basic operations to promote the learning of each table. The emphasis is on understanding rather than rote learning.

(B) Using your tables

Recording the basic times table answers to assist in recall and application in related activities.

Activities enabling pupils to apply tables knowledge to solve everyday mathematical problems.

Simple number charts or fun games like 'Tables Battleships' or 'Snakes 'n' Ladders' to reinforce pupil learning in an enjoyable, relevant way. (See page iv for game instructions.)

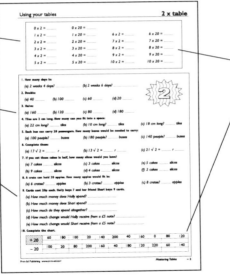

Recording and learning the derivatives of the times table.

(C) Assessing your tables

Two sets of 40 mental calculations to use as separate lessons for reinforcement and assessment of multiplication tables.

Space provided for pupils to record their score and times as they race against themselves and the clock. (See instructions for time recordings on page iii.)

Pupils will want to learn and improve their times tables as they race against themselves in these speed and accuracy activities for each multiplication table.

For each multiplication table there is a choice of two set activities (A or B) for the pupils to complete as directed by the teacher.

Self-evaluation, where pupils can select the facial expression that best describes their feelings about their results. Pupils can also comment on their successes or where they think they could improve.

Each assessment test is designed to test each individual against himself/herself, much the same as a golfer tries to lower his/her handicap score.

Teachers notes

Timing

- *Each pupil begins with the maximum time allowance of 3 minutes.*

- *Pupils mark their answers (provided on pages 48 – 52) to get a score and colour their progress on the 'Pupil progress graph' (pages viii – ix).*

- *The pupils need to work out their time allowance for the next day/lesson. Those with a perfect score (40) will reduce their times to 2 minutes. Those who did not obtain a perfect score remain on 3 minutes.*

- *Each time a pupil scores a perfect score, his/her time is further reduced by 30 seconds, making each test more challenging. Pupils with perfect scores move from 3 minutes to 2 minutes to 90 seconds and finally to 60 seconds.*

- *Those pupils not scoring 40 will remain on the same time frame until they are directed by a teacher or until they score 40 correct answers.*

Pupil progress graphs have been included on pages viii – ix.

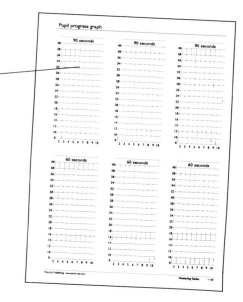

(D) Reviewing your tables

Two sets of 40 problems to revise and assess a combination of multiplication tables.

Review sheets use the four basic operations and the combination of two different multiplication tables.

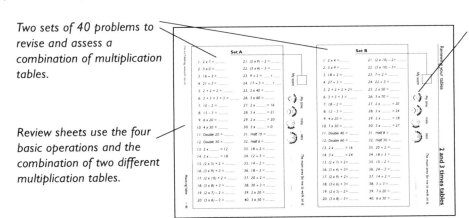

Self-evaluation, where pupils can select the facial expression that best describes their feelings in relation to their results. Pupils can also comment on their successes or where they think they could improve.

Marking

Marking is simple. Answers are provided. There are several ways you might like to arrange for answers to be marked. Remember, mental sessions should be brief and to the point so whichever method you choose needs to be efficient while identifying potential problem areas.

Methods could include:

- *whole-class: the teacher calls the answers to pupils who either self-check or partner-check.*

- *pupil checking: pupils use answer sheets provided to either self-check or partner-check.*

- *collection: the teacher collects the worksheets to mark individual pupil work. This can be a useful process to check accuracy of other methods used.*

Games

(a) Tables Battleships *(found on pages 29, 32, 35, 38 and 41)*

A game for 2 players.

Each player has a 16-squared grid with coordinates A, B, C, D and 1, 2, 3, 4. Each player fills in seven multiples of the designated table. The remaining squares are filled with the word 'miss'. Players then take turns locating the other player's 'ships' (multiples) by calling coordinates; e.g. B4.

For example (x 6 table grid shown)

If a player calls 'B4', the other player calls 'ship 48'. If the first player calls out the correct times table for 48 (i.e. 6 x 8) then that 'ship' is 'sunk' and crossed out. The winner is the first player to sink all 7 'ships' belonging to the other player.

4	12	48	miss	54
3	miss	42	miss	miss
2	6	miss	miss	18
1	miss	miss	30	miss
	A	B	C	D

(b) Snakes 'n' Ladders *(found on pages 14, 17, 20, 23 and 26)*

A game for 2 players.

Colour each number on the gameboard which is a multiple of the assigned times table; e.g. 7 times table—7, 14, 21, 28 …. Draw 4 ladders from coloured multiples to higher numbers. Draw 4 snakes from coloured multiples and leading down to lower numbers. Pupils will need a die and two small counters. To start from the number 1, pupils will need to throw a 6 on the die. If a counter lands on a ladder it is moved up to the number at the top of the ladder. If a counter lands on a snake, it is moved down to the number at the base of the snake. The first player to reach 100 wins the game.

(c) Tables Bingo *(see page xv for templates.)*

Teachers select a times table grid that pupils will play in. Fill in the squares of that bingo grid with multiples of the number in the centre. (Multiples are numbers that a given number will divide into exactly. Multiples of 3, for example, are 3, 6, 9, 12, 15 etc.) Teachers orally call a multiplication sum from the allotted table; e.g. 3 x 5. If the answer is on a pupil's grid he/she crosses it off. Pupils call out 'Bingo' when a line (across, down or diagonally) or all numbers are crossed. (To be determined by the teacher before the game commences.)

(d) Tables Spinners *(see page xiv for templates.)*

Copy spinners onto thick card. Cut and colour the spinners and use a pencil or similar object to poke through the centre. The teacher or pupil leaders, in small groups, can nominate a table orally; e.g. 5 times table. Pupils take turns to spin the appropriate spinner to match the selected table. Pupils record the multiplication answers when the number the spinner lands on is multiplied by the nominated table. As pupils get more competent with the game, perhaps time limits could be set to test and improve recall.

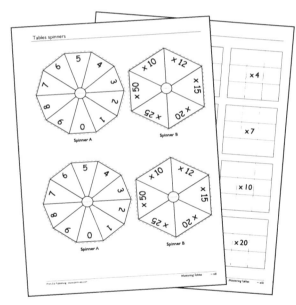

Merit certificates have been included for positive reinforcement of pupils' progress in Mastering Tables. (See page xvi)

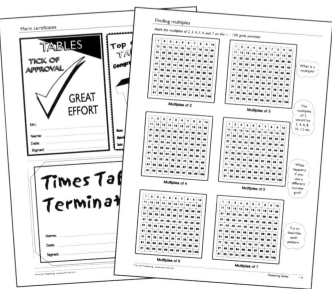

Finding Multiples (see pages xii – xiii)

Easy to use, timesaving multiple grids to increase pupils' knowledge of multiples related to the multiplication tables. Multiples are numbers that a given number will divide into exactly; e.g. multiples of 5 are 5, 10, 15, 20 etc. Discuss the patterns found.

Curriculum links

The activities in this book have been written to develop the following objectives in mathematics:

Country/ Subject	Year/ Level	Strand/Unit	Objectives
England Numeracy	Year 2	Numbers and the number system	• count on in steps of 2, 3, 4, 5 and 10
		Calculations	• know by heart all addition and subtraction facts for each number to at least 10 • know all pairs of numbers with a total of 20 • know all pairs of multiples of 10 with a total of 100 • use known number facts to add and subtract mentally • understand the operation of multiplication as repeated addition and begin to understand division as sharing • know by heart multiplication facts for the 2 and 10 times-tables • begin to know multiplication facts for the 5 times-table • derive quickly division facts corresponding to the 2 and 10 times-tables and doubles and halves of multiples to 100 • use known number facts and place value to carry out mentally simple multiplications and divisions
		Solving problems	• choose and use appropriate operations and efficient calculation strategies to solve problems • use mental addition and subtraction, simple multiplication and division, to solve simple word problems involving number and money • find totals and give change with money
	Year 3	Numbers and the number system	• describe and extend number sequences – 3, 4, 5 and 10 • recognise two-digit and three-digit multiples of 2, 5 or 10 and three-digit multiples of 50 and 100
		Calculations	• extend understanding of the operations of addition and subtraction • know by heart all addition and subtraction facts for each number to 20 • know all pairs of multiples of 5 with a total of 100 • use known number facts and place value to add and subtract mentally • understand multiplication as repeated addition • understand division as sharing • begin to find remainders after simple division • know by heart multiplication facts for the 2, 5 and 10 times-tables • begin to know the 3 and 4 times-tables • derive quickly division facts corresponding to the 2, 5 and 10 times-tables and doubles and halves of multiples • use known number facts and place value to carry out mentally simple multiplications and divisions
		Solving problems	• choose and use appropriate operations (including multiplication and division) to solve word problems • solve word problems involving numbers in 'real life' and money, including finding totals and giving change
	Year 4	Numbers and the number system	• multiply or divide any integer by 10 • begin to multiply by 100 • recognise multiples of 2, 3, 4, 5 and 10
		Calculations	• consolidate knowing by heart addition and subtraction facts for all numbers to 20 • use known number facts and place value to add or subtract mentally, including any pair of two-digit whole numbers • extend understanding of the operations of x and ÷, and their relationship to each other and to + and - • find remainders after division

Curriculum links

Country/ Subject	Year/ Level	Strand/Unit	Objectives
England Numeracy	Year 4	Calculations	• know by heart multiplication facts for 2, 3, 4, 5 and 10 times-tables • begin to know multiplication facts for 6, 7, 8 and 9 times-tables • derive quickly division facts corresponding to 2, 3, 4, 5 and 10 times-tables and doubles and halves of multiples • use known number facts and place value to multiply and divide integers, including by 10 and then 100
		Solving problems	• choose and use appropriate number operations and appropriate ways of calculating to solve problems • use all four operations to solve word problems involving numbers in 'real life' and money
	Year 5	Numbers and the number system	• recognise multiples of 6, 7, 8 and 9
		Calculations	• use known number facts and place value for mental addition and subtraction • know by heart all multiplication facts up to 10 x 10 • derive quickly division facts corresponding to tables up to 10 x 10 and doubles and halves of multiples • use known facts and place value to multiply and divide mentally
		Solving problems	• choose and use appropriate number operations to solve problems
Northern Ireland Mathematics	KS 1	Processes in mathematics	• select and use the mathematics appropriate to a task • recognise simple patterns and relationships and make predictions about them
		Number	• explore and record addition and multiplication patterns in number tables • understand the operations of addition and subtraction • add and subtract, initially using small numbers and progressing to working with hundreds, tens and units • solve problems involving whole numbers using addition and subtraction • progress to understanding the operations of multiplication and division and use them to solve problems with whole numbers • work with remainders in division • know addition and subtraction facts, initially to 10 and then to 20 • subtract mentally a single digit number from a two-digit number • know multiplication tables relating to the 2s, 5s and 10s and other tables, as appropriate • use times-tables facts in problem-solving situations • add and subtract money and use these skills in problem-solving situations
	KS 2	Number	• consolidate knowledge of addition and subtraction facts to 20 • understand and use this knowledge to calculate quickly facts that they cannot recall • add mentally two two-digit numbers • subtract mentally one two-digit number from another • know the multiplication facts to 10 x 10 • use multiplication facts when solving problems • engage in a range of activities to develop understanding of the four operations of number and their interrelationships • use the four operations to solve money problems
Scotland Mathematics	Level B	Number, money and measurement	• add and subtract numbers 0 to 20 mentally • multiply and divide mentally by 2, 3, 4, 5 and 10 within the confines of these tables • multiply and divide two-digit numbers multiplied by 2, 3, 4, 5 or 10

Curriculum links

Country/ Subject	Year/ Level	Strand/Unit	Objectives
Scotland Mathematics	Level C	Number, money and measurement	• use coins/notes to £5 worth or more, including exchange • add and subtract mentally for one-digit to or from whole numbers up to three-digits; beyond in cases involving multiples of 10 • add and subtract in applications in number and money to £20 • multiply and divide mentally within the confines of all tables to 10 • multiply and divide for any two or three-digit whole number by 10
	Level D	Number, money and measurement	• use all coins/notes to £20 worth or more, including exchange • multiply and divide mentally for whole numbers by single digits
Wales Mathematics	KS 1	Number	• 1.1 count in steps of different sizes • 2.2 explore and record patterns of multiples • 2.2 explore patterns involving multiplication and division, including those within a hundred-square of multiplication facts • 2.2 use the relationship between halving and doubling • 2.3 know addition and subtraction facts to 20 • 2.3 learn multiplication and division facts relating to the 2s, 5s, 10s, and use these to deduce other facts or to find new results • 3.1 understand the operations of addition and subtraction and the relationship between them • 3.1 recognise situations that require use of addition and subtraction and use them to solve problems with whole numbers and money • 3.2 understand the operations of multiplication and division • 3.2 recognise situations that require use of multiplication and division and use them to solve problems with whole numbers and money, understanding and dealing appropriately with remainders
	KS 2	Number	• 2.3 consolidate knowledge of addition and subtraction facts for numbers to 20 and use these, along with knowledge of place value and structure, to mentally obtain further results • 2.3 know the multiplication facts to 10 x 10 and use them to derive quickly the corresponding division facts • 2.3 develop a range of mental methods for finding, from known facts, those that they have not learned • 2.5 understand and use the relationships between the four operations and recognise situations in which the operations apply • 3.1 develop understanding and use of the four operations to solve problems, including those involving money

Pupil progress graph

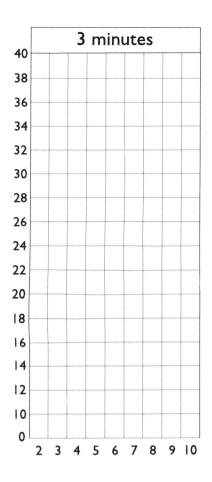

3 minutes

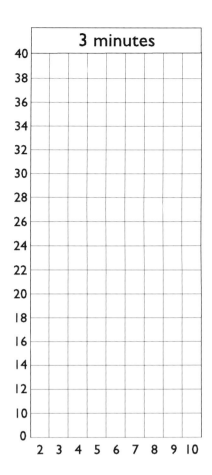

3 minutes

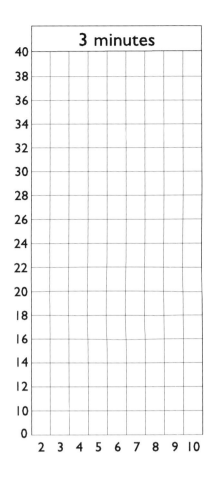

3 minutes

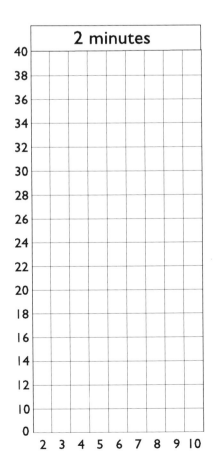

2 minutes

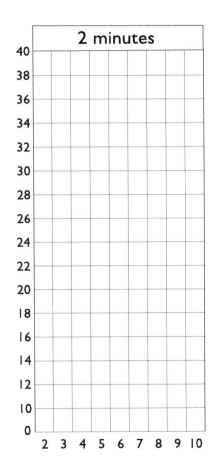

2 minutes

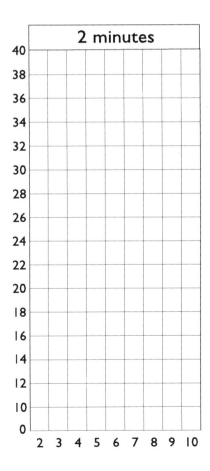

2 minutes

Pupil progress graph

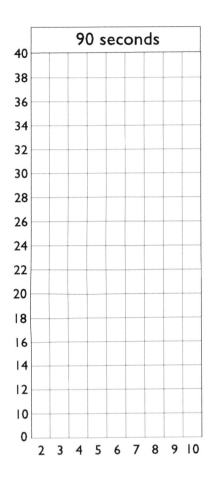

90 seconds

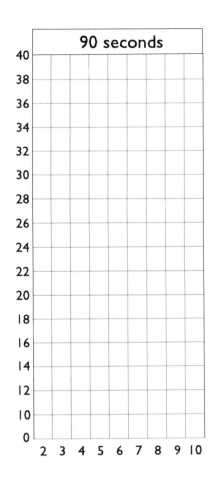

90 seconds

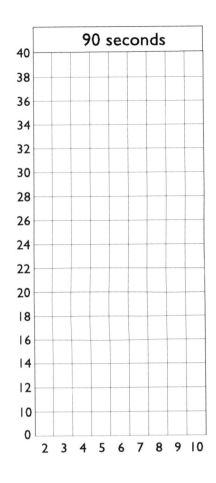

90 seconds

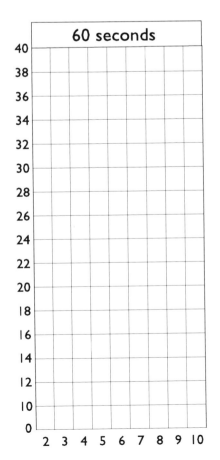

60 seconds

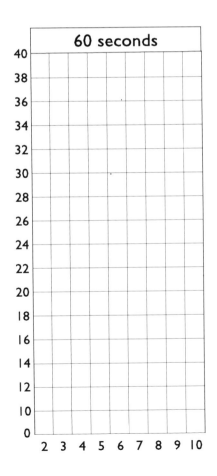

60 seconds

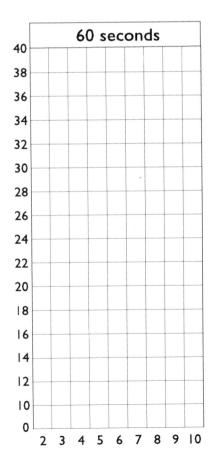

60 seconds

x 1 Table

1 x 1 = 1
2 x 1 = 2
3 x 1 = 3
4 x 1 = 4
5 x 1 = 5
6 x 1 = 6
7 x 1 = 7
8 x 1 = 8
9 x 1 = 9
10 x 1 = 10

x 2 Table

1 x 2 = 2
2 x 2 = 4
3 x 2 = 6
4 x 2 = 8
5 x 2 = 10
6 x 2 = 12
7 x 2 = 14
8 x 2 = 16
9 x 2 = 18
10 x 2 = 20

x 3 Table

1 x 3 = 3
2 x 3 = 6
3 x 3 = 9
4 x 3 = 12
5 x 3 = 15
6 x 3 = 18
7 x 3 = 21
8 x 3 = 24
9 x 3 = 27
10 x 3 = 30

x 4 Table

1 x 4 = 4
2 x 4 = 8
3 x 4 = 12
4 x 4 = 16
5 x 4 = 20
6 x 4 = 24
7 x 4 = 28
8 x 4 = 32
9 x 4 = 36
10 x 4 = 40

x 5 Table

1 x 5 = 5
2 x 5 = 10
3 x 5 = 15
4 x 5 = 20
5 x 5 = 25
6 x 5 = 30
7 x 5 = 35
8 x 5 = 40
9 x 5 = 45
10 x 5 = 50

x 6 Table

1 x 6 = 6
2 x 6 = 12
3 x 6 = 18
4 x 6 = 24
5 x 6 = 30
6 x 6 = 36
7 x 6 = 42
8 x 6 = 48
9 x 6 = 54
10 x 6 = 60

x 7 Table

1 x 7 = 7
2 x 7 = 14
3 x 7 = 21
4 x 7 = 28
5 x 7 = 35
6 x 7 = 42
7 x 7 = 49
8 x 7 = 56
9 x 7 = 63
10 x 7 = 70

x 8 Table

1 x 8 = 8
2 x 8 = 16
3 x 8 = 24
4 x 8 = 32
5 x 8 = 40
6 x 8 = 48
7 x 8 = 56
8 x 8 = 64
9 x 8 = 72
10 x 8 = 80

x 9 Table

1 x 9 = 9
2 x 9 = 18
3 x 9 = 27
4 x 9 = 36
5 x 9 = 45
6 x 9 = 54
7 x 9 = 63
8 x 9 = 72
9 x 9 = 81
10 x 9 = 90

x 10 Table

1 x 10 = 10
2 x 10 = 20
3 x 10 = 30
4 x 10 = 40
5 x 10 = 50
6 x 10 = 60
7 x 10 = 70
8 x 10 = 80
9 x 10 = 90
10 x 10 = 100

x 12 Table

1 x 12 = 12
2 x 12 = 24
3 x 12 = 36
4 x 12 = 48
5 x 12 = 60
6 x 12 = 72
7 x 12 = 84
8 x 12 = 96
9 x 12 = 108
10 x 12 = 120

x 15 Table

1 x 15 = 15
2 x 15 = 30
3 x 15 = 45
4 x 15 = 60
5 x 15 = 75
6 x 15 = 90
7 x 15 = 105
8 x 15 = 120
9 x 15 = 135
10 x 15 = 150

x 20 Table

1 x 20 = 20
2 x 20 = 40
3 x 20 = 60
4 x 20 = 80
5 x 20 = 100
6 x 20 = 120
7 x 20 = 140
8 x 20 = 160
9 x 20 = 180
10 x 20 = 200

x 25 Table

1 x 25 = 25
2 x 25 = 50
3 x 25 = 75
4 x 25 = 100
5 x 25 = 125
6 x 25 = 150
7 x 25 = 175
8 x 25 = 200
9 x 25 = 225
10 x 25 = 250

x 50 Table

1 x 50 = 50
2 x 50 = 100
3 x 50 = 150
4 x 50 = 200
5 x 50 = 250
6 x 50 = 300
7 x 50 = 350
8 x 50 = 400
9 x 50 = 450
10 x 50 = 500

Finding multiples

Mark the multiples of 2, 3, 4, 5, 6 and 7 on the 1 – 100 grids provided.

1	2	3	4	5	6	7	8	9	10
11	12	13	14	15	16	17	18	19	20
21	22	23	24	25	26	27	28	29	30
31	32	33	34	35	36	37	38	39	40
41	42	43	44	45	46	47	48	49	50
51	52	53	54	55	56	57	58	59	60
61	62	63	64	65	66	67	68	69	70
71	72	73	74	75	76	77	78	79	80
81	82	83	84	85	86	87	88	89	90
91	92	93	94	95	96	97	98	99	100

Multiples of 2

1	2	3	4	5	6	7	8	9	10
11	12	13	14	15	16	17	18	19	20
21	22	23	24	25	26	27	28	29	30
31	32	33	34	35	36	37	38	39	40
41	42	43	44	45	46	47	48	49	50
51	52	53	54	55	56	57	58	59	60
61	62	63	64	65	66	67	68	69	70
71	72	73	74	75	76	77	78	79	80
81	82	83	84	85	86	87	88	89	90
91	92	93	94	95	96	97	98	99	100

Multiples of 3

1	2	3	4	5	6	7	8	9	10
11	12	13	14	15	16	17	18	19	20
21	22	23	24	25	26	27	28	29	30
31	32	33	34	35	36	37	38	39	40
41	42	43	44	45	46	47	48	49	50
51	52	53	54	55	56	57	58	59	60
61	62	63	64	65	66	67	68	69	70
71	72	73	74	75	76	77	78	79	80
81	82	83	84	85	86	87	88	89	90
91	92	93	94	95	96	97	98	99	100

Multiples of 4

1	2	3	4	5	6	7	8	9	10
11	12	13	14	15	16	17	18	19	20
21	22	23	24	25	26	27	28	29	30
31	32	33	34	35	36	37	38	39	40
41	42	43	44	45	46	47	48	49	50
51	52	53	54	55	56	57	58	59	60
61	62	63	64	65	66	67	68	69	70
71	72	73	74	75	76	77	78	79	80
81	82	83	84	85	86	87	88	89	90
91	92	93	94	95	96	97	98	99	100

Multiples of 5

1	2	3	4	5	6	7	8	9	10
11	12	13	14	15	16	17	18	19	20
21	22	23	24	25	26	27	28	29	30
31	32	33	34	35	36	37	38	39	40
41	42	43	44	45	46	47	48	49	50
51	52	53	54	55	56	57	58	59	60
61	62	63	64	65	66	67	68	69	70
71	72	73	74	75	76	77	78	79	80
81	82	83	84	85	86	87	88	89	90
91	92	93	94	95	96	97	98	99	100

Multiples of 6

1	2	3	4	5	6	7	8	9	10
11	12	13	14	15	16	17	18	19	20
21	22	23	24	25	26	27	28	29	30
31	32	33	34	35	36	37	38	39	40
41	42	43	44	45	46	47	48	49	50
51	52	53	54	55	56	57	58	59	60
61	62	63	64	65	66	67	68	69	70
71	72	73	74	75	76	77	78	79	80
81	82	83	84	85	86	87	88	89	90
91	92	93	94	95	96	97	98	99	100

Multiples of 7

What is a multiple?

The multiples of 2 would be 2, 4, 6, 8, 10, 12 etc.

What happens if you use a different number grid?

Try to describe each pattern.

Finding multiples

Mark the multiples of 8, 9, 10, 12 and 15 on the 1 – 100 grids provided.

What is a multiple?

1	2	3	4	5	6	7	8	9	10
11	12	13	14	15	16	17	18	19	20
21	22	23	24	25	26	27	28	29	30
31	32	33	34	35	36	37	38	39	40
41	42	43	44	45	46	47	48	49	50
51	52	53	54	55	56	57	58	59	60
61	62	63	64	65	66	67	68	69	70
71	72	73	74	75	76	77	78	79	80
81	82	83	84	85	86	87	88	89	90
91	92	93	94	95	96	97	98	99	100

Multiples of 8

1	2	3	4	5	6	7	8	9	10
11	12	13	14	15	16	17	18	19	20
21	22	23	24	25	26	27	28	29	30
31	32	33	34	35	36	37	38	39	40
41	42	43	44	45	46	47	48	49	50
51	52	53	54	55	56	57	58	59	60
61	62	63	64	65	66	67	68	69	70
71	72	73	74	75	76	77	78	79	80
81	82	83	84	85	86	87	88	89	90
91	92	93	94	95	96	97	98	99	100

Multiples of 9

The multiples of 8 would be 8, 16, 24, 32 etc.

1	2	3	4	5	6	7	8	9	10
11	12	13	14	15	16	17	18	19	20
21	22	23	24	25	26	27	28	29	30
31	32	33	34	35	36	37	38	39	40
41	42	43	44	45	46	47	48	49	50
51	52	53	54	55	56	57	58	59	60
61	62	63	64	65	66	67	68	69	70
71	72	73	74	75	76	77	78	79	80
81	82	83	84	85	86	87	88	89	90
91	92	93	94	95	96	97	98	99	100

Multiples of 10

1	2	3	4	5	6	7	8	9	10
11	12	13	14	15	16	17	18	19	20
21	22	23	24	25	26	27	28	29	30
31	32	33	34	35	36	37	38	39	40
41	42	43	44	45	46	47	48	49	50
51	52	53	54	55	56	57	58	59	60
61	62	63	64	65	66	67	68	69	70
71	72	73	74	75	76	77	78	79	80
81	82	83	84	85	86	87	88	89	90
91	92	93	94	95	96	97	98	99	100

Multiples of 12

What happens if you use a different number grid?

Try to describe each pattern.

1	2	3	4	5	6	7	8	9	10
11	12	13	14	15	16	17	18	19	20
21	22	23	24	25	26	27	28	29	30
31	32	33	34	35	36	37	38	39	40
41	42	43	44	45	46	47	48	49	50
51	52	53	54	55	56	57	58	59	60
61	62	63	64	65	66	67	68	69	70
71	72	73	74	75	76	77	78	79	80
81	82	83	84	85	86	87	88	89	90
91	92	93	94	95	96	97	98	99	100

Multiples of 15

Tables spinners

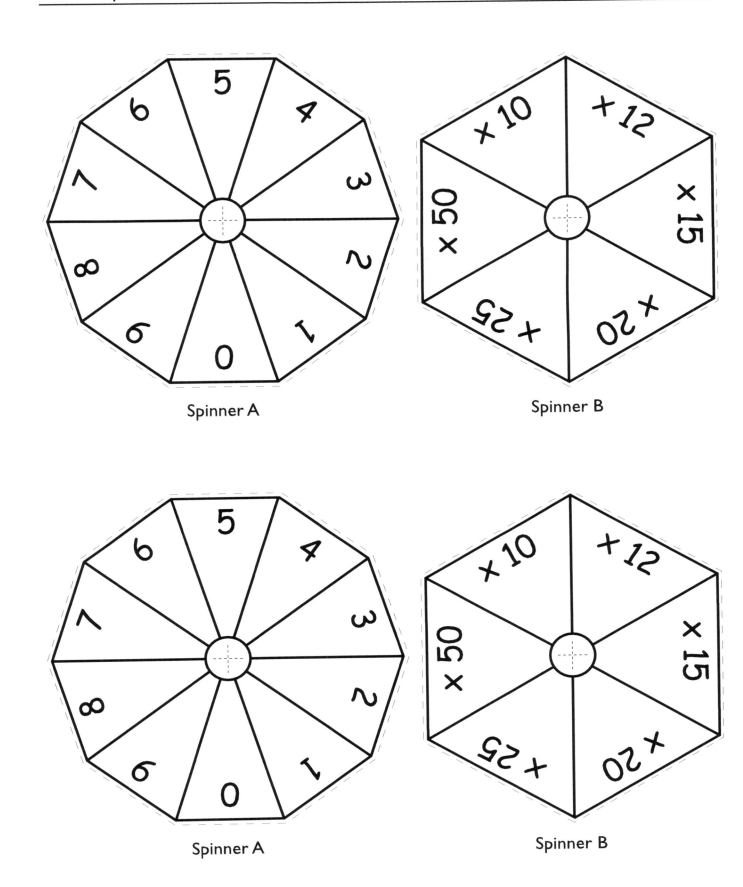

Spinner A

Spinner B

Spinner A

Spinner B

Tables bingo

	x 2	

	x 3	

	x 4	

	x 5	

	x 6	

	x 7	

	x 8	

	x 9	

	x 10	

	x 12	

	x 15	

	x 20	

TABLES

TICK OF APPROVAL

GREAT EFFORT

in:
_____

Name: _____

Date: _____

Signed: _____

Top of the TABLES

Congratulations

TOP! in

_____

Name: _____

Signed: _____

Date: _____

Times Table Terminator X

Name: _____

Date: _____

Signed: _____

Set A

1. Add 2 to the following:

(a) 14 _____   (c) 20 _____

(b) 4 _____   (d) 18 _____

2. How many groups of 2 in:

(a) 6? _____   (c) 12? _____

(b) 20? _____   (d) 16? _____

3. Subtract 2 from the following:

(a) 18 _____   (c) 12 _____

(b) 8 _____   (d) 10 _____

4. Which multiple of 2 is closest to:

(a) 5? _____   (c) 11? _____

(b) 3? _____   (d) 21? _____

5. Add:

(a) 2 + 2 + 2 + 2 = _____

(b) 2 + 2 + 2 + 2 + 2 = _____

(c) 2 + 2 + 2 + 2 + 2 + 2 + 2 = _____

6. Complete the number sequence:

0, 2, 4, _____, 8, _____, _____, 14, _____, _____, 20, _____

7. Complete the number sentences:

(a) 2 x _____ = 14

(b) 2 x _____ = 10

(c) 8 x _____ = 16

8. Complete the following:

(a) (2 x 5) + 2 = _____

(b) (2 x 7) – 2 = _____

(c) (2 x 9) + 2 = _____

(f) 9 x 20 = 160 □

(g) 8 ÷ 2 = 4 □

(h) 16 ÷ 2 = 8 □

(i) 6 ÷ 2 = 3 □

(j) 10 ÷ 2 = 6 □

9. True (✓) False (X):

(a) 3 x 2 = 6 □

(b) 9 x 2 = 16 □

(c) 6 x 2 = 14 □

(d) 7 x 20 = 140 □

(e) 5 x 20 = 100 □

10. Say your 2 x tables backwards.

Set B

1. Add 2 to the following:

(a) 10 _____   (c) 18 _____

(b) 8 _____   (d) 20 _____

2. How many groups of 2 in:

(a) 16? _____   (c) 10? _____

(b) 2? _____   (d) 14? _____

3. Subtract 2 from the following:

(a) 4 _____   (c) 20 _____

(b) 14 _____   (d) 22 _____

4. Which multiple of 2 is closest to:

(a) 9? _____   (c) 7? _____

(b) 13? _____   (d) 15? _____

5. Add:

(a) 2 + 2 + 2 + 2 + 2 + 2 = _____

(b) 2 + 2 + 2 + 2 + 2 + 2 + 2 = _____

(c) 2 + 2 + 2 + 2 + 2 + 2 + 2 + 2 + 2 = _____

6. Complete the number sequence:

20, _____, _____, 14, _____, 10, _____, _____, _____, 2,

7. Complete the number sentences:

(a) 2 x _____ = 8

(b) 3 x _____ = 6

(c) 2 x _____ = 18

8. Complete the following:

(a) (2 x 6) – 2 = _____

(b) (2 x 8) – 2 = _____

(c) (2 x 2) + 2 = _____

(f) 6 x 20 = 100 □

(g) 8 x 20 = 160 □

(h) 18 ÷ 2 = 9 □

(i) 14 ÷ 2 = 7 □

(j) 12 ÷ 2 = 8 □

9. True (✓) False (X):

(a) 8 x 2 = 16 □

(b) 5 x 2 = 10 □

(c) 7 x 2 = 12 □

(d) 4 x 20 = 80 □

(e) 3 x 20 = 60 □

10. Count by 20s to 200.

0 x 2 = _____	0 x 20 = _____		
1 x 2 = _____	1 x 20 = _____	6 x 2 = _____	6 x 20 = _____
2 x 2 = _____	2 x 20 = _____	7 x 2 = _____	7 x 20 = _____
3 x 2 = _____	3 x 20 = _____	8 x 2 = _____	8 x 20 = _____
4 x 2 = _____	4 x 20 = _____	9 x 2 = _____	9 x 20 = _____
5 x 2 = _____	5 x 20 = _____	10 x 2 = _____	10 x 20 = _____

1. How many days in:

(a) 2 weeks 4 days? _____ (b) 2 weeks 6 days? _____

2. Double:

(a) 40 _____ (b) 100 _____ (c) 60 _____ (d) 20 _____

3. Halve:

(a) 160 _____ (b) 120 _____ (c) 80 _____ (d) 180 _____

4. Tiles are 2 cm long. How many can you fit into a space:

(a) 22 cm long? _____ tiles (b) 10 cm long? _____ tiles (c) 18 cm long? _____ tiles

5. Each bus can carry 20 passengers. How many buses would be needed to carry:

(a) 100 people? _____ buses (b) 180 people? _____ buses (c) 140 people? _____ buses

6. Complete these:

(a) 17 ÷ 2 = _____ r _____ (b) 13 ÷ 2 = _____ r _____ (c) 21 ÷ 2 = _____ r _____

7. If you cut these cakes in half, how many slices would you have?

(a) 7 cakes _____ slices (c) 3 cakes _____ slices (e) 5 cakes _____ slices

(b) 9 cakes _____ slices (d) 4 cakes _____ slices (f) 2 cakes _____ slices

8. A crate can hold 20 apples. How many apples would fit in:

(a) 6 crates? _____ apples (b) 3 crates? _____ apples (c) 8 crates? _____ apples

9. Cards cost 20p each. Holly buys 7 and her friend Shari buys 9 cards.

(a) How much money does Holly spend? _____

(b) How much money does Shari spend? _____

(c) How much do they spend altogether? _____

(d) How much change would Holly receive from a £5 note? _____

(e) How much change would Shari receive from a £5 note? _____

10. Complete the chart.

+ 20	60	180	100	20	140	200	40	160	0	80	120
− 20	100	20	80	200	160	40	180	120	220	60	140

2 x table

Set B

My score:

My time: _____ mins _____ secs

I'm happy :)   I'm not happy :(

I didn't understand   OOPS!

The main area for me to work on is:

_____

_____

_____

1. 2 + 16 = _____
2. 2 x 4 = _____
3. 20 ÷ 2 = _____
4. 12 − 2 = _____
5. 2 + 20 = _____
6. 2 x 8 = _____
7. 10 ÷ 2 = _____
8. 24 − 2 = _____
9. 2 + 18 = _____
10. 2 x 10 = _____
11. 14 ÷ 2 = _____
12. 6 − 2 = _____
13. 22 + 2 = _____
14. 2 x 2 = _____
15. 24 ÷ 2 = _____
16. 8 − 2 = _____
17. 2 + 14 = _____
18. 2 x 5 = _____
19. 6 ÷ 2 = _____
20. 10 − 2 = _____

21. 2 + 12 = _____
22. 2 x 9 = _____
23. 12 ÷ 2 = _____
24. 14 − 2 = _____
25. 2 + 8 = _____
26. 7 x 2 = _____
27. 16 ÷ 2 = _____
28. 18 − 2 = _____
29. 2 + 10 = _____
30. 2 x 6 = _____
31. 2 ÷ 2 = _____
32. 20 − 2 = _____
33. 6 + 2 = _____
34. 2 x 20 = _____
35. 18 ÷ 2 = _____
36. 22 − 2 = _____
37. 2 + 2 = _____
38. 0 x 2 = _____
39. 8 ÷ 2 = _____
40. 4 − 2 = _____

Set A

My score:

My time: _____ mins _____ secs

I'm happy :)   I'm not happy :(

I didn't understand   OOPS!

The main area for me to work on is:

_____

_____

_____

1. 2 + 6 = _____
2. 2 x 7 = _____
3. 12 ÷ 2 = _____
4. 16 − 2 = _____
5. 2 + 10 = _____
6. 2 x 0 = _____
7. 8 ÷ 2 = _____
8. 20 − 2 = _____
9. 2 + 14 = _____
10. 2 x 5 = _____
11. 24 ÷ 2 = _____
12. 14 − 2 = _____
13. 18 + 2 = _____
14. 10 x 2 = _____
15. 10 ÷ 2 = _____
16. 18 − 2 = _____
17. 2 + 22 = _____
18. 2 x 4 = _____
19. 16 ÷ 2 = _____
20. 22 − 2 = _____

21. 4 + 2 = _____
22. 8 x 2 = _____
23. 2 ÷ 2 = _____
24. 24 − 2 = _____
25. 2 + 8 = _____
26. 9 x 2 = _____
27. 18 ÷ 2 = _____
28. 12 − 2 = _____
29. 2 + 12 = _____
30. 2 x 6 = _____
31. 6 ÷ 2 = _____
32. 8 − 2 = _____
33. 16 + 2 = _____
34. 0 x 2 = _____
35. 20 ÷ 2 = _____
36. 10 − 2 = _____
37. 2 + 20 = _____
38. 2 x 10 = _____
39. 14 ÷ 2 = _____
40. 6 − 2 = _____

Set B

1. Add 3 to the following:

(a) 9 _____   (c) 3 _____

(b) 18 _____   (d) 15 _____

2. How many groups of 3 in:

(a) 21? _____   (c) 12? _____

(b) 24? _____   (d) 3? _____

3. Subtract 3 from the following:

(a) 9 _____   (c) 30 _____

(b) 18 _____   (d) 6 _____

4. Which multiple of 3 is closest to:

(a) 8? _____   (c) 29? _____

(b) 11? _____   (d) 17? _____

5. Add:

(a) $3 + 3 + 3 =$ _____

(b) $3 + 3 + 3 + 3 + 3 =$ _____

(c) $3 + 3 + 3 + 3 + 3 + 3 + 3 + 3 =$ _____

6. Complete the number sequence:

30, _____, _____, 21, _____, 15, _____, _____, _____, 3,

7. Complete the number sentences:

(a) $3 \times$ _____ $= 12$

(b) $10 \times$ _____ $= 30$

(c) $3 \times$ _____ $= 15$

8. Complete the following:

(a) $(3 \times 3) + 3 =$ _____

(b) $(3 \times 7) + 3 =$ _____

(c) $(3 \times 10) - 3 =$ _____

9. True (✓) False (X):

(a) $8 \times 3 = 21$ ☐

(b) $5 \times 3 = 15$ ☐

(c) $7 \times 3 = 21$ ☐

(d) $10 \times 3 = 30$ ☐

(e) $4 \times 30 = 120$ ☐

(f) $4 \times 30 = 90$ ☐

(g) $6 \times 30 = 180$ ☐

(h) $8 \times 30 = 240$ ☐

(i) $27 \div 3 = 9$ ☐

(j) $21 \div 3 = 6$ ☐

10. Count by 30s to 300.

Set A

1. Add 3 to the following:

(a) 12 _____   (c) 21 _____

(b) 27 _____   (d) 6 _____

2. How many groups of 3 in:

(a) 30? _____   (c) 9? _____

(b) 15? _____   (d) 18? _____

3. Subtract 3 from the following:

(a) 27 _____   (c) 21 _____

(b) 15 _____   (d) 12 _____

4. Which multiple of 3 is closest to:

(a) 19? _____   (c) 23? _____

(b) 16? _____   (d) 31? _____

5. Add:

(a) $3 + 3 + 3 + 3 =$ _____

(b) $3 + 3 + 3 + 3 + 3 =$ _____

(c) $3 + 3 + 3 + 3 + 3 + 3 + 3 + 3 =$ _____

6. Complete the number sequence:

0, 3, 6, _____, 12, _____, 21, _____, _____, 30

7. Complete the number sentences:

(a) $3 \times$ _____ $= 27$

(b) $6 \times$ _____ $= 18$

(c) $3 \times$ _____ $= 9$

8. Complete the following:

(a) $(3 \times 5) + 3 =$ _____

(b) $(3 \times 4) + 3 =$ _____

(c) $(3 \times 9) - 3 =$ _____

9. True (✓) False (X):

(a) $3 \times 3 = 9$ ☐

(b) $9 \times 3 = 27$ ☐

(c) $6 \times 3 = 15$ ☐

(d) $7 \times 30 = 210$ ☐

(e) $5 \times 30 = 180$ ☐

(f) $9 \times 30 = 240$ ☐

(g) $12 \div 3 = 4$ ☐

(h) $24 \div 3 = 9$ ☐

(i) $9 \div 3 = 3$ ☐

(j) $15 \div 5 = 3$ ☐

10. Say your 3 x tables backwards.

3 x table

0 x 3 = _____	0 x 30 = _____		
1 x 3 = _____	1 x 30 = _____	6 x 3 = _____	6 x 30 = _____
2 x 3 = _____	2 x 30 = _____	7 x 3 = _____	7 x 30 = _____
3 x 3 = _____	3 x 30 = _____	8 x 3 = _____	8 x 30 = _____
4 x 3 = _____	4 x 30 = _____	9 x 3 = _____	9 x 30 = _____
5 x 3 = _____	5 x 30 = _____	10 x 3 = _____	10 x 30 = _____

1. How many days in:

(a) 3 weeks 5 days? _____ (b) 3 weeks 3 days? _____

2. Double:

(a) 60 _____   (b) 90 _____   (c) 120 _____   (d) 15 _____

3. Halve:

(a) 300 _____   (b) 180 _____   (c) 240 _____   (d) 420 _____

4. Tiles are 3 cm long. How many can you fit into a space:

(a) 15 cm long? _____ tiles   (b) 30 cm long? _____ tiles   (c) 27 cm long? _____ tiles

5. Each tram can carry 30 passengers. How many trams would be needed to carry:

(a) 150 people? _____ trams   (b) 270 people? _____ trams   (c) 120 people? _____ trams

6. Complete these:

(a) 29 ÷ 3 = _____ r _____   (b) 11 ÷ 3 = _____ r _____   (c) 19 ÷ 3 = _____ r _____

7. If you cut these pizzas into thirds, how many slices would you have?

(a) 4 pizzas _____ slices   (c) 9 pizzas _____ slices   (e) 5 pizzas _____ slices

(b) 6 pizzas _____ slices   (d) 2 pizzas _____ slices   (f) 10 pizzas _____ slices

8. A box can hold 30 oranges. How many oranges would fit in:

(a) 6 boxes? _____ oranges   (b) 4 boxes? _____ oranges   (c) 7 boxes? _____ oranges

9. Eggs cost 30p each. Josh buys 8 and Lauren buys 5 eggs.

(a) How much money does Josh spend? _____

(b) How much money does Lauren spend? _____

(c) How much more does Josh spend than Lauren? _____

(d) How much change would Josh get if he paid with a £5 note? _____

(e) How much change would Lauren get if she paid with a £5 note? _____

10. Complete the chart.

+ 30	120	30	270	180	90	300	150	210	60	240	0
− 30	180	300	210	120	60	270	90	240	330	30	150

Set A

1. 3 + 6 =
2. 3 x 7 =
3. 30 ÷ 3 =
4. 18 - 3 =
5. 3 + 9 =
6. 3 x 8 =
7. 12 ÷ 3 =
8. 27 - 3 =
9. 3 + 12 =
10. 3 x 9 =
11. 21 ÷ 3 =
12. 24 - 3 =
13. 3 + 15 =
14. 3 x 0 =
15. 18 ÷ 3 =
16. 30 - 3 =
17. 3 + 18 =
18. 3 x 6 =
19. 24 ÷ 3 =
20. 12 - 3 =
21. 3 + 3 =
22. 5 x 3 =
23. 27 ÷ 3 =
24. 21 - 3 =
25. 3 + 21 =
26. 4 x 3 =
27. 15 ÷ 3 =
28. 15 - 3 =
29. 27 + 3 =
30. 3 x 2 =
31. 6 ÷ 3 =
32. 9 - 3 =
33. 24 + 3 =
34. 3 x 3 =
35. 9 ÷ 3 =
36. 3 - 3 =
37. 30 + 3 =
38. 3 x 0 =
39. 3 ÷ 3 =
40. 6 - 3 =

Set B

1. 3 + 9 =
2. 3 x 6 =
3. 15 ÷ 3 =
4. 27 - 3 =
5. 3 + 21 =
6. 3 x 0 =
7. 24 ÷ 3 =
8. 18 - 3 =
9. 3 + 27 =
10. 3 x 8 =
11. 9 ÷ 3 =
12. 30 - 3 =
13. 3 + 6 =
14. 3 x 2 =
15. 30 ÷ 10 =
16. 9 - 3 =
17. 12 + 3 =
18. 3 x 4 =
19. 3 ÷ 3 =
20. 12 - 3 =
21. 3 + 18 =
22. 3 x 7 =
23. 21 ÷ 3 =
24. 33 - 3 =
25. 3 + 24 =
26. 10 x 3 =
27. 6 ÷ 3 =
28. 21 - 3 =
29. 3 + 30 =
30. 3 x 30 =
31. 18 ÷ 3 =
32. 24 - 3 =
33. 3 + 3 =
34. 9 x 3 =
35. 12 ÷ 3 =
36. 36 - 3 =
37. 3 + 15 =
38. 3 x 3 =
39. 27 ÷ 3 =
40. 15 - 3 =

My score:

My time:

_____ mins _____ secs

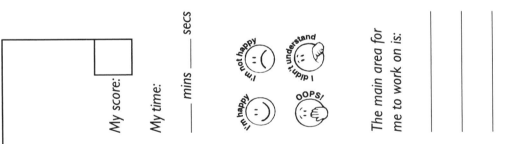

I'm happy

I'm not happy

I didn't understand

OOPS!

The main area for me to work on is:

Set B

1. Add 4 to the following:
(a) 20 ___   (c) 36 ___
(b) 24 ___   (d) 40 ___

2. How many groups of 4 in:
(a) 40? ___   (c) 12? ___
(b) 20? ___   (d) 36? ___

4. Which multiple of 4 is closest to:
(a) 11? ___   (c) 19? ___
(b) 3? ___   (d) 27? ___

3. Subtract 4 from the following:
(a) 16 ___   (c) 8 ___
(b) 32 ___   (d) 40 ___

5. Add:
(a) 4 + 4 + 4 + 4 + 4 + 4 = ___
(b) 4 + 4 + 4 + 4 + 4 + 4 + 4 = ___
(c) 4 + 4 + 4 + 4 + 4 + 4 + 4 + 4 + 4 + 4 = ___

6. Complete the number sequence:
40, ___, 28, ___, 16, ___, 4, ___

7. Complete the number sentences:
(a) 4 x ___ = 36
(b) 8 x ___ = 32
(c) 4 x ___ = 28

8. Complete the following:
(a) (4 x 4) + 4 = ___
(b) (4 x 8) + 4 = ___
(c) (4 x 6) – 4 = ___

9. True (✓) False (X):
(a) 8 x 4 = 36 □
(b) 5 x 4 = 24 □
(c) 7 x 4 = 28 □
(d) 10 x 4 = 40 □
(e) 3 x 40 = 120 □
(f) 6 x 40 = 240 □
(g) 8 x 40 = 280 □
(h) 36 ÷ 4 = 8 □
(i) 28 ÷ 4 = 7 □
(j) 24 ÷ 4 = 6 □

10. Count by 40s to 400.

Set A

1. Add 4 to the following:
(a) 16 ___   (c) 32 ___
(b) 8 ___   (d) 28 ___

2. How many groups of 4 in:
(a) 24? ___   (c) 16? ___
(b) 32? ___   (d) 8? ___

4. Which multiple of 4 is closest to:
(a) 39? ___   (c) 23? ___
(b) 17? ___   (d) 31? ___

3. Subtract 4 from the following:
(a) 28 ___   (c) 12 ___
(b) 36 ___   (d) 20 ___

5. Add:
(a) 4 + 4 + 4 = ___
(b) 4 + 4 + 4 + 4 = ___
(c) 4 + 4 + 4 + 4 + 4 + 4 + 4 + 4 = ___

6. Complete the number sequence:
0, 4, ___, 12, ___, 20, ___, ___, 32, ___, 40

7. Complete the number sentences:
(a) 4 x ___ = 20
(b) 4 x ___ = 0
(c) 4 x ___ = 12

8. Complete the following:
(a) (4 x 7) + 4 = ___
(b) (4 x 5) + 4 = ___
(c) (4 x 10) – 4 = ___

9. True (✓) False (X):
(a) 3 x 4 = 12 □
(b) 9 x 4 = 32 □
(c) 6 x 4 = 24 □
(d) 7 x 40 = 320 □
(e) 5 x 40 = 200 □
(f) 9 x 40 = 360 □
(g) 16 ÷ 4 = 5 □
(h) 32 ÷ 4 = 8 □
(i) 12 ÷ 4 = 3 □
(j) 20 ÷ 4 = 4 □

10. Say your 4 x tables backwards.

0 x 4 = _____	0 x 40 = _____		
1 x 4 = _____	1 x 40 = _____	6 x 4 = _____	6 x 40 = _____
2 x 4 = _____	2 x 40 = _____	7 x 4 = _____	7 x 40 = _____
3 x 4 = _____	3 x 40 = _____	8 x 4 = _____	8 x 40 = _____
4 x 4 = _____	4 x 40 = _____	9 x 4 = _____	9 x 40 = _____
5 x 4 = _____	5 x 40 = _____	10 x 4 = _____	10 x 40 = _____

1. How many days in:

(a) 4 weeks 3 days? _____ (b) 4 weeks 6 days? _____

2. Double:

(a) 80 _____   (b) 120 _____   (c) 40 _____   (d) 160 _____

3. Halve:

(a) 400 _____   (b) 320 _____   (c) 80 _____   (d) 280 _____

4. Tiles are 4 cm long. How many can you fit into a space:

(a) 20 cm long? _____ tiles   (b) 40 cm long? _____ tiles   (c) 36 cm long? _____ tiles

5. Each train carriage can carry 40 passengers. How many carriages would be needed to carry:

(a) 160 people? _____ carriages   (b) 360 people? _____ carriages   (c) 280 people? _____ carriages

6. Complete these:

(a) 25 ÷ 4 = _____ r _____   (b) 30 ÷ 4 = _____ r _____   (c) 18 ÷ 4 = _____ r _____

7. If you cut these pies into quarters, how many slices would you have?

(a) 3 pies _____ slices   (c) 7 pies _____ slices   (e) 5 pies _____ slices

(b) 9 pies _____ slices   (d) 4 pies _____ slices   (f) 8 pies _____ slices

8. A crate can hold 40 mangoes. How many mangoes would fit in:

(a) 5 crates? _____ mangoes   (b) 3 crates? _____ mangoes   (c) 8 crates? _____ mangoes

9. Collectable cards cost 40p each. Kellan buys 9 and his friend Nathan buys 6 cards.

(a) How much money does Kellan spend? _____

(b) How much money does Nathan spend? _____

(c) How much do they spend altogether? _____

(d) How much change would Kellan receive from a £10 note? _____

(e) How much change would Nathan receive from a £10 note? _____

10. Complete the chart.

+ 40	240	80	160	280	360	40	120	200	320	400	0
− 40	80	320	200	40	360	280	120	400	240	160	440

My score:

My time: _____ mins _____ secs

I'm happy I'm not happy

OOPS! I didn't understand

The main area for me to work on is:

_____

_____

_____

_____

Set B

1. 4 + 12 = _____	21. 32 + 4 = _____
2. 4 x 7 = _____	22. 8 x 40 = _____
3. 24 ÷ 4 = _____	23. 28 ÷ 4 = _____
4. 8 − 4 = _____	24. 16 − 4 = _____
5. 4 + 20 = _____	25. 4 + 40 = _____
6. 4 x 9 = _____	26. 4 x 8 = _____
7. 8 ÷ 4 = _____	27. 20 ÷ 4 = _____
8. 32 − 4 = _____	28. 20 − 4 = _____
9. 4 + 16 = _____	29. 40 + 4 = _____
10. 4 x 3 = _____	30. 5 x 40 = _____
11. 32 ÷ 4 = _____	31. 36 ÷ 4 = _____
12. 44 − 4 = _____	32. 12 − 4 = _____
13. 4 + 8 = _____	33. 24 + 4 = _____
14. 4 x 6 = _____	34. 4 x 0 = _____
15. 12 ÷ 4 = _____	35. 4 ÷ 4 = _____
16. 36 − 4 = _____	36. 28 − 4 = _____
17. 4 + 4 = _____	37. 4 + 36 = _____
18. 4 x 10 = _____	38. 4 x 4 = _____
19. 16 ÷ 4 = _____	39. 40 ÷ 4 = _____
20. 24 − 4 = _____	40. 40 − 4 = _____

My score:

My time: _____ mins _____ secs

I'm happy I'm not happy

OOPS! I didn't understand

The main area for me to work on is:

_____

_____

_____

_____

Set A

1. 4 + 4 = _____	21. 4 + 16 = _____
2. 4 x 5 = _____	22. 4 x 8 = _____
3. 40 ÷ 4 = _____	23. 20 ÷ 4 = _____
4. 12 − 4 = _____	24. 28 − 4 = _____
5. 4 + 12 = _____	25. 32 + 4 = _____
6. 4 x 7 = _____	26. 4 x 4 = _____
7. 16 ÷ 4 = _____	27. 28 ÷ 4 = _____
8. 24 − 4 = _____	28. 16 − 4 = _____
9. 4 + 28 = _____	29. 40 + 4 = _____
10. 4 x 3 = _____	30. 4 x 6 = _____
11. 8 ÷ 4 = _____	31. 36 ÷ 4 = _____
12. 8 − 4 = _____	32. 20 − 4 = _____
13. 4 + 8 = _____	33. 24 + 4 = _____
14. 4 x 9 = _____	34. 2 x 4 = _____
15. 12 ÷ 4 = _____	35. 24 ÷ 4 = _____
16. 36 − 4 = _____	36. 4 − 4 = _____
17. 4 + 20 = _____	37. 36 + 4 = _____
18. 4 x 10 = _____	38. 4 x 0 = _____
19. 32 ÷ 4 = _____	39. 40 ÷ 4 = _____
20. 40 − 4 = _____	40. 32 − 4 = _____

5 x table

Set A

1. Add 5 to the following:

(a) 15 _____   (c) 35 _____

(b) 20 _____   (d) 30 _____

2. How many groups of 5 in:

(a) 10? _____   (c) 45? _____

(b) 25? _____   (d) 30? _____

3. Subtract 5 from the following:

(a) 30 _____   (c) 50 _____

(b) 25 _____   (d) 15 _____

4. Which multiple of 5 is closest to:

(a) 47? _____   (c) 14? _____

(b) 33? _____   (d) 39? _____

5. Add:

(a) 5 + 5 + 5 = _____

(b) 5 + 5 + 5 + 5 + 5 = _____

(c) 5 + 5 + 5 + 5 + 5 + 5 + 5 + 5 = _____

6. Complete the number sequence:

0, 5, _____, 15, _____, _____, 30, _____, 40, _____, _____

7. Complete the number sentences:

(a) 5 x _____ = 50

(b) 5 x _____ = 0

(c) 5 x _____ = 30

8. Complete the following:

(a) (5 x 6) + 5 = _____

(b) (5 x 3) + 5 = _____

(c) (5 x 8) – 5 = _____

(f) 4 x 50 = 200 ☐

(g) 3 x 50 = 150 ☐

(h) 20 ÷ 5 = 4 ☐

(i) 40 ÷ 5 = 10 ☐

(j) 15 ÷ 5 = 3 ☐

9. True (✓) False (✗):

(a) 3 x 5 = 15 ☐

(b) 9 x 5 = 45 ☐

(c) 6 x 5 = 35 ☐

(d) 8 x 5 = 40 ☐

(e) 9 x 50 = 400 ☐

10. Say your 5 x tables backwards.

Set B

1. Add 5 to the following:

(a) 5 _____   (c) 40 _____

(b) 25 _____   (d) 10 _____

2. How many groups of 5 in:

(a) 50? _____   (c) 20? _____

(b) 35? _____   (d) 40? _____

3. Subtract 5 from the following:

(a) 10 _____   (c) 20 _____

(b) 45 _____   (d) 35 _____

4. Which multiple of 5 is closest to:

(a) 52? _____   (c) 8? _____

(b) 27? _____   (d) 17? _____

5. Add:

(a) 5 + 5 + 5 + 5 + 5 + 5 + 5 = _____

(b) 5 + 5 + 5 + 5 = _____

(c) 5 + 5 + 5 + 5 + 5 + 5 + 5 + 5 + 5 + 5 = _____

6. Complete the number sequence:

_____, 45, _____, 35, _____, _____, 20, 15, _____, _____, 0

7. Complete the number sentences:

(a) 5 x _____ = 45

(b) 5 x _____ = 10

(c) 8 x _____ = 40

8. Complete the following:

(a) (5 x 9) + 5 = _____

(b) (5 x 10) – 5 = _____

(c) (5 x 7) – 5 = _____

(f) 6 x 50 = 350 ☐

(g) 8 x 50 = 400 ☐

(h) 25 ÷ 5 = 5 ☐

(i) 45 ÷ 5 = 8 ☐

(j) 30 ÷ 5 = 6 ☐

9. True (✓) False (✗):

(a) 5 x 5 = 20 ☐

(b) 7 x 5 = 30 ☐

(c) 10 x 5 = 50 ☐

(d) 7 x 50 = 300 ☐

(e) 5 x 50 = 250 ☐

10. Count by 50s to 500.

0 x 5 = _____	0 x 50 = _____		
1 x 5 = _____	1 x 50 = _____	6 x 5 = _____	6 x 50 = _____
2 x 5 = _____	2 x 50 = _____	7 x 5 = _____	7 x 50 = _____
3 x 5 = _____	3 x 50 = _____	8 x 5 = _____	8 x 50 = _____
4 x 5 = _____	4 x 50 = _____	9 x 5 = _____	9 x 50 = _____
5 x 5 = _____	5 x 50 = _____	10 x 5 = _____	10 x 50 = _____

1. How many days in:

(a) 5 weeks 5 days? _____ (b) 5 weeks 2 days? _____

2. Double:

(a) 150 _____   (b) 250 _____   (c) 25 _____   (d) 100 _____

3. Halve:

(a) 200 _____   (b) 300 _____   (c) 100 _____   (d) 500 _____

4. Lollies cost 5p each. How many can you buy with:

(a) 30p? _____   (b) 45p? _____   (c) 50p? _____   (d) 25p? _____

5. Each plane can carry 50 passengers. How many planes would be needed to carry:

(a) 350 people? _____ planes   (b) 200 people? _____ planes   (c) 150 people? _____ planes

6. Complete these:

(a) $27 \div 5 =$ _____ r _____   (b) $39 \div 5 =$ _____ r _____   (c) $48 \div 5 =$ _____ r _____

7. If you cut these oranges into fifths, how many slices would you have?

(a) 6 oranges _____ slices   (c) 4 oranges _____ slices   (e) 2 oranges _____ slices

(b) 5 oranges _____ slices   (d) 10 oranges _____ slices   (f) 20 oranges _____ slices

8. Each cattle truck can hold 50 cattle. How many cattle would fit in:

(a) 3 trucks? _____ cattle   (b) 8 trucks? _____ cattle   (c) 6 trucks? _____ cattle

9. Phone calls cost 50p each. Troy made 7 calls and Asha made 9 calls.

(a) How much money does Troy spend? _____

(b) How much money does Asha spend? _____

(c) How much more does Asha spend than Troy? _____

(d) How much change would Troy receive from a £5 note? _____

(e) How much change would Asha receive from a £5 note? _____

10. Complete the chart.

+ 50	200	50	450	300	150	500	250	350	100	400	0
− 50	300	450	50	100	350	250	500	150	400	200	50

Set B

1. 5 + 45 = ____		21. 5 + 50 = ____	
2. 5 x 5 = ____		22. 5 x 3 = ____	
3. 45 ÷ 5 = ____		23. 50 ÷ 5 = ____	
4. 15 – 5 = ____		24. 25 – 5 = ____	
5. 5 + 5 = ____		25. 5 + 25 = ____	
6. 5 x 0 = ____		26. 5 x 9 = ____	
7. 5 ÷ 5 = ____		27. 20 ÷ 5 = ____	
8. 20 – 5 = ____		28. 10 – 5 = ____	
9. 5 + 10 = ____		29. 5 + 20 = ____	
10. 5 x 7 = ____		30. 5 x 2 = ____	
11. 40 ÷ 5 = ____		31. 35 ÷ 5 = ____	
12. 35 – 5 = ____		32. 40 – 5 = ____	
13. 5 + 30 = ____		33. 5 + 45 = ____	
14. 5 x 3 = ____		34. 6 x 5 = ____	
15. 25 ÷ 5 = ____		35. 15 ÷ 5 = ____	
16. 55 – 5 = ____		36. 60 – 5 = ____	
17. 5 + 35 = ____		37. 15 + 5 = ____	
18. 5 x 10 = ____		38. 5 x 8 = ____	
19. 10 ÷ 5 = ____		39. 40 ÷ 5 = ____	
20. 45 – 5 = ____		40. 30 – 5 = ____	

My score: _____

My time: ____ mins ____ secs

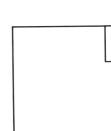

The main area for me to work on is: _____

Set A

1. 5 + 5 = ____		21. 5 + 35 = ____	
2. 5 x 8 = ____		22. 5 x 10 = ____	
3. 15 ÷ 5 = ____		23. 25 ÷ 5 = ____	
4. 30 – 5 = ____		24. 45 – 5 = ____	
5. 5 + 40 = ____		25. 30 + 5 = ____	
6. 5 x 6 = ____		26. 5 x 4 = ____	
7. 35 ÷ 5 = ____		27. 30 ÷ 5 = ____	
8. 60 – 5 = ____		28. 55 – 5 = ____	
9. 5 + 20 = ____		29. 5 + 10 = ____	
10. 5 x 2 = ____		30. 5 x 7 = ____	
11. 20 ÷ 5 = ____		31. 45 ÷ 5 = ____	
12. 40 – 5 = ____		32. 20 – 5 = ____	
13. 25 + 5 = ____		33. 5 + 45 = ____	
14. 9 x 5 = ____		34. 5 x 5 = ____	
15. 50 ÷ 5 = ____		35. 5 ÷ 5 = ____	
16. 10 – 5 = ____		36. 15 – 5 = ____	
17. 5 + 50 = ____		37. 5 – 5 = ____	
18. 5 x 3 = ____		38. 3 x 50 = ____	
19. 10 ÷ 5 = ____		39. 40 ÷ 5 = ____	
20. 25 – 5 = ____		40. 35 – 5 = ____	

My score: _____

My time: ____ mins ____ secs

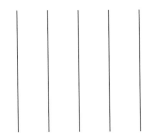

The main area for me to work on is: _____

6 x table

Set B

1. Add 6 to the following:

(a) 12 _____   (c) 42 _____

(b) 54 _____   (d) 30 _____

2. How many groups of 6 in:

(a) 36? _____   (c) 6? _____

(b) 42? _____   (d) 24? _____

3. Subtract 6 from the following:

(a) 18 _____   (c) 60 _____

(b) 48 _____   (d) 42 _____

4. Which multiple of 6 is closest to:

(a) 44? _____   (c) 25? _____

(b) 46? _____   (d) 14? _____

5. Add:

(a) 6 + 6 + 6 = _____

(b) 6 + 6 + 6 + 6 + 6 + 6 = _____

(c) 6 + 6 + 6 + 6 + 6 + 6 + 6 + 6 = _____

6. Complete the number sequence:

60, _____, _____, 42, _____, _____, 24, 18, _____, _____, 0

7. Complete the number sentences:

(a) 6 x _____ = 36

(b) 6 x _____ = 0

(c) 6 x _____ = 12

8. Complete the following:

(a) (6 x 9) + 6 = _____

(b) (6 x 4) − 6 = _____

(c) (6 x 6) − 6 = _____

9. True (✓) False (X):

(a) 5 x 6 = 30 ☐

(b) 7 x 6 = 36 ☐

(c) 10 x 6 = 60 ☐

(d) 4 x 60 = 240 ☐

(e) 3 x 60 = 120 ☐

(f) 6 x 60 = 360 ☐

(g) 54 ÷ 6 = 4 ☐

(h) 48 ÷ 6 = 8 ☐

(i) 18 ÷ 6 = 3 ☐

(j) 30 ÷ 6 = 6 ☐

10. Count by 60s to 600.

Set A

1. Add 6 to the following:

(a) 36 _____   (c) 48 _____

(b) 24 _____   (d) 18 _____

2. How many groups of 6 in:

(a) 18? _____   (c) 30? _____

(b) 54? _____   (d) 60? _____

3. Subtract 6 from the following:

(a) 12 _____   (c) 54 _____

(b) 30 _____   (d) 24 _____

4. Which multiple of 6 is closest to:

(a) 58? _____   (c) 34? _____

(b) 19? _____   (d) 53? _____

5. Add:

(a) 6 + 6 + 6 + 6 + 6 + 6 + 6 = _____

(b) 6 + 6 + 6 + 6 + 6 = _____

(c) 6 + 6 + 6 + 6 + 6 + 6 + 6 = _____

6. Complete the number sequence:

0, 6, _____, _____, 24, _____, _____, 42, _____, _____

7. Complete the number sentences:

(a) 6 x _____ = 54

(b) 3 x _____ = 18

(c) 6 x _____ = 24

8. Complete the following:

(a) (6 x 7) + 6 = _____

(b) (6 x 3) + 6 = _____

(c) (6 x 10) − 6 = _____

9. True (✓) False (X):

(a) 3 x 6 = 21 ☐

(b) 9 x 6 = 54 ☐

(c) 6 x 6 = 30 ☐

(d) 8 x 6 = 48 ☐

(e) 7 x 60 = 420 ☐

(f) 5 x 60 = 300 ☐

(g) 9 x 60 = 480 ☐

(h) 54 ÷ 6 = 9 ☐

(i) 42 ÷ 6 = 7 ☐

(j) 36 ÷ 6 = 5 ☐

10. Say your 6 x tables backwards.

0 x 6 = _____	0 x 60 = _____		
1 x 6 = _____	1 x 60 = _____	6 x 6 = _____	6 x 60 = _____
2 x 6 = _____	2 x 60 = _____	7 x 6 = _____	7 x 60 = _____
3 x 6 = _____	3 x 60 = _____	8 x 6 = _____	8 x 60 = _____
4 x 6 = _____	4 x 60 = _____	9 x 6 = _____	9 x 60 = _____
5 x 6 = _____	5 x 60 = _____	10 x 6 = _____	10 x 60 = _____

1. How many days in:

(a) 6 weeks 4 days? _____ (b) 6 weeks 3 days? _____

2. Double:

(a) 12 _____ (b) 180 _____ (c) 30 _____ (d) 300 _____

3. Halve:

(a) 120 _____ (b) 240 _____ (c) 480 _____ (d) 60 _____

4. Tiles are 6 cm long. How many can you fit into a space:

(a) 42 cm long? _____ tiles (b) 54 cm long? _____ tiles (c) 60 cm long? _____ tiles

5. Each bus can carry 60 passengers. How many buses would be needed to carry:

(a) 300 people? _____ buses (b) 480 people? _____ buses (c) 180 people? _____ buses

6. Complete these:

(a) 26 ÷ 6 = _____ r _____ (b) 57 ÷ 6 = _____ r _____ (c) 40 ÷ 6 = _____ r _____

7. If you cut these cakes into sixths, how many slices would you have?

(a) 3 cakes _____ slices (c) 5 cakes _____ slices (e) 6 cakes _____ slices

(b) 8 cakes _____ slices (d) 10 cakes _____ slices (f) 9 cakes _____ slices

8. A crate can hold 60 apples. How many apples would fit in:

(a) 2 crates? _____ apples (b) 6 crates? _____ apples (c) 9 crates? _____ apples

9. Cards cost 60p each. Ben buys 6 cards and his friend Josh buys 9.

(a) How much money does Ben spend? _____

(b) How much money does Josh spend? _____

(c) How much do Ben and Josh spend altogether? _____

(d) How much change would Ben receive from a £10 note? _____

(e) How much change would Josh receive from a £10 note? _____

10. **S n a k e s 'n'** **L a d d e r s**

Finish

81	82	83	84	85	86	87	88	89	90	91	92	93	94	95	96	97	98	99	100
80	79	78	77	76	75	74	73	72	71	70	69	68	67	66	65	64	63	62	61
41	42	43	44	45	46	47	48	49	50	51	52	53	54	55	56	57	58	59	60
40	39	38	37	36	35	34	33	32	31	30	29	28	27	26	25	24	23	22	21
1	2	3	4	5	6	7	8	9	10	11	12	13	14	15	16	17	18	19	20

Start

Set B

My score:

My time: _____ mins _____ secs

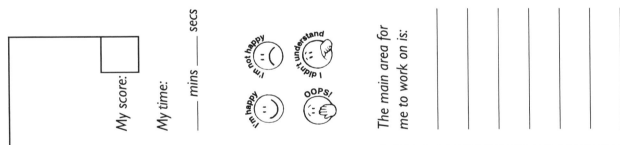

I'm happy

I'm not happy

I didn't understand

OOPS!

The main area for me to work on is:

1. 54 ÷ 6 =
2. 6 x 3 =
3. 18 ÷ 6 =
4. 54 – 6 =
5. 6 + 30 =
6. 6 x 6 =
7. 6 ÷ 6 =
8. 66 – 6 =
9. 6 + 0 =
10. 6 x 5 =
11. 42 ÷ 6 =
12. 60 – 6 =
13. 6 + 18 =
14. 6 x 0 =
15. 36 ÷ 6 =
16. 42 – 6 =
17. 6 + 42 =
18. 6 x 9 =
19. 30 ÷ 6 =
20. 12 – 6 =

21. 6 + 48 =
22. 3 x 60 =
23. 12 ÷ 6 =
24. 48 – 6 =
25. 6 + 24 =
26. 6 x 8 =
27. 60 ÷ 6 =
28. 24 – 6 =
29. 6 + 12 =
30. 6 x 4 =
31. 54 ÷ 6 =
32. 36 – 6 =
33. 6 + 36 =
34. 6 x 10 =
35. 24 ÷ 6 =
36. 18 – 6 =
37. 6 + 6 =
38. 6 x 7 =
39. 48 ÷ 6 =
40. 30 – 6 =

Set A

My score:

My time: _____ mins _____ secs

I'm happy

I'm not happy

I didn't understand

OOPS!

The main area for me to work on is:

1. 6 + 6 =
2. 6 x 7 =
3. 24 ÷ 6 =
4. 30 – 6 =
5. 6 + 36 =
6. 6 x 10 =
7. 48 ÷ 6 =
8. 18 – 6 =
9. 12 + 6 =
10. 6 x 4 =
11. 12 ÷ 6 =
12. 36 – 6 =
13. 6 + 54 =
14. 6 x 8 =
15. 54 ÷ 6 =
16. 24 – 6 =
17. 6 + 30 =
18. 6 x 0 =
19. 60 ÷ 6 =
20. 48 – 6 =

21. 60 ÷ 6 =
22. 6 x 9 =
23. 18 ÷ 6 =
24. 12 – 6 =
25. 6 + 18 =
26. 6 x 60 =
27. 6 ÷ 6 =
28. 42 – 6 =
29. 6 + 42 =
30. 6 x 5 =
31. 42 ÷ 6 =
32. 54 – 6 =
33. 6 + 48 =
34. 6 x 3 =
35. 30 ÷ 6 =
36. 60 – 6 =
37. 24 ÷ 6 =
38. 6 x 6 =
39. 36 ÷ 6 =
40. 66 – 6 =

Set B

1. Add 7 to the following:
(a) 14 _____   (c) 42 _____
(b) 28 _____   (d) 63 _____

2. How many groups of 7 in:
(a) 7?   (c) 70?
(b) 63?   (d) 21?

3. Subtract 7 from the following:
(a) 49 _____   (c) 63 _____
(b) 21 _____   (d) 56 _____

4. Which multiple of 7 is closest to:
(a) 30?   (c) 59?
(b) 12?   (d) 51?

5. Add:
(a) 7 + 7 + 7 + 7 + 7 + 7 + 7 + 7 = _____
(b) 7 + 7 + 7 + 7 = _____
(c) 7 + 7 + 7 + 7 + 7 + 7 + 7 + 7 = _____

6. Complete the number sequence:
_____, 63, _____, 49, _____, 28, _____, _____, 7, 0

7. Complete the number sentences:
(a) 7 x _____ = 28
(b) 9 x _____ = 63
(c) 7 x _____ = 42

8. Complete the following:
(a) (7 x 8) + 7 = _____
(b) (7 x 10) − 7 = _____
(c) (7 x 5) − 7 = _____
(f) 5 x 70 = 350 □
(g) 9 x 70 = 560 □
(h) 28 ÷ 7 = 4 □
(i) 56 ÷ 7 = 8 □
(j) 21 ÷ 7 = 3 □

9. True (✓) False (X):
(a) 8 x 7 = 56 □
(b) 5 x 7 = 42 □
(c) 7 x 7 = 49 □
(d) 10 x 7 = 70 □
(e) 7 x 70 = 560 □

10. Count by 70s to 700.

Set A

1. Add 7 to the following:
(a) 21 _____   (c) 56 _____
(b) 63 _____   (d) 7 _____

2. How many groups of 7 in:
(a) 14?   (c) 35?
(b) 56?   (d) 42?

3. Subtract 7 from the following:
(a) 70 _____   (c) 14 _____
(b) 35 _____   (d) 42 _____

4. Which multiple of 7 is closest to:
(a) 22?   (c) 40?
(b) 17?   (d) 9?

5. Add:
(a) 7 + 7 + 7 = _____
(b) 7 + 7 + 7 + 7 + 7 + 7 + 7 = _____
(c) 7 + 7 + 7 + 7 + 7 = _____

6. Complete the number sequence:
0, 7, _____, _____, _____, 35, 42, _____, _____, 63

7. Complete the number sentences:
(a) 7 x _____ = 56
(b) 2 x _____ = 14
(c) 7 x _____ = 70

8. Complete the following:
(a) (7 x 9) + 7 = _____
(b) (7 x 3) + 7 = _____
(c) (7 x 4) − 7 = _____
(f) 6 x 70 = 420 □
(g) 8 x 70 = 630 □
(h) 42 ÷ 7 = 6 □
(i) 49 ÷ 7 = 8 □
(j) 63 ÷ 7 = 9 □

9. True (✓) False (X):
(a) 3 x 7 = 21 □
(b) 9 x 7 = 56 □
(c) 6 x 7 = 49 □
(d) 4 x 70 = 280 □
(e) 3 x 70 = 210 □

10. Say your 7 x tables backwards.

0 x 7 = _____	0 x 70 = _____		
1 x 7 = _____	1 x 70 = _____	6 x 7 = _____	6 x 70 = _____
2 x 7 = _____	2 x 70 = _____	7 x 7 = _____	7 x 70 = _____
3 x 7 = _____	3 x 70 = _____	8 x 7 = _____	8 x 70 = _____
4 x 7 = _____	4 x 70 = _____	9 x 7 = _____	9 x 70 = _____
5 x 7 = _____	5 x 70 = _____	10 x 7 = _____	10 x 70 = _____

1. How many days in:

(a) 7 weeks 5 days? _____ (b) 7 weeks 4 days? _____

2. Double:

(a) 210 _____ (b) 280 _____ (c) 35 _____ (d) 21 _____

3. Halve:

(a) 700 _____ (b) 280 _____ (c) 70 _____ (d) 14 _____

4. Tiles are 7 cm long. How many can you fit into a space:

(a) 42 cm long? _____ tiles (b) 35 cm long? _____ tiles (c) 63 cm long? _____ tiles

5. Each tram can carry 70 passengers. How many trams would be needed to carry:

(a) 560 people? _____ trams (b) 420 people? _____ trams (c) 210 people? _____ trams

6. Complete these:

(a) 37 ÷ 7 = _____ r _____ (b) 64 ÷ 7 = _____ r _____ (c) 25 ÷ 7 = _____ r _____

7. If you cut these pizzas into sevenths, how many slices would you have?

(a) 4 pizzas _____ slices (c) 7 pizzas _____ slices (e) 3 pizzas _____ slices

(b) 5 pizzas _____ slices (d) 9 pizzas _____ slices (f) 6 pizzas _____ slices

8. A crate can hold 70 pears. How many pears would fit in:

(a) 3 crates? _____ pears (b) 6 crates? _____ pears (c) 10 crates? _____ pears

9. Stamps cost 70p each. Karl buys 5 and his friend Ahmed buys 8 stamps.

(a) How much money does Karl spend? _____   (e) How much change would Ahmed

(b) How much money does Ahmed spend? _____   receive from a £10 note? _____

(c) How much more does Ahmed spend than Karl? _____

(d) How much change would Karl receive from a £10 note? _____

10.

																			Finish
81	82	83	84	85	86	87	88	89	90	91	92	93	94	95	96	97	98	99	100
80	79	78	77	76	75	74	73	72	71	70	69	68	67	66	65	64	63	62	61
41	42	43	44	45	46	47	48	49	50	51	52	53	54	55	56	57	58	59	60
40	39	38	37	36	35	34	33	32	31	30	29	28	27	26	25	24	23	22	21
1	2	3	4	5	6	7	8	9	10	11	12	13	14	15	16	17	18	19	20

Start

7 x table

Set B

My score:

My time:

_____ mins _____ secs

I'm happy — I'm not happy — I didn't understand — OOPS!

The main area for me to work on is:

_____

_____

1. 7 + 7 =
2. 7 x 8 =
3. 42 ÷ 7 =
4. 70 − 7 =
5. 21 + 7 =
6. 7 x 5 =
7. 7 ÷ 7 =
8. 28 − 7 =
9. 7 + 63 =
10. 7 x 3 =
11. 35 ÷ 7 =
12. 14 − 7 =
13. 7 − 7 =
14. 7 x 9 =
15. 14 ÷ 7 =
16. 2 x 70 =
17. 42 + 7 =
18. 7 x 7 =
19. 7 x 0 =
20. 21 − 7 =

21. 7 + 56 =
22. 3 x 70 =
23. 28 ÷ 7 =
24. 35 − 7 =
25. 7 + 49 =
26. 7 x 4 =
27. 49 ÷ 7 =
28. 49 − 7 =
29. 7 + 35 =
30. 7 x 6 =
31. 56 ÷ 7 =
32. 63 − 7 =
33. 28 + 7 =
34. 4 x 70 =
35. 21 ÷ 7 =
36. 56 − 7 =
37. 14 + 7 =
38. 7 x 10 =
39. 56 ÷ 7 =
40. 42 − 7 =

Set A

My score:

My time:

_____ mins _____ secs

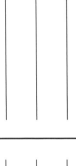

I'm happy — I'm not happy — I didn't understand — OOPS!

The main area for me to work on is:

_____

_____

1. 7 + 14 =
2. 7 x 6 =
3. 21 ÷ 7 =
4. 14 − 7 =
5. 7 + 28 =
6. 7 x 3 =
7. 49 ÷ 7 =
8. 70 − 7 =
9. 35 + 7 =
10. 7 x 7 =
11. 14 ÷ 7 =
12. 21 − 7 =
13. 49 + 7 =
14. 7 x 0 =
15. 35 ÷ 7 =
16. 35 − 7 =
17. 7 + 70 =
18. 7 x 70 =
19. 63 ÷ 7 =
20. 28 − 7 =

21. 7 + 21 =
22. 7 x 2 =
23. 28 ÷ 7 =
24. 49 − 7 =
25. 7 + 42 =
26. 7 x 5 =
27. 42 ÷ 7 =
28. 77 − 7 =
29. 56 + 7 =
30. 7 x 9 =
31. 70 ÷ 7 =
32. 42 − 7 =
33. 7 x 70 =
34. 7 x 10 =
35. 7 ÷ 7 =
36. 63 − 7 =
37. 7 + 63 =
38. 7 x 4 =
39. 56 ÷ 7 =
40. 70 x 0 =

Set B

1. Add 8 to the following:
(a) 16 _____   (c) 56 _____
(b) 72 _____   (d) 32 _____

2. How many groups of 8 in:
(a) 56? _____   (c) 8? _____
(b) 64? _____   (d) 24? _____

3. Subtract 8 from the following:
(a) 80 _____   (c) 24 _____
(b) 56 _____   (d) 40 _____

4. Which multiple of 8 is closest to:
(a) 18? _____   (c) 27? _____
(b) 45? _____   (d) 82? _____

5. Add:
(a) 8 + 8 + 8 + 8 + 8 + 8 + 8 = _____
(b) 8 + 8 + 8 + 8 + 8 = _____
(c) 8 + 8 + 8 + 8 + 8 + 8 + 8 + 8 + 8 = _____

6. Complete the number sequence:
80, _____, _____, 56, _____, 40, _____, _____, 8

7. Complete the number sentences:
(a) 8 x _____ = 24
(b) 7 x _____ = 56
(c) 8 x _____ = 32

8. Complete the following:
(a) (8 x 7) + 8 = _____
(b) (8 x 6) − 8 = _____
(c) (8 x 8) − 8 = _____

9. True (✓) False (X):
(a) 8 x 8 = 72 ☐
(b) 8 x 5 = 40 ☐
(c) 7 x 8 = 56 ☐
(d) 10 x 8 = 80 ☐
(e) 4 x 80 = 240 ☐
(f) 3 x 80 = 240 ☐
(g) 8 x 80 = 640 ☐
(h) 72 ÷ 8 = 8 ☐
(i) 56 ÷ 8 = 7 ☐
(j) 48 ÷ 8 = 6 ☐

10. Count by 80s to 800.

Set A

1. Add 8 to the following:
(a) 48 _____   (c) 24 _____
(b) 40 _____   (d) 64 _____

2. How many groups of 8 in:
(a) 32? _____   (c) 80? _____
(b) 40? _____   (d) 16? _____

3. Subtract 8 from the following:
(a) 72 _____   (c) 48 _____
(b) 64 _____   (d) 16 _____

4. Which multiple of 8 is closest to:
(a) 66? _____   (c) 33? _____
(b) 53? _____   (d) 10? _____

5. Add:
(a) 8 + 8 + 8 + 8 + 8 + 8 = _____
(b) 8 + 8 + 8 = _____
(c) 8 + 8 + 8 + 8 + 8 + 8 + 8 + 8 = _____

6. Complete the number sequence:
_____, 8, _____, _____, 32, _____, _____, 56, _____, _____, 80

7. Complete the number sentences:
(a) 8 x _____ = 48
(b) 2 x _____ = 16
(c) 8 x _____ = 72

8. Complete the following:
(a) (8 x 4) + 8 = _____
(b) (8 x 9) + 8 = _____
(c) (8 x 10) − 8 = _____

9. True (✓) False (X):
(a) 3 x 8 = 24 ☐
(b) 9 x 8 = 64 ☐
(c) 6 x 8 = 48 ☐
(d) 4 x 80 = 480 ☐
(e) 5 x 80 = 400 ☐
(f) 9 x 80 = 720 ☐
(g) 32 ÷ 8 = 5 ☐
(h) 64 ÷ 8 = 8 ☐
(i) 24 ÷ 8 = 3 ☐
(j) 40 ÷ 8 = 6 ☐

10. Say your 8 x tables backwards.

8 x table

0 x 8 = _____	0 x 80 = _____		
1 x 8 = _____	1 x 80 = _____	6 x 8 = _____	6 x 80 = _____
2 x 8 = _____	2 x 80 = _____	7 x 8 = _____	7 x 80 = _____
3 x 8 = _____	3 x 80 = _____	8 x 8 = _____	8 x 80 = _____
4 x 8 = _____	4 x 80 = _____	9 x 8 = _____	9 x 80 = _____
5 x 8 = _____	5 x 80 = _____	10 x 8 = _____	10 x 80 = _____

1. How many days in:

(a) 8 weeks 4 days? _____

(b) 8 weeks 2 days? _____

2. Double:

(a) 160 _____   (b) 240 _____   (c) 80 _____   (d) 8 _____

3. Halve:

(a) 64 _____   (b) 48 _____   (c) 16 _____   (d) 80 _____

4. Tiles are 8 cm long. How many can you fit into a space:

(a) 40 cm long? _____ tiles   (b) 80 cm long? _____ tiles   (c) 56 cm long? _____ tiles

5. Each train carriage can carry 80 passengers. How many carriages would be needed to carry:

(a) 320 people? _____ carriages   (b) 640 people? _____ carriages   (c) 160 people? _____ carriages

6. Complete these:

(a) 74 ÷ 8 = _____ r _____   (b) 35 ÷ 8 = _____ r _____   (c) 21 ÷ 8 = _____ r _____

7. If you cut these apples pies into eighths, how many slices would you have?

(a) 3 pies _____ slices   (c) 9 pies _____ slices   (e) 5 pies _____ slices

(b) 6 pies _____ slices   (d) 4 pies _____ slices   (f) 10 pies _____ slices

8. A crate can hold 80 bottles. How many bottles would fit in:

(a) 5 crates? _____ bottles   (b) 9 crates? _____ bottles   (c) 7 crates? _____ bottles

9. Tennis balls cost 80p each. Sarah buys 4 and her sister Leah buys 6 tennis balls.

(a) How much money does Sarah spend? _____

(b) How much money does Leah spend? _____

(c) How much do they spend altogether? _____

(d) How much change would Sarah receive from a £10 note? _____

(e) How much change would Leah receive from a £10 note? _____

10. Snakes 'n' Ladders

																			Finish
81	82	83	84	85	86	87	88	89	90	91	92	93	94	95	96	97	98	99	100
80	79	78	77	76	75	74	73	72	71	70	69	68	67	66	65	64	63	62	61
41	42	43	44	45	46	47	48	49	50	51	52	53	54	55	56	57	58	59	60
40	39	38	37	36	35	34	33	32	31	30	29	28	27	26	25	24	23	22	21
1	2	3	4	5	6	7	8	9	10	11	12	13	14	15	16	17	18	19	20

Start

Set B

1. 80 + 8 =
2. 8 x 8 =
3. 48 ÷ 8 =
4. 80 − 8 =
5. 24 + 8 =
6. 8 x 5 =
7. 8 ÷ 8 =
8. 32 − 8 =
9. 8 + 72 =
10. 8 x 3 =
11. 40 ÷ 8 =
12. 16 − 8 =
13. 8 + 8 =
14. 9 x 8 =
15. 16 ÷ 8 =
16. 88 − 8 =
17. 48 + 8 =
18. 8 x 7 =
19. 2 x 80 =
20. 24 − 8 =

21. 72 + 8 =
22. 80 x 0 =
23. 32 ÷ 8 =
24. 40 − 8 =
25. 8 + 56 =
26. 8 x 4 =
27. 56 ÷ 8 =
28. 56 − 8 =
29. 8 + 40 =
30. 6 x 8 =
31. 64 ÷ 8 =
32. 72 − 8 =
33. 8 + 32 =
34. 5 x 80 =
35. 24 ÷ 8 =
36. 64 − 8 =
37. 16 + 8 =
38. 10 x 8 =
39. 72 ÷ 8 =
40. 48 − 8 =

My score:

My time: _____ mins _____ secs

I'm happy

I'm not happy

I didn't understand

OOPS!

The main area for me to work on is:

Set A

1. 16 + 8 =
2. 6 x 8 =
3. 24 ÷ 8 =
4. 16 − 8 =
5. 8 + 32 =
6. 8 x 3 =
7. 56 ÷ 8 =
8. 80 − 8 =
9. 8 + 40 =
10. 8 x 8 =
11. 16 ÷ 8 =
12. 24 − 8 =
13. 56 + 8 =
14. 8 x 0 =
15. 40 ÷ 8 =
16. 40 − 8 =
17. 8 + 80 =
18. 8 x 80 =
19. 64 ÷ 8 =
20. 32 − 8 =

21. 24 + 8 =
22. 8 x 2 =
23. 32 ÷ 8 =
24. 56 − 8 =
25. 8 + 48 =
26. 8 x 5 =
27. 48 ÷ 8 =
28. 88 − 8 =
29. 64 + 8 =
30. 8 x 9 =
31. 80 ÷ 8 =
32. 48 − 8 =
33. 3 x 80 =
34. 8 x 10 =
35. 8 ÷ 8 =
36. 72 − 8 =
37. 8 + 72 =
38. 8 x 4 =
39. 72 ÷ 8 =
40. 2 x 80 =

My score:

My time: _____ mins _____ secs

I'm happy

I'm not happy

I didn't understand

OOPS!

The main area for me to work on is:

Set B

1. Add 9 to the following:

(a) 54 ____   (c) 81 ____

(b) 9 ____   (d) 63 ____

2. How many groups of 9 in:

(a) 18? ____   (c) 54?

(b) 72? ____   (d) 27?

3. Subtract 9 from the following:

(a) 63 ____   (c) 90 ____

(b) 27 ____   (d) 45 ____

4. Which multiple of 9 is closest to:

(a) 35?   (c) 65?

(b) 70?   (d) 89?

5. Add:

(a) 9 + 9 + 9 + 9 + 9 + 9 + 9 = ____

(b) 9 + 9 + 9 + 9 = ____

(c) 9 + 9 + 9 + 9 + 9 + 9 + 9 + 9 + 9 = ____

6. Complete the number sequence:

____, ____, 72, ____, 45, ____, ____, 18, ____, ____

7. Complete the number sentences:

(a) 9 x ____ = 36

(b) 9 x ____ = 0

(c) 9 x ____ = 81

8. Complete the following:

(a) (9 x 9) + 9 = ____

(b) (9 x 10) – 9 = ____

(c) (9 x 2) – 9 = ____

(f) 9 x 90 = 810 ☐

(g) 4 x 90 = 270 ☐

(h) 45 ÷ 9 = 5 ☐

(i) 27 ÷ 9 = 4 ☐

(j) 72 ÷ 9 = 8 ☐

9. True (✓) False (✗):

(a) 5 x 9 = 36 ☐

(b) 7 x 9 = 72 ☐

(c) 10 x 9 = 90 ☐

(d) 7 x 90 = 630 ☐

(e) 5 x 90 = 450 ☐

10. Count by 90s to 900.

Set A

1. Add 9 to the following:

(a) 27 ____   (c) 72 ____

(b) 45 ____   (d) 18 ____

2. How many groups of 9 in:

(a) 90? ____   (c) 36?

(b) 63? ____   (d) 81?

3. Subtract 9 from the following:

(a) 18 ____   (c) 36 ____

(b) 81 ____   (d) 54 ____

4. Which multiple of 9 is closest to:

(a) 83?   (c) 50?

(b) 21?   (d) 30?

5. Add:

(a) 9 + 9 + 9 + 9 + 9 = ____

(b) 9 + 9 + 9 = ____

(c) 9 + 9 + 9 + 9 + 9 + 9 + 9 + 9 = ____

6. Complete the number sequence:

0, 9, ____, ____, 36, ____, ____, 63, ____, ____, 90

7. Complete the number sentences:

(a) 9 x ____ = 45

(b) 3 x ____ = 27

(c) 9 x ____ = 72

8. Complete the following:

(a) (9 x 3) + 9 = ____

(b) (9 x 5) + 9 = ____

(c) (9 x 6) – 9 = ____

(f) 6 x 90 = 630 ☐

(g) 8 x 90 = 720 ☐

(h) 54 ÷ 9 = 6 ☐

(i) 63 ÷ 9 = 7 ☐

(j) 81 ÷ 9 = 8 ☐

9. True (✓) False (✗):

(a) 3 x 9 = 27 ☐

(b) 9 x 9 = 81 ☐

(c) 6 x 9 = 54 ☐

(d) 8 x 9 = 63 ☐

(e) 3 x 90 = 270 ☐

10. Say your 9 x table backwards.

0 x 9 = _____	0 x 90 = _____		
1 x 9 = _____	1 x 90 = _____	6 x 9 = _____	6 x 90 = _____
2 x 9 = _____	2 x 90 = _____	7 x 9 = _____	7 x 90 = _____
3 x 9 = _____	3 x 90 = _____	8 x 9 = _____	8 x 90 = _____
4 x 9 = _____	4 x 90 = _____	9 x 9 = _____	9 x 90 = _____
5 x 9 = _____	5 x 90 = _____	10 x 9 = _____	10 x 90 = _____

1. How many days in:

(a) 9 weeks 3 days? _____ (b) 9 weeks 5 days? _____

2. Double:

(a) 180 _____ (b) 450 _____ (c) 90 _____ (d) 18 _____

3. Halve:

(a) 180 _____ (b) 54 _____ (c) 18 _____ (d) 90 _____

4. Tiles are 9 cm long. How many can you fit into a space:

(a) 45 cm long? _____ tiles (b) 90 cm long? _____ tiles (c) 72 cm long? _____ tiles

5. Each plane can carry 90 passengers. How many planes would be needed to carry:

(a) 270 people? _____ planes (b) 540 people? _____ planes (c) 810 people? _____ planes

6. Complete these:

(a) $38 \div 9 =$ _____ r _____ (b) $59 \div 9 =$ _____ r _____ (c) $79 \div 9 =$ _____ r _____

7. If you cut these cakes into ninths, how many pieces would you have?

(a) 4 cakes _____ slices (c) 6 cakes _____ slices (e) 2 cakes _____ slices

(b) 9 cakes _____ slices (d) 5 cakes _____ slices (f) 7 cakes _____ slices

8. A pouch can hold 90 marbles. How many marbles would fit in:

(a) 7 pouches? _____ marbles (b) 9 pouches? _____ marbles (c) 3 pouches? _____ marbles

9. Comic books cost 90p each. Hanna buys 8 and her friend Toshia buys 4 comic books.

(a) How much money does Hanna spend? _____

(b) How much money does Toshia spend? _____

(c) How much more does Hanna spend than Toshia? _____

(d) How much change would Hanna receive from a £10 note? _____

(e) How much change would Toshia receive from a £10 note? _____

10. Snakes 'n' Ladders

																			Finish
81	82	83	84	85	86	87	88	89	90	91	92	93	94	95	96	97	98	99	100
80	79	78	77	76	75	74	73	72	71	70	69	68	67	66	65	64	63	62	61
41	42	43	44	45	46	47	48	49	50	51	52	53	54	55	56	57	58	59	60
40	39	38	37	36	35	34	33	32	31	30	29	28	27	26	25	24	23	22	21
1	2	3	4	5	6	7	8	9	10	11	12	13	14	15	16	17	18	19	20

Start

9 x table

Set B

My score:

My time: _____ mins _____ secs

I'm happy I'm not happy

OOPS! I didn't understand

The main area for me to work on is:

_____

_____

_____

1. 27 + 9 =
2. 9 x 10 =
3. 18 ÷ 2 =
4. 81 – 9 =
5. 9 + 54 =
6. 9 x 4 =
7. 45 ÷ 9 =
8. 54 – 9 =
9. 72 + 9 =
10. 9 x 9 =
11. 81 ÷ 9 =
12. 90 x 0 =
13. 9 + 18 =
14. 9 x 5 =
15. 36 ÷ 9 =
16. 27 – 9 =
17. 36 + 9 =
18. 9 x 2 =
19. 54 ÷ 9 =
20. 90 – 9 =

21. 9 + 45 =
22. 9 x 0 =
23. 27 ÷ 9 =
24. 36 – 9 =
25. 2 x 90 =
26. 3 x 90 =
27. 63 ÷ 9 =
28. 45 – 9 =
29. 9 + 81 =
30. 9 x 7 =
31. 90 ÷ 9 =
32. 18 – 9 =
33. 63 + 9 =
34. 9 x 3 =
35. 72 ÷ 9 =
36. 63 – 9 =
37. 9 + 90 =
38. 6 x 9 =
39. 9 ÷ 9 =
40. 99 – 9 =

Set A

My score:

My time: _____ mins _____ secs

I'm happy I'm not happy

OOPS! I didn't understand

The main area for me to work on is:

_____

_____

_____

1. 9 + 18 =
2. 6 x 9 =
3. 27 ÷ 9 =
4. 18 – 9 =
5. 36 + 9 =
6. 9 x 3 =
7. 63 ÷ 9 =
8. 45 – 9 =
9. 45 + 9 =
10. 9 x 7 =
11. 18 ÷ 9 =
12. 27 – 9 =
13. 63 + 9 =
14. 9 x 0 =
15. 45 ÷ 9 =
16. 90 – 9 =
17. 9 + 90 =
18. 9 x 1 =
19. 81 ÷ 9 =
20. 36 – 9 =

21. 27 + 9 =
22. 9 x 2 =
23. 36 ÷ 9 =
24. 63 – 9 =
25. 54 + 9 =
26. 9 x 5 =
27. 54 ÷ 9 =
28. 99 – 9 =
29. 72 + 9 =
30. 9 x 9 =
31. 90 ÷ 9 =
32. 81 – 9 =
33. 9 x 90 =
34. 9 x 10 =
35. 9 ÷ 9 =
36. 54 – 9 =
37. 9 + 81 =
38. 9 x 4 =
39. 72 ÷ 9 =
40. 4 x 90 =

10 x table

Set B

1. Add 10 to the following:
(a) 10 _____   (c) 80 _____
(b) 70 _____   (d) 110 _____

2. How many groups of 10 in:
(a) 50?   (c) 90?
(b) 60?   (d) 200?

3. Subtract 10 from the following:
(a) 80 _____   (c) 60 _____
(b) 110 _____   (d) 100 _____

4. Which multiple of 10 is closest to:
(a) 18?   (c) 27?
(b) 74?   (d) 98?

5. Add:
(a) $10 + 10 + 10 + 10 =$ _____
(b) $10 + 10 + 10 + 10 + 10 + 10 + 10 + 10 =$ _____
(c) $10 + 10 + 10 + 10 + 10 + 10 + 10 + 10 + 10 + 10 =$ _____

6. Complete the number sequence:
100, _____, _____, 70, _____, 50, _____, _____, 10,

7. Complete the number sentences:
(a) $10 \times$ _____ $= 20$
(b) $8 \times$ _____ $= 80$
(c) $10 \times$ _____ $= 60$

8. Complete the following:
(a) $(10 \times 4) + 10 =$
(b) $(10 \times 7) - 10 =$
(c) $(10 \times 5) - 10 =$

(f) $3 \times 100 = 500$ ☐
(g) $6 \times 100 = 600$ ☐
(h) $40 \div 10 = 5$ ☐
(i) $80 \div 10 = 8$ ☐
(j) $50 \div 10 = 6$ ☐

9. True (✓) False (X):
(a) $8 \times 10 = 80$ ☐
(b) $5 \times 10 = 40$ ☐
(c) $7 \times 10 = 60$ ☐
(d) $10 \times 10 = 100$ ☐
(e) $4 \times 100 = 400$ ☐

10. Count by 100s to 1000.

Set A

1. Add 10 to the following:
(a) 40 _____   (c) 20 _____
(b) 50 _____   (d) 90 _____

2. How many groups of 10 in:
(a) 30?   (c) 80?
(b) 40?   (d) 110?

3. Subtract 10 from the following:
(a) 50 _____   (c) 90 _____
(b) 20 _____   (d) 40 _____

4. Which multiple of 10 is closest to:
(a) 57?   (c) 48?
(b) 33?   (d) 87?

5. Add:
(a) $10 + 10 + 10 + 10 =$ _____
(b) $10 + 10 + 10 + 10 + 10 + 10 + 10 =$ _____
(c) $10 + 10 + 10 + 10 + 10 + 10 + 10 + 10 + 10 =$ _____

6. Complete the number sequence:
0, _____, _____, 40, _____, 70, _____, _____, 100

7. Complete the number sentences:
(a) $10 \times$ _____ $= 70$
(b) $10 \times$ _____ $= 100$
(c) $10 \times$ _____ $= 50$

8. Complete the following:
(a) $(10 \times 10) + 10 =$
(b) $(10 \times 6) + 10 =$
(c) $(10 \times 10) - 10 =$

(f) $9 \times 100 = 800$ ☐
(g) $90 \div 10 = 8$ ☐
(h) $70 \div 10 = 7$ ☐
(i) $60 \div 10 = 6$ ☐
(j) $30 \div 10 = 2$ ☐

9. True (✓) False (X):
(a) $3 \times 10 = 30$ ☐
(b) $9 \times 10 = 90$ ☐
(c) $6 \times 10 = 70$ ☐
(d) $7 \times 100 = 700$ ☐
(e) $5 \times 100 = 500$ ☐

10. Say your 10 x tables backwards.

0 x 10 = _____	0 x 100 = _____		
1 x 10 = _____	1 x 100 = _____	6 x 10 = _____	6 x 100 = _____
2 x 10 = _____	2 x 100 = _____	7 x 10 = _____	7 x 100 = _____
3 x 10 = _____	3 x 100 = _____	8 x 10 = _____	8 x 100 = _____
4 x 10 = _____	4 x 100 = _____	9 x 10 = _____	9 x 100 = _____
5 x 10 = _____	5 x 100 = _____	10 x 10 = _____	10 x 100 = _____

1. How many days in:

(a) 10 weeks 4 days? _____ (b) 10 weeks 1 day? _____

2. Double:

(a) 500 _____ (b) 300 _____ (c) 40 _____ (d) 20 _____

3. Halve:

(a) 20 _____ (b) 60 _____ (c) 800 _____ (d) 100 _____

4. Lollies cost 10p each. How many can you buy with:

(a) £1.50? _____ (b) £2.70? _____ (c) £1.20? _____ (d) £6.00? _____

5. Each bus can carry 100 passengers. How many buses would be needed to carry:

(a) 800 people? _____ buses (b) 1000 people? _____ buses (c) 200 people? _____ buses

6. Complete these:

(a) 72 ÷ 10 = _____ r _____ (b) 67 ÷ 10 = _____ r _____ (c) 103 ÷ 10 = _____ r _____

7. If you cut these pizzas into tenths, how many slices would you have?

(a) 10 pizzas _____ slices (b) 7 pizzas _____ slices (c) 2 pizzas _____ slices

(d) 4 pizzas _____ slices (e) 15 pizzas _____ slices (f) 20 pizzas _____ slices

8. A crate can hold 100 bottles. How many bottles would fit in:

(a) 6 crates? _____ bottles (b) 10 crates? _____ bottles (c) 20 crates? _____ bottles

9. Notepads cost £1.00 each. Jamie buys 8 and Nikki buys 4 pads.

(a) How much money does Jamie spend? _____ (e) How much change would Nikki receive

(b) How much money does Nikki spend? _____ from a £20 note? _____

(c) How much do Jamie and Nikki spend altogether? _____

(d) How much change would Jamie receive from a £20 note? _____

10. Snakes 'n' Ladders

Finish

81	82	83	84	85	86	87	88	89	90	91	92	93	94	95	96	97	98	99	100
80	79	78	77	76	75	74	73	72	71	70	69	68	67	66	65	64	63	62	61
41	42	43	44	45	46	47	48	49	50	51	52	53	54	55	56	57	58	59	60
40	39	38	37	36	35	34	33	32	31	30	29	28	27	26	25	24	23	22	21
1	2	3	4	5	6	7	8	9	10	11	12	13	14	15	16	17	18	19	20

Start

10 x table

Set B

My score: _____

My time: _____ mins _____ secs

I'm happy · I'm not happy · I didn't understand · OOPS!

The main area for me to work on is:

_____

_____

_____

1. $10 + 80 =$ _____
2. $4 \times 10 =$ _____
3. $100 \div 10 =$ _____
4. $50 - 10 =$ _____
5. $40 + 10 =$ _____
6. $9 \times 10 =$ _____
7. $150 \div 10 =$ _____
8. $90 - 10 =$ _____
9. $10 + 70 =$ _____
10. $10 \times 10 =$ _____
11. $700 \div 10 =$ _____
12. $10 - 10 =$ _____
13. $10 + 90 =$ _____
14. $70 \times 10 =$ _____
15. $400 \div 10 =$ _____
16. $100 - 10 =$ _____
17. $10 + 100 =$ _____
18. $20 \times 10 =$ _____
19. $60 \times 10 =$ _____
20. $120 - 10 =$ _____

21. $100 + 60 =$ _____
22. $50 \times 10 =$ _____
23. $200 \div 10 =$ _____
24. $150 - 10 =$ _____
25. $10 + 20 =$ _____
26. $30 \times 10 =$ _____
27. $600 \div 10 =$ _____
28. $200 - 10 =$ _____
29. $10 + 140 =$ _____
30. $10 \times 0 =$ _____
31. $800 \div 10 =$ _____
32. $170 - 10 =$ _____
33. $200 + 10 =$ _____
34. $4 \times 100 =$ _____
35. $500 \div 10 =$ _____
36. $300 - 10 =$ _____
37. $190 + 10 =$ _____
38. $9 \times 10 =$ _____
39. $300 \div 10 =$ _____
40. $250 - 10 =$ _____

Set A

My score: _____

My time: _____ mins _____ secs

I'm happy · I'm not happy · I didn't understand · OOPS!

The main area for me to work on is:

_____

_____

_____

1. $10 + 30 =$ _____
2. $10 \times 8 =$ _____
3. $70 \div 10 =$ _____
4. $500 - 10 =$ _____
5. $10 + 90 =$ _____
6. $10 \times 10 =$ _____
7. $40 \div 10 =$ _____
8. $800 - 10 =$ _____
9. $10 + 50 =$ _____
10. $10 \times 6 =$ _____
11. $100 \div 10 =$ _____
12. $100 - 10 =$ _____
13. $120 + 10 =$ _____
14. $10 \times 0 =$ _____
15. $50 \div 10 =$ _____
16. $300 - 10 =$ _____
17. $10 + 40 =$ _____
18. $20 \times 10 =$ _____
19. $300 \div 10 =$ _____
20. $900 - 10 =$ _____

21. $100 + 70 =$ _____
22. $8 \times 10 =$ _____
23. $150 \div 10 =$ _____
24. $110 - 10 =$ _____
25. $10 + 20 =$ _____
26. $2 \times 10 =$ _____
27. $200 \div 10 =$ _____
28. $120 - 10 =$ _____
29. $100 + 10 =$ _____
30. $6 \times 10 =$ _____
31. $40 \div 10 =$ _____
32. $20 - 10 =$ _____
33. $10 + 200 =$ _____
34. $10 \times 100 =$ _____
35. $70 \div 10 =$ _____
36. $40 - 10 =$ _____
37. $10 + 60 =$ _____
38. $10 \times 9 =$ _____
39. $60 \div 10 =$ _____
40. $150 - 10 =$ _____

12 x table

Set B

1. Add 12 to the following:

(a) 12 _____   (c) 48 _____

(b) 84 _____   (d) 108 _____

2. How many groups of 12 in:

(a) 60? _____   (c) 36? _____

(b) 120? _____   (d) 48? _____

3. Subtract 12 from the following:

(a) 60 _____   (c) 120 _____

(b) 84 _____   (d) 36 _____

4. Which multiple of 12 is closest to:

(a) 100? _____   (c) 25? _____

(b) 42? _____   (d) 63? _____

5. Add:

(a) 12 + 12 + 12 + 12 = _____

(b) 12 + 12 + 12 + 12 + 12 + 12 = _____

(c) 12 + 12 + 12 + 12 + 12 + 12 + 12 + 12 + 12 = _____

6. Complete the number sequence:

120, _____, _____, 84, _____, 60, _____, _____, 12, _____

7. Complete the number sentences:

(a) 12 x _____ = 108

(b) 12 x _____ = 0

(c) 12 x _____ = 96

8. Complete the following:

(a) (12 x 7) + 12 = _____

(b) (12 x 5) − 12 = _____

(c) (12 x 8) − 12 = _____

(f) 6 x 120 = 720 ☐

(g) 48 ÷ 12 = 5 ☐

(h) 96 ÷ 12 = 8 ☐

(i) 36 ÷ 12 = 3 ☐

(j) 60 ÷ 12 = 6 ☐

9. True (✓) False (X):

(a) 5 x 12 = 60 ☐

(b) 7 x 12 = 72 ☐

(c) 10 x 12 = 120 ☐

(d) 4 x 120 = 600 ☐

(e) 3 x 120 = 360 ☐

10. Count by 12s to 120.

Set A

1. Add 12 to the following:

(a) 36 _____   (c) 60 _____

(b) 96 _____   (d) 24 _____

2. How many groups of 12 in:

(a) 24? _____   (c) 72? _____

(b) 108? _____   (d) 84? _____

3. Subtract 12 from the following:

(a) 48 _____   (c) 108 _____

(b) 24 _____   (d) 72 _____

4. Which multiple of 12 is closest to:

(a) 38? _____   (c) 80? _____

(b) 57? _____   (d) 94? _____

5. Add:

(a) 12 + 12 + 12 = _____

(b) 12 + 12 + 12 + 12 + 12 + 12 = _____

(c) 12 + 12 + 12 + 12 + 12 + 12 = _____

6. Complete the number sequence:

0, _____, 24, 48, _____, _____, 84, _____, _____, 120

7. Complete the number sentences:

(a) 12 x _____ = 24

(b) 12 x _____ = 120

(c) 12 x _____ = 72

8. Complete the following:

(a) (12 x 6) + 12 = _____

(b) (12 x 10) − 12 = _____

(c) (12 x 4) + 12 = _____

(f) 5 x 120 = 600 ☐

(g) 2 x 120 = 240 ☐

(h) 108 ÷ 12 = 8 ☐

(i) 84 ÷ 12 = 7 ☐

(j) 72 ÷ 12 = 6 ☐

9. True (✓) False (X):

(a) 3 x 12 = 36 ☐

(b) 9 x 12 = 96 ☐

(c) 6 x 12 = 72 ☐

(d) 8 x 12 = 84 ☐

(e) 7 x 12 = 840 ☐

10. Say your 12 x tables.

0 x 12 = _____	0 x 120 = _____		
1 x 12 = _____	1 x 120 = _____	6 x 12 = _____	6 x 120 = _____
2 x 12 = _____	2 x 120 = _____	7 x 12 = _____	7 x 120 = _____
3 x 12 = _____	3 x 120 = _____	8 x 12 = _____	8 x 120 = _____
4 x 12 = _____	4 x 120 = _____	9 x 12 = _____	9 x 120 = _____
5 x 12 = _____	5 x 120 = _____	10 x 12 = _____	10 x 120 = _____

1. How many days in:

(a) 12 weeks 3 days? _____   (b) 12 weeks 5 days? _____

2. Double:

(a) 60 _____   (b) 48 _____   (c) 36 _____   (d) 24 _____

3. Halve:

(a) 24 _____   (b) 120 _____   (c) 108 _____   (d) 60 _____

4. Tiles are 12 cm long. How many can you fit into a space:

(a) 60 cm long? _____ tiles   (b) 120 cm long? _____ tiles   (c) 96 cm long? _____ tiles

5. Each ferry can carry 120 passengers. How many ferries would be needed to carry:

(a) 360 people? _____ ferries   (b) 600 people? _____ ferries   (c) 1200 people? _____ ferries

6. Complete these:

(a) 50 ÷ 12 = _____ r _____   (b) 41 ÷ 12 = _____ r _____   (c) 27 ÷ 12 = _____ r _____

7. If you cut these oranges into twelfths, how many slices would you have?

(a) 2 oranges _____ slices   (b) 5 oranges _____ slices   (c) 4 oranges _____ slices

(d) 10 oranges _____ slices   (e) 7 oranges _____ slices   (f) 8 oranges _____ slices

8. A crate can hold 120 pineapples. How many pineapples would fit in:

(a) 3 crates? _____ pineapples   (b) 7 crates? _____ pineapples   (c) 9 crates? _____ pineapples

9. Snake sweets cost 12p each. Emily buys 10 and her friend Anita buys 5 snakes.

(a) How much money does Emily spend? _____

(b) How much money does Anita spend? _____

(c) How much more does Emily spend than Anita? _____

(d) How much change would Emily receive from a £5 note? _____

(e) How much change would Anita receive from a £5 note? _____

10. Tables Battleships.

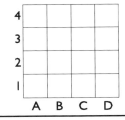 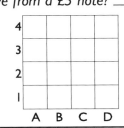 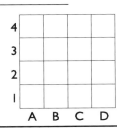 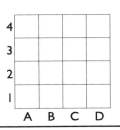

12 x table

Set A

1. 12 + 24 =
2. 6 x 12 =
3. 36 ÷ 12 =
4. 24 – 12 =
5. 48 + 12 =
6. 3 x 12 =
7. 84 ÷ 12 =
8. 60 – 12 =
9. 12 + 60 =
10. 12 x 0 =
11. 24 ÷ 12 =
12. 36 – 12 =
13. 84 + 12 =
14. 7 x 12 =
15. 60 ÷ 12 =
16. 120 – 12 =
17. 120 + 12 =
18. 12 x 1 =
19. 108 ÷ 12 =
20. 48 – 12 =

21. 12 + 36 =
22. 2 x 12 =
23. 48 ÷ 12 =
24. 84 – 12 =
25. 12 + 72 =
26. 5 x 12 =
27. 72 ÷ 12 =
28. 12 – 12 =
29. 96 + 12 =
30. 12 x 3 =
31. 120 ÷ 12 =
32. 108 – 12 =
33. 12 + 0 =
34. 10 x 12 =
35. 12 ÷ 12 =
36. 72 – 12 =
37. 108 + 12 =
38. 4 x 12 =
39. 96 ÷ 12 =
40. 120 x 0 =

My score:

My time: ____ mins ____ secs

I'm happy

I'm not happy

I didn't understand

OOPS!

The main area for me to work on is:

_____

Set B

1. 12 + 36 =
2. 10 x 12 =
3. 96 ÷ 12 =
4. 108 – 12 =
5. 72 + 12 =
6. 4 x 12 =
7. 72 ÷ 12 =
8. 72 – 12 =
9. 96 + 12 =
10. 12 x 0 =
11. 24 ÷ 12 =
12. 12 – 12 =
13. 12 + 12 =
14. 5 x 12 =
15. 48 ÷ 12 =
16. 84 – 12 =
17. 108 + 12 =
18. 2 x 12 =
19. 108 ÷ 12 =
20. 48 – 12 =

21. 12 + 24 =
22. 12 x 10 =
23. 12 ÷ 12 =
24. 120 – 12 =
25. 48 + 12 =
26. 9 x 12 =
27. 84 ÷ 12 =
28. 36 – 12 =
29. 12 + 60 =
30. 7 x 12 =
31. 36 ÷ 12 =
32. 60 – 12 =
33. 84 + 12 =
34. 12 x 3 =
35. 60 ÷ 12 =
36. 24 – 12 =
37. 120 + 12 =
38. 6 x 12 =
39. 120 x 0 =
40. 96 – 12 =

My score:

My time: ____ mins ____ secs

I'm happy

I'm not happy

I didn't understand

OOPS!

The main area for me to work on is:

_____

Set B

1. Add 15 to the following:
(a) 135 _____   (c) 90 _____
(b) 60 _____   (d) 15 _____

2. How many groups of 15 in:
(a) 150? _____   (c) 30? _____
(b) 90? _____   (d) 45? _____

3. Subtract 15 from the following:
(a) 75 _____   (c) 90 _____
(b) 135 _____   (d) 30 _____

4. Which multiple of 15 is closest to:
(a) 100? _____   (c) 25? _____
(b) 42? _____   (d) 133? _____

5. Add:
(a) $15 + 15 + 15 + 15 =$ _____
(b) $15 + 15 + 15 + 15 + 15 + 15 + 15 =$ _____
(c) $15 + 15 + 15 + 15 + 15 + 15 + 15 + 15 + 15 + 15 =$ _____

6. Complete the number sequence:
150, _____, _____, 105, _____, 75, _____, _____, 15,

7. Complete the number sentences:
(a) $15 \times$ _____ $= 150$
(b) $15 \times$ _____ $= 75$
(c) $15 \times$ _____ $= 30$

8. Complete the following:
(a) $(15 \times 5) + 15 =$ _____
(b) $(15 \times 4) - 15 =$ _____
(c) $(15 \times 8) - 15 =$ _____
(f) $5 \times 150 = 750$ □
(g) $6 \times 150 = 900$ □
(h) $60 \div 15 = 4$ □
(i) $120 \div 15 = 7$ □
(j) $45 \div 15 = 3$ □

9. True (✓) False (X):
(a) $4 \times 15 = 60$ □
(b) $1 \times 15 = 15$ □
(c) $6 \times 15 = 90$ □
(d) $7 \times 15 = 110$ □
(e) $2 \times 150 = 450$ □

10. Count by 15s to 150.

Set A

1. Add 15 to the following:
(a) 75 _____   (c) 105 _____
(b) 45 _____   (d) 120 _____

2. How many groups of 15 in:
(a) 120? _____   (c) 15? _____
(b) 75? _____   (d) 105? _____

3. Subtract 15 from the following:
(a) 150 _____   (c) 45 _____
(b) 120 _____   (d) 60 _____

4. Which multiple of 15 is closest to:
(a) 151? _____   (c) 92? _____
(b) 33? _____   (d) 17? _____

5. Add:
(a) $15 + 15 + 15 =$ _____
(b) $15 + 15 + 15 + 15 + 15 =$ _____
(c) $15 + 15 + 15 + 15 + 15 + 15 + 15 + 15 + 15 =$ _____

6. Complete the number sequence:
0, 15, _____, _____, 60, _____, _____, 105, _____, _____, 150

7. Complete the number sentences:
(a) $15 \times$ _____ $= 45$
(b) $15 \times$ _____ $= 60$
(c) $15 \times$ _____ $= 90$

8. Complete the following:
(a) $(15 \times 3) + 15 =$ _____
(b) $(15 \times 7) + 15 =$ _____
(c) $(15 \times 6) - 15 =$ _____
(f) $2 \times 150 = 300$ □
(g) $4 \times 150 = 600$ □
(h) $75 \div 15 = 6$ □
(i) $30 \div 15 = 2$ □
(j) $150 \div 15 = 10$ □

9. True (✓) False (X):
(a) $3 \times 15 = 60$ □
(b) $5 \times 15 = 75$ □
(c) $10 \times 15 = 150$ □
(d) $2 \times 15 = 45$ □
(e) $7 \times 150 = 1050$ □

10. Say your 15 x tables.

0 x 15 = _____	0 x 150 = _____		
1 x 15 = _____	1 x 150 = _____	6 x 15 = _____	6 x 150 = _____
2 x 15 = _____	2 x 150 = _____	7 x 15 = _____	7 x 150 = _____
3 x 15 = _____	3 x 150 = _____	8 x 15 = _____	8 x 150 = _____
4 x 15 = _____	4 x 150 = _____	9 x 15 = _____	9 x 150 = _____
5 x 15 = _____	5 x 150 = _____	10 x 15 = _____	10 x 150 = _____

1. How many days in:

(a) 15 weeks 3 days? _____ (b) 15 weeks 5 days? _____

2. Double:

(a) 60 _____   (b) 45 _____   (c) 15 _____   (d) 75 _____

3. Halve:

(a) 120 _____   (b) 150 _____   (c) 60 _____   (d) 30 _____

4. Sweets cost 15p each. How many can you buy with:

(a) 45p? _____   (b) £1.20? _____   (c) £1.35? _____   (d) £1.50? _____

5. Each maxi-taxi can carry 15 passengers. How many taxis would be needed to carry:

(a) 60 people? _____ taxis   (b) 150 people? _____ taxis   (c) 105 people? _____ taxis

6. Complete these:

(a) 48 ÷ 15 = _____ r _____   (b) 107 ÷ 15 = _____ r _____   (c) 140 ÷ 15 = _____ r _____

7. If you cut these meat pies into fifteenths, how many slices would you have?

(a) 4 pies _____ slices   (b) 5 pies _____ slices   (c) 2 pies _____ slices

(d) 7 pies _____ slices   (e) 3 pies _____ slices   (f) 9 pies _____ slices

8. A crate can hold 150 bananas. How many bananas would fit in:

(a) 3 crates? _____   (b) 6 crates? _____   (c) 9 crates? _____

9. Football stickers cost £1.50 each. Jordan buys 3 and his friend Jack buys 7 stickers.

(a) How much money does Jordan spend? _____

(b) How much money does Jack spend? _____

(c) How much do Jordan and Jack spend altogether? _____

(d) How much change would Jordan receive from a £10 note? _____

(e) How much change would Jack receive from a £20 note? _____

10. Tables Battleships.

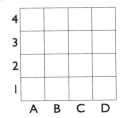 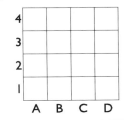 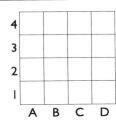 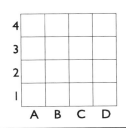

15 x table

Set B

My score:

My time: _____ mins _____ secs

I'm not happy

I didn't understand

I'm happy

OOPS!

The main area for me to work on is:

_____

_____

_____

_____

1. $120 \div 15 =$ _____
2. $15 \times 1 =$ _____
3. $60 \div 15 =$ _____
4. $60 - 15 =$ _____
5. $90 + 15 =$ _____
6. $15 \times 7 =$ _____
7. $90 \div 15 =$ _____
8. $45 - 15 =$ _____
9. $15 \times 0 =$ _____
10. $15 \times 5 =$ _____
11. $15 \div 15 =$ _____
12. $15 - 15 =$ _____
13. $135 + 15 =$ _____
14. $15 \times 9 =$ _____
15. $120 \div 15 =$ _____
16. $30 - 15 =$ _____
17. $105 + 15 =$ _____
18. $8 \times 15 =$ _____
19. $150 \div 15 =$ _____
20. $90 - 15 =$ _____

21. $15 + 15 =$ _____
22. $15 \times 4 =$ _____
23. $135 \div 15 =$ _____
24. $75 - 15 =$ _____
25. $30 + 15 =$ _____
26. $15 \times 2 =$ _____
27. $75 \div 15 =$ _____
28. $120 - 15 =$ _____
29. $60 + 15 =$ _____
30. $15 \times 10 =$ _____
31. $30 \div 15 =$ _____
32. $150 - 15 =$ _____
33. $45 + 15 =$ _____
34. $15 \times 3 =$ _____
35. $105 \div 15 =$ _____
36. $135 - 15 =$ _____
37. $75 + 15 =$ _____
38. $6 \times 15 =$ _____
39. $45 \div 15 =$ _____
40. $105 - 15 =$ _____

Set A

My score:

My time: _____ mins _____ secs

I'm not happy

I didn't understand

I'm happy

OOPS!

The main area for me to work on is:

_____

_____

_____

_____

1. $30 + 15 =$ _____
2. $15 \times 6 =$ _____
3. $45 \div 15 =$ _____
4. $30 - 15 =$ _____
5. $60 + 15 =$ _____
6. $15 \times 3 =$ _____
7. $105 \div 15 =$ _____
8. $75 - 15 =$ _____
9. $75 + 15 =$ _____
10. $15 \times 10 =$ _____
11. $30 \div 15 =$ _____
12. $45 - 15 =$ _____
13. $45 + 15 =$ _____
14. $15 \times 2 =$ _____
15. $75 \div 15 =$ _____
16. $15 - 15 =$ _____
17. $15 + 15 =$ _____
18. $15 \times 4 =$ _____
19. $135 \div 15 =$ _____
20. $60 - 15 =$ _____

21. $120 + 15 =$ _____
22. $15 \times 5 =$ _____
23. $60 \div 15 =$ _____
24. $105 - 15 =$ _____
25. $90 + 15 =$ _____
26. $15 \times 8 =$ _____
27. $90 \div 15 =$ _____
28. $90 - 15 =$ _____
29. $150 \times 0 =$ _____
30. $15 \times 9 =$ _____
31. $15 \div 15 =$ _____
32. $150 - 15 =$ _____
33. $135 + 15 =$ _____
34. $15 \times 1 =$ _____
35. $120 \div 15 =$ _____
36. $120 - 15 =$ _____
37. $105 + 15 =$ _____
38. $15 \times 7 =$ _____
39. $150 \div 15 =$ _____
40. $135 - 15 =$ _____

20 x table

Set B

1. Add 20 to the following:
(a) 40 _____   (c) 140 _____
(b) 20 _____   (d) 180 _____

2. How many groups of 20 in:
(a) 80?   (c) 200?
(b) 180?   (d) 40?

3. Subtract 20 from the following:
(a) 140 _____   (c) 200 _____
(b) 60 _____   (d) 160 _____

4. Which multiple of 20 is closest to:
(a) 116?   (c) 168?
(b) 94?   (d) 192?

5. Add:
(a) 20 + 20 + 20 + 20 + 20 + 20 + 20 + 20 = _____
(b) 20 + 20 + 20 = _____
(c) 20 + 20 + 20 + 20 + 20 + 20 + 20 + 20 + 20 + 20 = _____

6. Complete the number sequence:
200, _____, 140, _____, 100, _____, _____, 20,

7. Complete the number sentences:
(a) 20 x _____ = 120
(b) 20 x _____ = 200
(c) 20 x _____ = 60

8. Complete the following:
(a) (20 x 9) + 20 =
(b) (20 x 5) – 20 =
(c) (20 x 8) – 20 =
(f) 6 x 200 = 1400
(g) 8 x 200 = 1600
(h) 80 ÷ 20 = 4
(i) 160 ÷ 20 = 8
(j) 60 ÷ 20 = 3

9. True (✓) False (X):
(a) 5 x 20 = 100 ☐
(b) 7 x 20 = 140 ☐
(c) 10 x 20 = 180 ☐
(d) 4 x 200 = 800 ☐
(e) 3 x 200 = 600 ☐

10. Count by 20s to 200.

Set A

1. Add 20 to the following:
(a) 80 _____   (c) 120 _____
(b) 160 _____   (d) 60 _____

2. How many groups of 20 in:
(a) 60?   (c) 100?
(b) 160?   (d) 120?

3. Subtract 20 from the following:
(a) 40 _____   (c) 180 _____
(b) 100 _____   (d) 80 _____

4. Which multiple of 20 is closest to:
(a) 38?   (c) 145?
(b) 55?   (d) 23?

5. Add:
(a) 20 + 20 + 20 + 20 = _____
(b) 20 + 20 + 20 + 20 + 20 + 20 = _____
(c) 20 + 20 + 20 + 20 + 20 + 20 + 20 + 20 + 20 = _____

6. Complete the number sequence:
0, 20, _____, 80, _____, _____, 140, _____, _____, 200

7. Complete the number sentences:
(a) 20 x _____ = 100
(b) 20 x _____ = 180
(c) 20 x _____ = 0

8. Complete the following:
(a) (20 x 7) + 20 =
(b) (20 x 4) + 20 =
(c) (20 x 10) – 20 =
(f) 5 x 200 = 1000
(g) 9 x 200 = 1600
(h) 100 ÷ 20 = 8
(i) 180 ÷ 20 = 9
(j) 140 ÷ 20 = 7

9. True (✓) False (X):
(a) 3 x 20 = 60 ☐
(b) 9 x 20 = 180 ☐
(c) 6 x 20 = 140 ☐
(d) 8 x 20 = 180 ☐
(e) 7 x 200 = 1400 ☐

10. Say your 20 x tables.

0 x 20 = _____	0 x 200 = _____		
1 x 20 = _____	1 x 200 = _____	6 x 20 = _____	6 x 200 = _____
2 x 20 = _____	2 x 200 = _____	7 x 20 = _____	7 x 200 = _____
3 x 20 = _____	3 x 200 = _____	8 x 20 = _____	8 x 200 = _____
4 x 20 = _____	4 x 200 = _____	9 x 20 = _____	9 x 200 = _____
5 x 20 = _____	5 x 200 = _____	10 x 20 = _____	10 x 200 = _____

1. How many days in:

(a) 20 weeks 5 days? _____   (b) 20 weeks 2 days? _____

2. Double:

(a) 80 _____   (b) 60 _____   (c) 20 _____   (d) 100 _____

3. Halve:

(a) 600 _____   (b) 160 _____   (c) 80 _____   (d) 40 _____

4. Lollies cost 20p each. How many can you buy with:

(a) £1.00? _____   (b) 60p? _____   (c) £2.00? _____   (d) £1.40? _____

5. Each bus can carry 20 passengers. How many buses would be needed to carry:

(a) 80 people? _____ buses   (b) 140 people? _____ buses   (c) 200 people? _____ buses

6. Complete these:

(a) 68 ÷ 20 = _____ r _____   (b) 105 ÷ 20 = _____ r _____   (c) 175 ÷ 20 = _____ r _____

7. If you cut these pizzas into twentieths, how many slices would you have?

(a) 2 pizzas _____ slices   (c) 5 pizzas _____ slices   (e) 10 pizzas _____ slices

(b) 7 pizzas _____ slices   (d) 8 pizzas _____ slices   (f) 4 pizzas _____ slices

8. Each cattle truck can hold 200 cattle. How many cattle would fit in:

(a) 3 trucks? _____   (b) 7 trucks? _____   (c) 10 trucks? _____

9. Ice-creams cost £2.00 each. Sasha buys 6 and her cousin Rosie buys 9 ice-creams.

(a) How much money does Sasha spend? _____

(b) How much money does Rosie spend? _____

(c) How much more does Rosie spend than Sasha? _____

(d) How much change would Sasha receive from a £20 note? _____

(e) How much change would Rosie receive from a £20 note? _____

10. Tables Battleships.

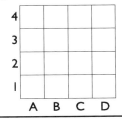   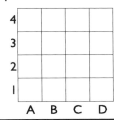   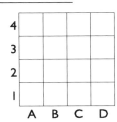   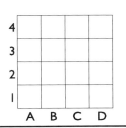

-

Set A

1. 20 + 80 =
2. 20 x 3 =
3. 100 ÷ 20 =
4. 80 – 20 =
5. 100 + 20 =
6. 10 x 20 =
7. 60 ÷ 20 =
8. 140 – 20 =
9. 160 + 20 =
10. 4 x 20 =
11. 160 ÷ 20 =
12. 100 – 20 =
13. 60 + 20 =
14. 9 x 20 =
15. 200 ÷ 20 =
16. 120 – 20 =
17. 40 + 20 =
18. 7 x 20 =
19. 40 ÷ 20 =
20. 200 – 20 =
21. 120 + 20 =
22. 20 x 2 =
23. 80 ÷ 20 =
24. 160 – 20 =
25. 220 + 20 =
26. 5 x 20 =
27. 120 ÷ 20 =
28. 60 – 20 =
29. 180 + 20 =
30. 8 x 20 =
31. 180 ÷ 20 =
32. 40 – 20 =
33. 200 x 0 =
34. 6 x 20 =
35. 140 ÷ 20 =
36. 180 – 20 =
37. 140 + 20 =
38. 20 x 0 =
39. 20 ÷ 20 =
40. 1 x 200 =

My score:

My time: _____ mins _____ secs

I'm happy   I'm not happy

OOPS!   I didn't understand

The main area for me to work on is:

Set B

1. 200 x 1 =
2. 6 x 20 =
3. 140 ÷ 20 =
4. 60 – 20 =
5. 120 + 20 =
6. 4 x 20 =
7. 100 ÷ 20 =
8. 120 – 20 =
9. 180 + 20 =
10. 2 x 20 =
11. 40 – 20 =
12. 240 – 20 =
13. 80 + 20 =
14. 7 x 20 =
15. 80 ÷ 20 =
16. 180 – 20 =
17. 60 + 20 =
18. 9 x 20 =
19. 200 ÷ 20 =
20. 40 – 20 =
21. 140 + 20 =
22. 20 x 3 =
23. 160 ÷ 20 =
24. 100 – 20 =
25. 160 + 20 =
26. 5 x 20 =
27. 60 ÷ 20 =
28. 80 – 20 =
29. 100 + 20 =
30. 8 x 20 =
31. 180 ÷ 20 =
32. 160 – 20 =
33. 40 + 20 =
34. 10 x 20 =
35. 120 ÷ 20 =
36. 140 – 20 =
37. 200 + 20 =
38. 20 x 0 =
39. 20 ÷ 20 =
40. 200 – 20 =

My score:

My time: _____ mins _____ secs

I'm happy   I'm not happy

OOPS!   I didn't understand

The main area for me to work on is:

25 x table

Set B

1. Add 25 to the following:

(a) 150 _____ (c) 50 _____

(b) 175 _____ (d) 200 _____

2. How many groups of 25 in:

(a) 200? _____ (c) 150? _____

(b) 225? _____ (d) 50? _____

3. Subtract 25 from the following:

(a) 50 _____ (c) 200 _____

(b) 75 _____ (d) 125 _____

4. Which multiple of 25 is closest to:

(a) 80? _____ (c) 155? _____

(b) 240? _____ (d) 96? _____

5. Add:

(a) 25 + 25 + 25 + 25 + 25 + 25 + 25 = _____

(b) 25 + 25 + 25 + 25 + 25 + 25 + 25 + 25 = _____

(c) 25 + 25 + 25 + 25 + 25 + 25 + 25 + 25 + 25 + 25 = _____

6. Complete the number sequence:

250, _____, _____, 175, _____, 125, _____, _____, 25, _____

7. Complete the number sentences:

(a) 25 x _____ = 100

(b) 25 x _____ = 250

(c) 25 x _____ = 175

8. Complete the following:

(a) (25 x 2) + 25 = _____

(b) (25 x 5) − 25 = _____

(c) (25 x 8) − 25 = _____

9. True (✓) False (X):

(a) 8 x 25 = 250 ☐

(b) 2 x 25 = 50 ☐

(c) 4 x 25 = 100 ☐

(d) 7 x 250 = 1750 ☐

(e) 5 x 250 = 1500 ☐

(f) 2 x 250 = 500 ☐

(g) 125 ÷ 25 = 6 ☐

(h) 250 ÷ 25 = 10 ☐

(i) 50 ÷ 25 = 2 ☐

(j) 150 ÷ 25 = 6 ☐

10. Count by 25s to 250.

Set A

1. Add 25 to the following:

(a) 125 _____ (c) 75 _____

(b) 225 _____ (d) 100 _____

2. How many groups of 25 in:

(a) 100? _____ (c) 250? _____

(b) 75? _____ (d) 175? _____

3. Subtract 25 from the following:

(a) 175 _____ (c) 100 _____

(b) 250 _____ (d) 150 _____

4. Which multiple of 25 is closest to:

(a) 180? _____ (c) 210? _____

(b) 65? _____ (d) 28? _____

5. Add:

(a) 25 + 25 + 25 + 25 = _____

(b) 25 + 25 + 25 + 25 + 25 + 25 = _____

(c) 25 + 25 + 25 + 25 + 25 + 25 + 25 + 25 + 25 = _____

6. Complete the number sequence:

0, _____, 50, _____, 100, _____, _____, 175, _____, _____, 250

7. Complete the number sentences:

(a) 25 x _____ = 200

(b) 25 x _____ = 150

(c) 25 x _____ = 225

8. Complete the following:

(a) (25 x 7) + 25 = _____

(b) (25 x 4) + 25 = _____

(c) (25 x 3) − 25 = _____

9. True (✓) False (X):

(a) 3 x 25 = 75 ☐

(b) 9 x 25 = 200 ☐

(c) 6 x 25 = 150 ☐

(d) 5 x 25 = 125 ☐

(e) 4 x 250 = 1000 ☐

(f) 5 x 250 = 2500 ☐

(g) 9 x 250 = 2250 ☐

(h) 100 ÷ 25 = 4 ☐

(i) 150 ÷ 25 = 7 ☐

(j) 75 ÷ 25 = 3 ☐

10. Say your 25 x tables.

0 x 25 = _____	0 x 250 = _____		
1 x 25 = _____	1 x 250 = _____	6 x 25 = _____	6 x 250 = _____
2 x 25 = _____	2 x 250 = _____	7 x 25 = _____	7 x 250 = _____
3 x 25 = _____	3 x 250 = _____	8 x 25 = _____	8 x 250 = _____
4 x 25 = _____	4 x 250 = _____	9 x 25 = _____	9 x 250 = _____
5 x 25 = _____	5 x 250 = _____	10 x 25 = _____	10 x 250 = _____

1. How many days in:

(a) 25 weeks 3 days? _____   (b) 25 weeks 5 days? _____

2. Double:

(a) 125 _____   (b) 75 _____   (c) 50 _____   (d) 25 _____

3. Halve:

(a) 150 _____   (b) 50 _____   (c) 200 _____   (d) 100 _____

4. Sweets cost 25p each. How many can you buy with:

(a) £1.25? _____   (b) £2.25? _____   (c) £1.00? _____   (d) £1.50? _____

5. Each bus can carry 25 passengers. How many buses would be needed to carry:

(a) 250 people? _____ buses   (b) 175 people? _____ buses   (c) 125 people? _____ buses

6. Complete these:

(a) 79 ÷ 25 = _____ r _____   (b) 130 ÷ 25 = _____ r _____   (c) 215 ÷ 25 = _____ r _____

7. If you cut these cakes into twenty-fifths, how many slices would you have?

(a) 3 cakes _____ slices   (c) 9 cakes _____ slices   (e) 5 cakes _____ slices

(b) 4 cakes _____ slices   (d) 7 cakes _____ slices   (f) 8 cakes _____ slices

8. A pallet can hold 250 house bricks. How many bricks would fit on:

(a) 4 pallets? _____ bricks   (b) 6 pallets? _____ bricks   (c) 10 pallets? _____ bricks

9. Calendars cost £2.50 each. Jon buys 3 and his friend Sam buys 7 calendars.

(a) How much money does Jon spend? _____

(b) How much money does Sam spend? _____

(c) How much do Jon and Sam spend altogether? _____

(d) How much change would Jon receive from a £10 note? _____

(e) How much change would Sam receive from a £20 note? _____

10. Tables Battleships.

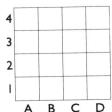 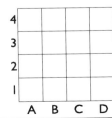 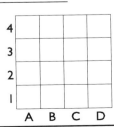 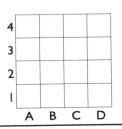

25 x table

Set B

My score:

My time: _____ mins _____ secs

I'm happy :-)   I'm not happy :-(

I didn't understand   OOPS!

The main area for me to work on is:

_____

_____

1. 250 x 4 =
2. 25 x 0 =
3. 50 ÷ 25 =
4. 100 − 25 =
5. 50 + 25 =
6. 9 x 25 =
7. 125 ÷ 25 =
8. 50 − 25 =
9. 200 + 25 =
10. 25 x 5 =
11. 175 ÷ 25 =
12. 150 − 25 =
13. 225 + 25 =
14. 25 x 2 =
15. 250 ÷ 25 =
16. 25 − 25 =
17. 175 + 25 =
18. 8 x 25 =
19. 225 ÷ 25 =
20. 75 − 25 =

21. 125 + 25 =
22. 7 x 25 =
23. 100 ÷ 25 =
24. 125 − 25 =
25. 75 + 25 =
26. 4 x 25 =
27. 200 ÷ 25 =
28. 175 − 25 =
29. 25 + 25 =
30. 25 x 3 =
31. 25 ÷ 25 =
32. 225 − 25 =
33. 150 + 25 =
34. 25 x 10 =
35. 75 ÷ 25 =
36. 200 − 25 =
37. 100 + 25 =
38. 6 x 25 =
39. 150 ÷ 25 =
40. 250 − 25 =

Set A

My score:

My time: _____ mins _____ secs

I'm happy :-)   I'm not happy :-(

I didn't understand   OOPS!

The main area for me to work on is:

_____

_____

1. 50 + 25 =
2. 25 x 6 =
3. 100 ÷ 25 =
4. 250 − 25 =
5. 100 + 25 =
6. 25 x 10 =
7. 200 ÷ 25 =
8. 200 − 25 =
9. 150 + 25 =
10. 25 x 3 =
11. 25 ÷ 25 =
12. 225 − 25 =
13. 25 + 25 =
14. 25 x 4 =
15. 75 ÷ 25 =
16. 175 − 25 =
17. 75 + 25 =
18. 25 x 7 =
19. 150 ÷ 25 =
20. 125 − 25 =

21. 125 + 25 =
22. 25 x 8 =
23. 50 ÷ 25 =
24. 75 − 25 =
25. 175 + 25 =
26. 25 x 2 =
27. 125 ÷ 25 =
28. 25 − 25 =
29. 225 + 25 =
30. 25 x 5 =
31. 175 ÷ 25 =
32. 150 − 25 =
33. 200 + 25 =
34. 25 x 9 =
35. 250 ÷ 25 =
36. 100 − 25 =
37. 2 x 250 =
38. 25 x 0 =
39. 225 ÷ 25 =
40. 50 − 25 =

Set B

1. Add 50 to the following:

(a) 450 _____   (c) 300 _____

(b) 250 _____   (d) 200 _____

2. How many groups of 50 in:

(a) 300? _____   (c) 450? _____

(b) 500? _____   (d) 250? _____

3. Subtract 50 from the following:

(a) 450 _____   (c) 100 _____

(b) 300 _____   (d) 550 _____

4. Which multiple of 50 is closest to:

(a) 415? _____   (c) 142? _____

(b) 280? _____   (d) 519? _____

5. Add:

(a) 50 + 50 + 50 + 50 + 50 + 50 = _____

(b) 50 + 50 + 50 + 50 + 50 + 50 + 50 = _____

(c) 50 + 50 + 50 + 50 + 50 + 50 + 50 + 50 + 50 + 50 = _____

6. Complete the number sequence:

_____, 450, _____, _____, 300, _____, _____, 100, _____

7. Complete the number sentences:

(a) 50 x _____ = 500

(b) 50 x _____ = 200

(c) 50 x _____ = 400

8. Complete the following:

(a) (50 x 4) + 50 = _____

(b) (50 x 10) − 50 = _____

(c) (50 x 7) − 50 = _____

9. True (✓) False (X):

(a) 10 x 50 = 500 □

(b) 7 x 50 = 350 □

(c) 5 x 50 = 200 □

(d) 2 x 500 = 1500 □

(e) 4 x 500 = 2000 □

(f) 6 x 500 = 3500 □

(g) 3 x 500 = 1500 □

(h) 250 ÷ 50 = 4 □

(i) 150 ÷ 50 = 3 □

(j) 400 ÷ 50 = 8 □

10. Count by 50s to 500.

Set A

1. Add 50 to the following:

(a) 150 _____   (c) 350 _____

(b) 50 _____   (d) 100 _____

2. How many groups of 50 in:

(a) 200? _____   (c) 350? _____

(b) 100? _____   (d) 400? _____

3. Subtract 50 from the following:

(a) 500 _____   (c) 150 _____

(b) 250 _____   (d) 200 _____

4. Which multiple of 50 is closest to:

(a) 108? _____   (c) 370? _____

(b) 490? _____   (d) 162? _____

5. Add:

(a) 50 + 50 + 50 + 50 = _____

(b) 50 + 50 + 50 + 50 + 50 = _____

(c) 50 + 50 + 50 + 50 + 50 + 50 + 50 + 50 = _____

6. Complete the number sequence:

0, 50, _____, _____, 200, _____, _____, 350, _____, _____, 500

7. Complete the number sentences:

(a) 50 x _____ = 350

(b) 50 x _____ = 250

(c) 50 x _____ = 450

8. Complete the following:

(a) (50 x 6) + 50 = _____

(b) (50 x 9) + 50 = _____

(c) (50 x 3) − 50 = _____

9. True (✓) False (X):

(a) 3 x 50 = 150 □

(b) 9 x 50 = 400 □

(c) 6 x 50 = 300 □

(d) 8 x 50 = 400 □

(e) 7 x 500 = 3500 □

(f) 5 x 500 = 2500 □

(g) 9 x 500 = 4000 □

(h) 100 ÷ 50 = 2 □

(i) 350 ÷ 50 = 6 □

(j) 50 ÷ 50 = 1 □

10. Say your 50 x tables.

0 x 50 = _____	0 x 500 = _____		
1 x 50 = _____	1 x 500 = _____	6 x 50 = _____	6 x 500 = _____
2 x 50 = _____	2 x 500 = _____	7 x 50 = _____	7 x 500 = _____
3 x 50 = _____	3 x 500 = _____	8 x 50 = _____	8 x 500 = _____
4 x 50 = _____	4 x 500 = _____	9 x 50 = _____	9 x 500 = _____
5 x 50 = _____	5 x 500 = _____	10 x 50 = _____	10 x 500 = _____

1. How many days in:

(a) 50 weeks 4 days? _____   (b) 50 weeks 1 day? _____

2. Double:

(a) 150 _____   (b) 200 _____   (c) 50 _____   (d) 400 _____

3. Halve:

(a) 500 _____   (b) 300 _____   (c) 100 _____   (d) 200 _____

4. Pencils cost 50p each. How many can you buy with:

(a) £2.50? _____   (b) £4.50? _____   (c) £1.50? _____   (d) £3.00? _____

5. Each tram can carry 50 passengers. How many trams would be needed to carry:

(a) 150 people? _____ trams   (b) 300 people? _____ trams   (c) 450 people? _____ trams

6. Complete these:

(a) 120 ÷ 50 = _____ r _____   (b) 380 ÷ 50 = _____ r _____   (c) 460 ÷ 50 = _____ r _____

7. If you cut these metre-long sweet snakes into fiftieths, how many pieces would you have?

(a) 3 snakes _____ pieces   (b) 8 snakes _____ pieces   (c) 10 snakes _____ pieces

(d) 5 snakes _____ pieces   (e) 7 snakes _____ pieces   (f) 9 snakes _____ pieces

8. Each submarine can hold 500 sailors. How many sailors would fit in:

(a) 6 submarines? _____ sailors   (b) 10 submarines? _____ sailors   (c) 7 submarines? _____ sailors

9. Magazines cost £5.00 each. Kate buys 5 and Harley buys 9 magazines.

(a) How much money does Kate spend? _____

(b) How much money does Harley spend? _____

(c) How much more does Harley spend than Kate? _____

(d) How much change would Kate receive from a £50 note? _____

(e) How much change would Harley receive from a £50 note? _____

10. Tables Battleships.

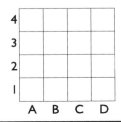
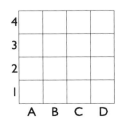
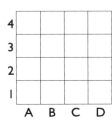
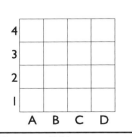

50 x table

Set B

My score:

My time: _____ mins _____ secs

I'm not happy

I'm happy

I didn't understand

OOPS!

The main area for me to work on is:
_____
_____
_____
_____
_____
_____

1. 500 x 1 =
2. 50 x 0 =
3. 100 ÷ 50 =
4. 200 – 50 =
5. 100 + 50 =
6. 50 x 9 =
7. 250 ÷ 50 =
8. 100 – 50 =
9. 400 + 50 =
10. 50 x 5 =
11. 350 ÷ 50 =
12. 300 – 50 =
13. 450 + 50 =
14. 50 x 2 =
15. 500 ÷ 50 =
16. 50 – 50 =
17. 350 + 50 =
18. 50 x 8 =
19. 450 ÷ 50 =
20. 150 – 50 =

21. 4 x 500 =
22. 50 x 7 =
23. 200 ÷ 50 =
24. 250 – 50 =
25. 150 + 50 =
26. 50 x 4 =
27. 400 ÷ 50 =
28. 350 – 50 =
29. 50 + 50 =
30. 50 x 5 =
31. 50 ÷ 50 =
32. 450 – 50 =
33. 300 + 50 =
34. 50 x 10 =
35. 150 ÷ 50 =
36. 400 – 50 =
37. 200 + 50 =
38. 50 x 6 =
39. 300 ÷ 50 =
40. 500 – 50 =

Set A

My score:

My time: _____ mins _____ secs

I'm not happy

I'm happy

I didn't understand

OOPS!

The main area for me to work on is:
_____
_____
_____
_____
_____
_____

1. 100 + 50 =
2. 50 x 6 =
3. 200 ÷ 50 =
4. 500 – 50 =
5. 200 + 50 =
6. 50 x 10 =
7. 400 ÷ 50 =
8. 400 – 50 =
9. 300 + 50 =
10. 50 x 3 =
11. 50 ÷ 50 =
12. 450 – 50 =
13. 50 + 50 =
14. 50 x 4 =
15. 150 ÷ 50 =
16. 350 – 50 =
17. 150 + 50 =
18. 50 x 7 =
19. 300 ÷ 50 =
20. 250 – 50 =

21. 250 + 50 =
22. 50 x 8 =
23. 100 ÷ 50 =
24. 150 – 50 =
25. 350 + 50 =
26. 500 x 0 =
27. 250 ÷ 50 =
28. 50 – 50 =
29. 450 + 50 =
30. 50 x 5 =
31. 350 ÷ 50 =
32. 300 – 50 =
33. 400 + 50 =
34. 50 x 9 =
35. 500 ÷ 50 =
36. 200 – 50 =
37. 50 x 0 =
38. 50 x 8 =
39. 450 ÷ 50 =
40. 100 – 50 =

2 and 3 times tables

My score

My time: _____ mins _____ secs

The main area for me to work on is:

_____

Set B

1. 2 x 4 = _____
2. 3 x 9 = _____
3. 18 ÷ 2 = _____
4. 27 ÷ 3 = _____
5. 2 + 2 + 2 + 2 = _____
6. 3 + 3 + 3 = _____
7. 18 − 2 = _____
8. 12 − 3 = _____
9. 4 x 20 = _____
10. 7 x 30 = _____
11. Double 40 = _____
12. Double 60 = _____
13. 2 x _____ = 16
14. 3 x _____ = 24
15. (2 x 7) + 2 = _____
16. (3 x 4) + 3 = _____
17. (2 x 9) + 2 = _____
18. (3 x 6) + 3 = _____
19. (2 x 5) − 2 = _____
20. (3 x 8) − 3 = _____

21. (2 x 10) − 2 = _____
22. (3 x 10) − 3 = _____
23. 7 ÷ 2 = _____ r _____
24. 22 ÷ 3 = _____ r _____
25. 2 x 50 = _____
26. 3 x 70 = _____
27. 2 x _____ = 20
28. 3 x _____ = 24
29. 2 x _____ = 18
30. 3 x _____ = 27
31. Half 8 = _____
32. Half 30 = _____
33. 20 ÷ 2 = _____
34. 18 ÷ 3 = _____
35. 10 − 2 = _____
36. 24 − 3 = _____
37. 14 ÷ 2 = _____
38. 3 ÷ 3 = _____
39. 7 x 20 = _____
40. 6 x 30 = _____

My score

My time: _____ mins _____ secs

The main area for me to work on is:

_____

Set A

1. 2 x 7 = _____
2. 3 x 0 = _____
3. 16 ÷ 2 = _____
4. 21 ÷ 3 = _____
5. 2 + 2 + 2 = _____
6. 3 + 3 + 3 + 3 = _____
7. 10 − 2 = _____
8. 15 − 3 = _____
9. 6 x 20 = _____
10. 4 x 30 = _____
11. Double 20 = _____
12. Double 30 = _____
13. 2 x _____ = 12
14. 3 x _____ = 18
15. (2 x 5) + 2 = _____
16. (3 x 9) + 3 = _____
17. (2 x 10) + 2 = _____
18. (3 x 8) + 3 = _____
19. (2 x 7) − 2 = _____
20. (3 x 6) − 3 = _____

21. (2 x 9) − 2 = _____
22. (3 x 4) − 3 = _____
23. 9 ÷ 2 = _____ r _____
24. 17 ÷ 3 = _____ r _____
25. 2 x 40 = _____
26. 3 x 60 = _____
27. 2 x _____ = 16
28. 3 x _____ = 21
29. 2 x _____ = 20
30. 3 x _____ = 0
31. Half 10 = _____
32. Half 6 = _____
33. 18 ÷ 2 = _____
34. 12 ÷ 3 = _____
35. 14 − 2 = _____
36. 18 − 3 = _____
37. 20 ÷ 2 = _____
38. 30 ÷ 3 = _____
39. 2 x 20 = _____
40. 3 x 30 = _____

My score

My time: ____ mins ____ secs

The main area for me to work on is:

_____

Set B

1. 9 × 4 = _____
2. 0 × 5 = _____
3. 18 ÷ 4 = _____ r _____
4. 27 ÷ 5 = _____ r _____
5. 4 + 4 + 4 + 4 = _____
6. 5 + 5 + 5 = _____
7. 28 – 4 = _____
8. 10 – 5 = _____
9. 6 × 40 = _____
10. 6 × 50 = _____
11. Double 40 = _____
12. Double 50 = _____
13. 4 × _____ = 20
14. 5 × _____ = 35
15. (3 × 4) + 4 = _____
16. (7 × 5) + 5 = _____
17. (9 × 4) + 4 = _____
18. (10 × 5) + 5 = _____
19. (1 × 4) – 4 = _____
20. (5 × 5) – 5 = _____

21. (7 × 4) – 4 = _____
22. (3 × 5) – 5 = _____
23. 23 ÷ 4 = _____ r _____
24. 42 ÷ 5 = _____ r _____
25. 5 × 40 = _____
26. 7 × 50 = _____
27. 4 × _____ = 28
28. 5 × 9 = _____
29. 4 × _____ = 16
30. 5 × _____ = 0
31. Half 40 = _____
32. Half 50 = _____
33. 28 ÷ 4 = _____
34. 20 ÷ 5 = _____
35. 16 – 4 = _____
36. 30 – 5 = _____
37. 40 ÷ 4 = _____
38. 25 ÷ 5 = _____
39. 10 × 40 = _____
40. 3 × 50 = _____

My score

My time: ____ mins ____ secs

The main area for me to work on is:

_____

Set A

1. 0 × 4 = _____
2. 5 × 5 = _____
3. 16 ÷ 4 = _____
4. 30 ÷ 5 = _____
5. 4 + 4 + 4 = _____
6. 5 + 5 + 5 + 5 = _____
7. 12 – 4 = _____
8. 40 – 5 = _____
9. 7 × 40 = _____
10. 8 × 50 = _____
11. Double 8 = _____
12. Double 10 = _____
13. 4 × _____ = 12
14. 5 × _____ = 50
15. (2 × 4) + 4 = _____
16. (6 × 5) + 5 = _____
17. (8 × 4) + 4 = _____
18. (9 × 5) + 5 = _____
19. (0 × 4) – 0 = _____
20. (7 × 5) – 5 = _____

21. (3 × 4) – 4 = _____
22. (9 × 5) – 5 = _____
23. 13 ÷ 4 = _____ r _____
24. 37 ÷ 5 = _____ r _____
25. 4 × 40 = _____
26. 5 × 50 = _____
27. 4 × _____ = 24
28. 5 × 6 = _____
29. 4 × _____ = 36
30. 5 × _____ = 50
31. Half 8 = _____
32. Half 10 = _____
33. 20 ÷ 4 = _____
34. 35 ÷ 5 = _____
35. 20 – 4 = _____
36. 50 – 5 = _____
37. 40 ÷ 4 = _____
38. 20 ÷ 5 = _____
39. 7 × 40 = _____
40. 6 × 50 = _____

My score   My time: _____ mins _____ secs   The main area for me to work on is:

_____

Set B

1. 5 x 6 = _____
2. 0 x 7 = _____
3. 42 ÷ 6 = _____
4. 56 ÷ 7 = _____
5. 6 + 6 + 6 + 6 = _____
6. 7 + 7 + 7 = _____
7. 48 – 6 = _____
8. 14 – 7 = _____
9. 3 x 60 = _____
10. 8 x 70 = _____
11. Double 60 = _____
12. Double 70 = _____
13. 6 x _____ = 18
14. 7 x _____ = 28
15. (6 x 3) + 6 = _____
16. (7 x 5) + 7 = _____
17. (6 x 4) + 6 = _____
18. (3 x 7) + 7 = _____
19. (3 x 6) – 6 = _____
20. (5 x 7) – 7 = _____

21. (1 x 6) – 6 = _____
22. (8 x 7) – 7 = _____
23. 20 ÷ 6 = _____ r _____
24. 51 ÷ 7 = _____ r _____
25. 5 x 60 = _____
26. 7 x 70 = _____
27. 6 x _____ = 60
28. 7 x _____ = 0
29. 6 x _____ = 36
30. 7 x _____ = 63
31. Half 12 = _____
32. Half 28 = _____
33. 18 ÷ 6 = _____
34. 28 ÷ 7 = _____
35. 12 – 6 = _____
36. 70 – 7 = _____
37. 48 ÷ 6 = _____
38. 7 ÷ 7 = _____
39. 4 x 60 = _____
40. 6 x 70 = _____

My score   My time: _____ mins _____ secs   The main area for me to work on is:

_____

Set A

1. 3 x 6 = _____
2. 8 x 7 = _____
3. 36 ÷ 6 = _____
4. 42 ÷ 7 = _____
5. 6 + 6 + 6 = _____
6. 7 + 7 + 7 + 7 = _____
7. 18 – 6 = _____
8. 49 – 7 = _____
9. 6 x 60 = _____
10. 3 x 70 = _____
11. Double 6 = _____
12. Double 7 = _____
13. 6 x _____ = 30
14. 7 x _____ = 63
15. (6 x 2) + 6 = _____
16. (7 x 7) + 7 = _____
17. (6 x 8) + 6 = _____
18. (2 x 7) + 7 = _____
19. (5 x 6) – 6 = _____
20. (4 x 7) – 7 = _____

21. (2 x 6) – 6 = _____
22. (10 x 7) – 7 = _____
23. 14 ÷ 6 = _____ r _____
24. 30 ÷ 7 = _____ r _____
25. 7 x 60 = _____
26. 9 x 70 = _____
27. 6 x _____ = 24
28. 7 x _____ = 35
29. 6 x _____ = 0
30. 7 x _____ = 14
31. Half 60 = _____
32. Half 70 = _____
33. 24 ÷ 6 = _____
34. 49 ÷ 7 = _____
35. 36 – 6 = _____
36. 56 – 7 = _____
37. 12 ÷ 6 = _____
38. 70 ÷ 7 = _____
39. 8 x 60 = _____
40. 5 x 70 = _____

Set B

My score

My time: _____ mins _____ secs

The main area for me to work on is: _____

1. 6 × 8 = _____
2. 0 × 9 = _____
3. 16 ÷ 8 = _____
4. 90 ÷ 9 = _____
5. 8 + 8 + 8 = _____
6. 9 + 9 + 9 = _____
7. 32 − 8 = _____
8. 81 − 9 = _____
9. 6 × 80 = _____
10. 5 × 90 = _____
11. Double 80 = _____
12. Double 90 = _____
13. 8 × _____ = 24
14. 9 × _____ = 81
15. (8 × 8) + 8 = _____
16. (9 × 9) + 9 = _____
17. (8 × 2) + 8 = _____
18. (9 × 1) + 9 = _____
19. (8 × 10) − 8 = _____
20. (9 × 6) − 9 = _____

21. (8 × 8) − 8 = _____
22. (9 × 2) − 9 = _____
23. 44 ÷ 8 = _____ r
24. 86 ÷ 9 = _____ r
25. 10 × 80 = _____
26. 6 × 90 = _____
27. 8 × _____ = 80
28. 9 × _____ = 63
29. 8 × _____ = 16
30. 9 × _____ = 90
31. Half 40 = _____
32. Half 18 = _____
33. 8 ÷ 8 = _____
34. 72 ÷ 9 = _____
35. 40 − 8 = _____
36. 90 − 9 = _____
37. 32 ÷ 8 = _____
38. 45 ÷ 9 = _____
39. 10 × 80 = _____
40. 7 × 90 = _____

Set A

My score

My time: _____ mins _____ secs

The main area for me to work on is: _____

1. 5 × 8 = _____
2. 9 × 9 = _____
3. 32 ÷ 8 = _____
4. 18 ÷ 9 = _____
5. 8 + 8 + 8 + 8 = _____
6. 9 + 9 + 9 + 9 = _____
7. 24 − 8 = _____
8. 72 − 9 = _____
9. 7 × 80 = _____
10. 3 × 90 = _____
11. Double 8 = _____
12. Double 9 = _____
13. 8 × _____ = 40
14. 9 × _____ = 9
15. (8 × 3) + 8 = _____
16. (9 × 2) + 9 = _____
17. (8 × 6) + 8 = _____
18. (9 × 5) + 9 = _____
19. (8 × 2) − 8 = _____
20. (9 × 4) − 9 = _____

21. (8 × 10) − 8 = _____
22. (9 × 10) − 9 = _____
23. 19 ÷ 8 = _____ r
24. 31 ÷ 9 = _____ r
25. 8 × 80 = _____
26. 9 × 90 = _____
27. 8 × _____ = 32
28. 9 × _____ = 45
29. 8 × _____ = 56
30. 9 × _____ = 72
31. Half 80 = _____
32. Half 90 = _____
33. 40 ÷ 8 = _____
34. 63 ÷ 9 = _____
35. 16 − 8 = _____
36. 45 − 9 = _____
37. 24 ÷ 8 = _____
38. 36 ÷ 9 = _____
39. 4 × 80 = _____
40. 10 × 90 = _____

10 and 12 times tables

Set B

My score

My time: _____ mins _____ secs

 I'm happy I'm not happy OOPS! I didn't understand

The main area for me to work on is:
_____

1. 0 x 10 = _____
2. 8 x 12 = _____
3. 100 ÷ 10 = _____
4. 84 ÷ 12 = _____
5. 10 + 10 – 10 = _____
6. 12 + 12 + 12 = _____
7. 20 – 10 = _____
8. 36 – 12 = _____
9. 5 x 100 = _____
10. 0 x 120 = _____
11. Double 100 = _____
12. Double 120 = _____
13. 10 x _____ = 60
14. 12 x _____ = 60
15. (10 x 4) + 10 = _____
16. (12 x 6) + 12 = _____
17. (10 x 8) + 10 = _____
18. (12 x 5) + 12 = _____
19. (10 x 10) – 10 = _____
20. (12 x 1) – 12 = _____

21. (10 x 9) – 10 = _____
22. (12 x 5) – 12 = _____
23. 94 ÷ 10 = _____ r _____
24. 50 ÷ 12 = _____ r _____
25. 2 x 100 = _____
26. 5 x 120 = _____
27. 10 x _____ = 70
28. 12 x _____ = 0
29. 10 x _____ = 100
30. 12 x _____ = 120
31. Half 100 = _____
32. Half 120 = _____
33. 40 ÷ 10 = _____
34. 48 ÷ 12 = _____
35. 70 – 10 = _____
36. 72 – 12 = _____
37. 60 ÷ 10 = _____
38. 48 ÷ 12 = _____
39. 5 x 100 = _____
40. 4 x 120 = _____

Set A

My score

My time: _____ mins _____ secs

 I'm happy I'm not happy OOPS! I didn't understand

The main area for me to work on is:
_____

1. 7 x 10 = _____
2. 0 x 12 = _____
3. 80 ÷ 10 = _____
4. 72 ÷ 12 = _____
5. 10 + 10 + 10 = _____
6. 12 + 12 + 12 = _____
7. 60 – 10 = _____
8. 24 – 12 = _____
9. 4 x 100 = _____
10. 2 x 120 = _____
11. Double 10 = _____
12. Double 12 = _____
13. 10 x _____ = 30
14. 12 x _____ = 108
15. (10 x 2) + 10 = _____
16. (12 x 3) + 12 = _____
17. (10 x 5) + 10 = _____
18. (12 x 2) + 12 = _____
19. (10 x 7) – 10 = _____
20. (12 x 4) – 12 = _____

21. (10 x 2) – 10 = _____
22. (12 x 6) – 12 = _____
23. 87 ÷ 10 = _____ r _____
24. 39 ÷ 12 = _____ r _____
25. 10 x 100 = _____
26. 3 x 120 = _____
27. 10 x _____ = 50
28. 12 x _____ = 48
29. 10 x _____ = 0
30. 12 x _____ = 96
31. Half 10 = _____
32. Half 12 = _____
33. 90 ÷ 10 = _____
34. 24 ÷ 12 = _____
35. 100 – 10 = _____
36. 60 – 12 = _____
37. 40 ÷ 10 = _____
38. 120 ÷ 12 = _____
39. 6 x 100 = _____
40. 10 x 120 = _____

Answers

Prim-Ed Publishing www.prim-ed.com

.... page 1

Set A

1. (a) 16   (c) 22
   (b) 6   (d) 20
2. (a) 3   (c) 6
   (b) 10   (d) 8
3. (a) 16   (c) 10
   (b) 6   (d) 8
4. (a) 4, 6   (c) 10, 12
   (b) 2, 4   (d) 20, 22
5. (a) 8   (c) 16
   (b) 10
6. 6, 10, 12, 16, 18, 22, 24
7. (a) 7   (c) 2
   (b) 5
8. (a) 12   (c) 20
   (b) 12
9. (a) ✔   (f) ✗
   (b) ✗   (g) ✔
   (c) ✗   (h) ✔
   (d) ✔   (i) ✔
   (e) ✔   (j) ✗
10. Teacher check

Set B

1. (a) 12   (c) 20
   (b) 10   (d) 22
2. (a) 8   (c) 5
   (b) 1   (d) 7
3. (a) 2   (c) 18
   (b) 12   (d) 20
4. (a) 8, 10   (c) 6, 8
   (b) 12, 14   (d) 14, 16
5. (a) 14   (c) 18
   (b) 12
6. 18, 16, 12, 8, 6, 4, 0
7. (a) 4   (c) 9
   (b) 2
8. (a) 10   (c) 6
   (b) 14
9. (a) ✔   (f) ✗
   (b) ✔   (g) ✔
   (c) ✗   (h) ✔
   (d) ✔   (i) ✔
   (e) ✔   (j) ✗
10. Teacher check

.... page 2

1. (a) 18   (b) 20
2. (a) 80   (c) 120
   (b) 200   (d) 40
3. (a) 80   (c) 40
   (b) 60   (d) 90
4. (a) 11   (c) 9
   (b) 5
5. (a) 5   (c) 7
   (b) 9
6. (a) 8 r1   (c) 10 r1
   (b) 6 r1
7. (a) 14   (d) 8
   (b) 18   (e) 10
   (c) 6   (f) 4
8. (a) 120   (c) 160
   (b) 60
9. (a) £1.40   (d) £3.60
   (b) £1.80   (e) £3.20
   (c) £3.20
10. Teacher check

.... page 3

Set A

1. 8	21. 6	3. 6	23. 1
2. 14	22. 16	4. 14	24. 22
		5. 12	25. 10
		6. 0	26. 18
		7. 4	27. 9
		8. 18	28. 10
		9. 16	29. 14
		10. 10	30. 12
		11. 12	31. 3
		12. 12	32. 6
		13. 20	33. 18
		14. 20	34. 0
		15. 5	35. 10
		16. 16	36. 8
		17. 24	37. 22
		18. 8	38. 20
		19. 8	39. 7
		20. 20	40. 4

Set B

1. 18	21. 14
2. 8	22. 18
3. 10	23. 6
4. 10	24. 12
5. 22	25. 10
6. 16	26. 14
7. 5	27. 8
8. 22	28. 16
9. 20	29. 12
10. 20	30. 12
11. 7	31. 1
12. 4	32. 18
13. 24	33. 8
14. 4	34. 40
15. 12	35. 9
16. 6	36. 20
17. 16	37. 4
18. 10	38. 0
19. 3	39. 4
20. 8	40. 2

.... page 4

Set A

1. (a) 15   (c) 24
   (b) 30   (d) 9
2. (a) 10   (c) 3
   (b) 5   (d) 6
3. (a) 24   (c) 18
   (b) 12   (d) 9
4. (a) 18   (c) 24
   (b) 15   (d) 30
5. (a) 12   (c) 24
   (b) 15
6. 9, 15, 18, 24, 27
7. (a) 9   (c) 3
   (b) 3
8. (a) 18   (c) 24
   (b) 15
9. (a) ✔   (f) ✗
   (b) ✔   (g) ✔
   (c) ✗   (h) ✗
   (d) ✔   (i) ✔
   (e) ✗   (j) ✔
10. Teacher check

Set B

1. (a) 12   (c) 6
   (b) 21   (d) 18
2. (a) 7   (c) 4
   (b) 8   (d) 1
3. (a) 6   (c) 27
   (b) 15   (d) 3
4. (a) 9   (c) 30
   (b) 12   (d) 18
5. (a) 9   (c) 27
   (b) 18
6. 27, 24, 18, 12, 9, 6, 0
7. (a) 4   (c) 5
   (b) 3
8. (a) 12   (c) 27
   (b) 24
9. (a) ✗   (f) ✗
   (b) ✗   (g) ✔
   (c) ✔   (h) ✔
   (d) ✔   (i) ✔
   (e) ✔   (j) ✗
10. Teacher check

.... page 5

1. (a) 26   (b) 24
2. (a) 120   (c) 240
   (b) 180   (d) 30
3. (a) 150   (c) 120
   (b) 90   (d) 210
4. (a) 5   (c) 9
   (b) 10
5. (a) 5   (c) 4
   (b) 9
6. (a) 9 r2   (c) 6 r1
   (b) 3 r2
7. (a) 12   (d) 6
   (b) 18   (e) 15
   (c) 27   (f) 30
8. (a) 180   (c) 210
   (b) 120
9. (a) £2.40   (d) £2.60
   (b) £1.50   (e) £3.50
   (c) 90p
10. Teacher check

.... page 6

Set A

1. 9	21. 6
2. 21	22. 15
3. 10	23. 9
4. 15	24. 18
5. 12	25. 24
6. 24	26. 12
7. 4	27. 5
8. 24	28. 12
9. 15	29. 30
10. 27	30. 6
11. 7	31. 2
12. 21	32. 6
13. 18	33. 27
14. 0	34. 9
15. 6	35. 3
16. 27	36. 0
17. 21	37. 33
18. 18	38. 0
19. 8	39. 1
20. 9	40. 3

Set B

1. 12	21. 21
2. 18	22. 21
3. 5	23. 7
4. 24	24. 30
5. 24	25. 27
6. 0	26. 30
7. 8	27. 2
8. 15	28. 18
9. 30	29. 33
10. 24	30. 90
11. 3	31. 6
12. 27	32. 21
13. 9	33. 6
14. 6	34. 27
15. 3	35. 4
16. 6	36. 33
17. 15	37. 18
18. 12	38. 9
19. 1	39. 9
20. 9	40. 12

.... page 7

Set A

1. (a) 20   (c) 36
   (b) 12   (d) 32
2. (a) 6   (c) 4
   (b) 8   (d) 2
3. (a) 24   (c) 8
   (b) 32   (d) 16
4. (a) 40   (c) 24
   (b) 16   (d) 32
5. (a) 12   (c) 32
6. 8, 16, 24, 28, 36
7. (a) 5   (c) 3
   (b) 0
8. (a) 32   (c) 36
   (b) 24
9. (a) ✔   (f) ✔
   (b) ✗   (g) ✗
   (c) ✔   (h) ✔
   (d) ✗   (i) ✔
   (e) ✔   (j) ✗
10. Teacher check

Set B

1. (a) 24   (c) 40
   (b) 28   (d) 44
2. (a) 10   (c) 3
   (b) 5   (d) 9
3. (a) 12   (c) 4
   (b) 28   (d) 36
4. (a) 12   (c) 20
   (b) 4   (d) 28
5. (a) 28   (c) 40
   (b) 24
6. 36, 32, 24, 20, 12, 8, 0
7. (a) 9   (c) 7
   (b) 4
8. (a) 20   (c) 20
   (b) 36
9. (a) ✗   (f) ✔
   (b) ✗   (g) ✗
   (c) ✔   (h) ✗
   (d) ✔   (i) ✔
   (e) ✔   (j) ✔
10. Teacher check

.... page 8

1. (a) 31   (b) 34
2. (a) 160   (c) 80
   (b) 240   (d) 320
3. (a) 200   (c) 40
   (b) 160   (d) 140
4. (a) 5   (c) 9
   (b) 10
5. (a) 4   (c) 7
   (b) 9
6. (a) 6 r1   (c) 4 r2
   (b) 7 r2
7. (a) 12   (d) 16
   (b) 36   (e) 20
   (c) 28   (f) 32
8. (a) 200   (c) 320
   (b) 120
9. (a) £3.60   (d) £6.40
   (b) £2.40   (e) £7.60
   (c) £6.00
10. Teacher check

.... page 9

Set A

1. 8	21. 20
2. 20	22. 32
3. 10	23. 5
4. 8	24. 24
5. 16	25. 36
6. 28	26. 16
7. 4	27. 7
8. 20	28. 12
9. 32	29. 44
10. 12	30. 24
11. 2	31. 9
12. 4	32. 16
13. 12	33. 28
14. 36	34. 8
15. 3	35. 6
16. 32	36. 0
17. 24	37. 40
18. 40	38. 0
19. 8	39. 10
20. 36	40. 28

Set B

1. 16	21. 36
2. 28	22. 320
3. 6	23. 7
4. 4	24. 12
5. 24	25. 44
6. 36	26. 32
7. 2	27. 5
8. 28	28. 16
9. 20	29. 44
10. 12	30. 200
11. 8	31. 9
12. 40	32. 8
13. 12	33. 28
14. 24	34. 0
15. 3	35. 1
16. 32	36. 24
17. 8	37. 40
18. 40	38. 16
19. 4	39. 10
20. 20	40. 36

.... page 10

Set A

1. (a) 20   (c) 40
   (b) 25   (d) 35
2. (a) 2   (c) 9
   (b) 5   (d) 6
3. (a) 25   (c) 45
   (b) 20   (d) 10
4. (a) 45   (c) 15
   (b) 35   (d) 40
5. (a) 15   (c) 40
   (b) 30
6. 10, 20, 25, 35, 45, 50
7. (a) 10   (c) 6
   (b) 0
8. (a) 35   (c) 35
   (b) 20
9. (a) ✔   (f) ✔
   (b) ✔   (g) ✔
   (c) ✗   (h) ✔
   (d) ✔   (i) ✗
   (e) ✗   (j) ✔
10. Teacher check

Set B

1. (a) 10   (c) 45
   (b) 30   (d) 15
2. (a) 10   (c) 4
   (b) 7   (d) 8

Answers

3. (a) 5   (c) 15
   (b) 40   (d) 30
4. (a) 50   (c) 10
   (b) 25   (d) 15
5. (a) 35   (c) 45
   (b) 20
6. 50, 40, 30, 25, 10, 5
7. (a) 9   (c) 5
   (b) 2
8. (a) 50   (c) 30
   (b) 45
9. (a) ✘   (f) ✘
   (b) ✘   (g) ✔
   (c) ✔   (h) ✔
   (d) ✘   (i) ✘
   (e) ✔   (j) ✔
10. Teacher check

·················· page 11

1. (a) 40   (b) 37
2. (a) 300 (c) 50
   (b) 500 (d) 200
3. (a) 100 (c) 50
   (b) 150 (d) 250
4. (a) 6   (c) 10
   (b) 9   (d) 5
5. (a) 7   (c) 3
   (b) 4
6. (a) 5 r2 (c) 9 r3
   (b) 7 r4
7. (a) 30   (d) 50
   (b) 25   (e) 10
   (c) 20   (f) 100
8. (a) 150 (c) 300
   (b) 400
9. (a) £3.50 (d) £1.50
   (b) £4.50 (e) 50p
   (c) £1.00
10. Teacher check

·················· page 12

Set A
1. 10   21. 40
2. 40   22. 50
3. 3   23. 5
4. 25   24. 40
5. 45   25. 35
6. 30   26. 20
7. 7   27. 6
8. 55   28. 50
9. 25   29. 15
10. 10   30. 35
11. 4   31. 9
12. 35   32. 15
13. 30   33. 50
14. 45   34. 25
15. 10   35. 1
16. 5   36. 10
17. 55   37. 0
18. 15   38. 150
19. 2   39. 8
20. 20   40. 30

Set B
1. 50   21. 55
2. 25   22. 15
3. 9   23. 10
4. 10   24. 20
5. 10   25. 30
6. 0   26. 45
7. 1   27. 4
8. 15   28. 5
9. 15   29. 25
10. 35   30. 10
11. 8   31. 7

12. 30   32. 35
13. 35   33. 50
14. 15   34. 30
15. 5   35. 3
16. 50   36. 55
17. 40   37. 20
18. 50   38. 40
19. 2   39. 8
20. 40   40. 25

·················· page 13

Set A
1. (a) 42   (c) 54
   (b) 30   (d) 24
2. (a) 3   (c) 5
   (b) 9   (d) 10
3. (a) 6   (c) 48
   (b) 24   (d) 18
4. (a) 60   (c) 36
   (b) 18   (d) 54
5. (a) 48   (c) 36
   (b) 30
6. 12, 18, 30, 36, 48, 54, 60
7. (a) 9   (c) 4
   (b) 6
8. (a) 48   (c) 54
   (b) 24
9. (a) ✘   (f) ✔
   (b) ✔   (g) ✘
   (c) ✘   (h) ✔
   (d) ✔   (i) ✔
   (e) ✔   (j) ✘
10. Teacher check

Set B
1. (a) 18   (c) 48
   (b) 60   (d) 36
2. (a) 6   (c) 1
   (b) 7   (d) 4
3. (a) 12   (c) 54
   (b) 42   (d) 36
4. (a) 42   (c) 24
   (b) 48   (d) 12
5. (a) 18   (c) 54
   (b) 42
6. 54, 48, 36, 30, 12, 6
7. (a) 6   (c) 2
   (b) 0
8. (a) 60   (c) 30
   (b) 18
9. (a) ✔   (f) ✔
   (b) ✘   (g) ✘
   (c) ✔   (h) ✔
   (d) ✔   (i) ✔
   (e) ✘   (j) ✘
10. Teacher check

·················· page 14

1. (a) 46   (b) 45
2. (a) 24   (c) 60
   (b) 360 (d) 600
3. (a) 60   (c) 240
   (b) 120 (d) 30
4. (a) 7   (c) 10
   (b) 9
5. (a) 5   (c) 3
   (b) 8
6. (a) 4 r2 (c) 6 r4
   (b) 9 r3
7. (a) 18   (d) 60
   (b) 48   (e) 36
   (c) 30   (f) 54
8. (a) 120 (c) 540
   (b) 360

9. (a) £3.60 (d) £6.40
   (b) £5.40 (e) £4.60
   (c) £9.00
10. Teacher check

·················· page 15

Set A
1. 12   21. 66
2. 42   22. 54
3. 4   23. 3
4. 24   24. 6
5. 42   25. 24
6. 60   26. 360
7. 8   27. 1
8. 12   28. 36
9. 18   29. 48
10. 24   30. 30
11. 2   31. 7
12. 30   32. 48
13. 60   33. 54
14. 48   34. 18
15. 9   35. 5
16. 18   36. 54
17. 36   37. 30
18. 0   38. 36
19. 10   39. 6
20. 42   40. 60

Set B
1. 60   21. 54
2. 18   22. 180
3. 3   23. 2
4. 48   24. 42
5. 36   25. 30
6. 36   26. 48
7. 1   27. 10
8. 60   28. 18
9. 6   29. 18
10. 30   30. 24
11. 7   31. 9
12. 54   32. 30
13. 24   33. 42
14. 0   34. 60
15. 6   35. 4
16. 36   36. 12
17. 48   37. 12
18. 54   38. 42
19. 5   39. 8
20. 6   40. 24

·················· page 16

Set A
1. (a) 28   (c) 63
   (b) 70   (d) 14
2. (a) 2   (c) 5
   (b) 8   (d) 6
3. (a) 63   (c) 7
   (b) 28   (d) 35
4. (a) 21   (c) 42
   (b) 14   (d) 7
5. (a) 21   (c) 35
   (b) 49
6. 14, 21, 28, 49, 56, 70
7. (a) 8   (c) 10
   (b) 7
8. (a) 70   (c) 21
   (b) 28
9. (a) ✔   (f) ✔
   (b) ✘   (g) ✘
   (c) ✘   (h) ✔
   (d) ✔   (i) ✘
   (e) ✔   (j) ✔
10. Teacher check

Set B
1. (a) 21   (c) 49
   (b) 35   (d) 70
2. (a) 1   (c) 10
   (b) 9   (d) 3
3. (a) 42   (c) 56
   (b) 14   (d) 49
4. (a) 28   (c) 56
   (b) 14   (d) 49
5. (a) 63   (c) 56
   (b) 28
6. 70, 56, 42, 35, 21, 14
7. (a) 4   (c) 6
   (b) 7
8. (a) 63   (c) 28
   (b) 63
9. (a) ✔   (f) ✔
   (b) ✘   (g) ✘
   (c) ✔   (h) ✔
   (d) ✔   (i) ✔
   (e) ✘   (j) ✔
10. Teacher check

·················· page 17

1. (a) 54   (b) 53
2. (a) 420 (c) 70
   (b) 560 (d) 42
3. (a) 350 (c) 35
   (b) 140 (d) 7
4. (a) 6   (c) 9
   (b) 5
5. (a) 8   (c) 3
   (b) 6
6. (a) 5 r2 (c) 3 r4
   (b) 9 r1
7. (a) 28   (d) 63
   (b) 35   (e) 21
   (c) 49   (f) 42
8. (a) 210 (c) 700
   (b) 420
9. (a) £3.50 (d) £6.50
   (b) £5.60 (e) £4.40
   (c) £2.10
10. Teacher check

·················· page 18

Set A
1. 21   21. 28
2. 42   22. 14
3. 3   23. 4
4. 7   24. 42
5. 35   25. 49
6. 21   26. 35
7. 7   27. 6
8. 63   28. 70
9. 42   29. 63
10. 49   30. 63
11. 2   31. 10
12. 14   32. 35
13. 56   33. 490
14. 0   34. 70
15. 5   35. 1
16. 28   36. 56
17. 77   37. 70
18. 490 38. 28
19. 9   39. 8
20. 21   40. 0

Set B
1. 14   21. 63
2. 56   22. 210
3. 6   23. 4
4. 63   24. 28
5. 28   25. 56
6. 35   26. 28

7. 1   27. 7
8. 21   28. 42
9. 70   29. 42
10. 21   30. 42
11. 5   31. 8
12. 7   32. 56
13. 0   33. 35
14. 63   34. 280
15. 2   35. 3
16. 140 36. 49
17. 49   37. 21
18. 49   38. 70
19. 0   39. 8
20. 14   40. 35

·················· page 19

Set A
1. (a) 56   (c) 32
   (b) 48   (d) 72
2. (a) 4   (c) 10
   (b) 5   (d) 2
3. (a) 64   (c) 40
   (b) 56   (d) 8
4. (a) 64   (c) 32
   (b) 56   (d) 8
5. (a) 48   (c) 64
   (b) 24
6. 0, 16, 24, 40, 48, 64, 72
7. (a) 6   (c) 9
   (b) 8
8. (a) 40   (c) 72
   (b) 80
9. (a) ✔   (f) ✔
   (b) ✘   (g) ✘
   (c) ✔   (h) ✔
   (d) ✘   (i) ✔
   (e) ✔   (j) ✘
10. Teacher check

Set B
1. (a) 24   (c) 64
   (b) 80   (d) 40
2. (a) 7   (c) 1
   (b) 8   (d) 3
3. (a) 72   (c) 16
   (b) 48   (d) 32
4. (a) 16   (c) 24
   (b) 48   (d) 80
5. (a) 56   (c) 72
   (b) 40
6. 72, 64, 48, 32, 24, 16, 0
7. (a) 3   (c) 4
   (b) 8
8. (a) 64   (c) 56
   (b) 40
9. (a) ✘   (f) ✔
   (b) ✔   (g) ✔
   (c) ✔   (h) ✘
   (d) ✔   (i) ✔
   (e) ✘   (j) ✔
10. Teacher check

·················· page 20

1. (a) 60   (b) 58
2. (a) 320 (c) 160
   (b) 480 (d) 16
3. (a) 32   (c) 8
   (b) 24   (d) 40
4. (a) 5   (c) 7
   (b) 10
5. (a) 4   (c) 2
   (b) 8
6. (a) 9 r2 (c) 2 r5

Prim-Ed Publishing www.prim-ed.com

(b) 4 r3
7. (a) 24   (d) 32
  (b) 48   (e) 40
  (c) 72   (f) 80
8. (a) 400   (c) 560
  (b) 720
9. (a) £3.20   (d) £6.80
  (b) £4.80   (e) £5.20
  (c) £8.00
10. Teacher check

.... page 21

Set A

1. 24	21. 32
2. 48	22. 16
3. 3	23. 4
4. 8	24. 48
5. 40	25. 56
6. 24	26. 40
7. 7	27. 6
8. 72	28. 80
9. 48	29. 72
10. 64	30. 72
11. 2	31. 10
12. 16	32. 40
13. 64	33. 240
14. 0	34. 80
15. 5	35. 1
16. 32	36. 64
17. 88	37. 80
18. 640	38. 32
19. 8	39. 9
20. 24	40. 160

Set B

1. 88	21. 80
2. 64	22. 0
3. 6	23. 4
4. 72	24. 32
5. 32	25. 64
6. 40	26. 32
7. 1	27. 7
8. 24	28. 48
9. 80	29. 48
10. 24	30. 48
11. 5	31. 8
12. 8	32. 64
13. 16	33. 40
14. 72	34. 400
15. 2	35. 3
16. 80	36. 56
17. 56	37. 24
18. 56	38. 80
19. 160	39. 9
20. 16	40. 40

.... page 22

Set A
1. (a) 36   (c) 81
  (b) 54   (d) 27
2. (a) 10   (c) 4
  (b) 7   (d) 9
3. (a) 9   (c) 27
  (b) 72   (d) 45
4. (a) 81   (c) 54
  (b) 18   (d) 27
5. (a) 45   (c) 72
  (b) 27
6. 18, 27, 45, 54, 72, 81
7. (a) 5   (c) 8
  (b) 9
8. (a) 36   (c) 45
  (b) 54
9. (a) ✔   (f) ✗
  (b) ✔   (g) ✔
  (c) ✔   (h) ✔
  (d) ✗   (i) ✔
  (e) ✔   (j) ✗
10. Teacher check

Set B
1. (a) 63   (c) 90
  (b) 18   (d) 72
2. (a) 2   (c) 6
  (b) 8   (d) 3
3. (a) 54   (c) 81
  (b) 18   (d) 36
4. (a) 36   (c) 63
  (b) 72   (d) 90
5. (a) 63   (c) 81
  (b) 36
6. 90, 81, 63, 54, 36, 27, 9, 0
7. (a) 4   (c) 9
  (b) 0
8. (a) 90   (c) 9
  (b) 81
9. (a) ✗   (f) ✔
  (b) ✗   (g) ✗
  (c) ✔   (h) ✔
  (d) ✔   (i) ✗
  (e) ✔   (j) ✔
10. Teacher check

.... page 23
1. (a) 66   (b) 68
2. (a) 360   (c) 180
  (b) 900   (d) 36
3. (a) 90   (c) 9
  (b) 27   (d) 45
4. (a) 5   (c) 8
  (b) 10
5. (a) 3   (c) 9
  (b) 6
6. (a) 4 r2   (c) 8 r7
  (b) 6 r5
7. (a) 36   (d) 45
  (b) 81   (e) 18
  (c) 54   (f) 63
8. (a) 630   (c) 270
  (b) 810
9. (a) £7.20   (d) £2.80
  (b) £3.60   (e) £6.40
  (c) £3.60
10. Teacher check

.... page 24

Set A

1. 27	21. 36
2. 54	22. 18
3. 3	23. 4
4. 9	24. 54
5. 45	25. 63
6. 27	26. 45
7. 7	27. 6
8. 36	28. 90
9. 54	29. 81
10. 63	30. 81
11. 2	31. 10
12. 18	32. 72
13. 72	33. 810
14. 0	34. 90
15. 5	35. 1
16. 81	36. 45
17. 99	37. 90
18. 9	38. 36
19. 9	39. 8
20. 27	40. 360

Set B

1. 36	21. 54
2. 90	22. 0
3. 9	23. 3
4. 72	24. 27
5. 63	25. 180
6. 36	26. 270
7. 5	27. 7
8. 45	28. 36
9. 81	29. 90
10. 81	30. 63
11. 9	31. 10
12. 0	32. 9
13. 27	33. 72
14. 45	34. 27
15. 4	35. 8
16. 18	36. 54
17. 45	37. 99
18. 18	38. 54
19. 6	39. 1
20. 81	40. 90

.... page 25

Set A
1. (a) 50   (c) 30
  (b) 60   (d) 100
2. (a) 3   (c) 8
  (b) 4   (d) 11
3. (a) 40   (c) 80
  (b) 10   (d) 30
4. (a) 60   (c) 50
  (b) 30   (d) 90
5. (a) 40   (c) 80
  (b) 60
6. 10, 20, 30, 50, 60, 80, 90
7. (a) 7   (c) 5
  (b) 10
8. (a) 110   (c) 90
  (b) 70
9. (a) ✔   (f) ✗
  (b) ✔   (g) ✗
  (c) ✗   (h) ✔
  (d) ✔   (i) ✔
  (e) ✔   (j) ✗
10. Teacher check

Set B
1. (a) 20   (c) 90
  (b) 80   (d) 120
2. (a) 5   (c) 9
  (b) 6   (d) 20
3. (a) 70   (c) 50
  (b) 100   (d) 90
4. (a) 20   (c) 30
  (b) 70   (d) 100
5. (a) 30   (c) 90
  (b) 70
6. 90, 80, 60, 40, 30, 20, 0
7. (a) 2   (c) 6
  (b) 10
8. (a) 50   (c) 40
  (b) 60
9. (a) ✔   (f) ✗
  (b) ✗   (g) ✔
  (c) ✗   (h) ✗
  (d) ✔   (i) ✔
  (e) ✔   (j) ✗
10. Teacher check

.... page 26
1. (a) 74   (b) 71
2. (a) 1000   (c) 80
  (b) 600   (d) 40
3. (a) 10   (c) 400
  (b) 30   (d) 50
4. (a) 15   (c) 12
  (b) 27   (d) 60
5. (a) 8   (c) 2
  (b) 10
6. (a) 7 r2   (c) 10 r3
  (b) 6 r7
7. (a) 100   (d) 40
  (b) 70   (e) 150
  (c) 20   (f) 200
8. (a) 600   (c) 2000
  (b) 1000
9. (a) £8.00   (d) £12.00
  (b) £4.00   (e) £16.00
  (c) £12.00
10. Teacher check

.... page 27

Set A

1. 40	21. 170
2. 80	22. 80
3. 7	23. 15
4. 490	24. 100
5. 100	25. 30
6. 100	26. 20
7. 4	27. 20
8. 790	28. 110
9. 60	29. 110
10. 60	30. 60
11. 10	31. 4
12. 90	32. 10
13. 130	33. 210
14. 0	34. 1 000
15. 5	35. 7
16. 290	36. 30
17. 50	37. 70
18. 200	38. 90
19. 30	39. 6
20. 890	40. 140

Set B

1. 90	21. 160
2. 40	22. 500
3. 10	23. 20
4. 40	24. 140
5. 50	25. 30
6. 90	26. 300
7. 15	27. 60
8. 80	28. 190
9. 80	29. 150
10. 100	30. 0
11. 70	31. 80
12. 0	32. 160
13. 100	33. 210
14. 700	34. 400
15. 40	35. 50
16. 90	36. 290
17. 110	37. 200
18. 200	38. 90
19. 600	39. 30
20. 110	40. 240

.... page 28

Set A
1. (a) 48   (c) 72
  (b) 108   (d) 36
2. (a) 2   (c) 6
  (b) 9   (d) 7
3. (a) 36   (c) 96
  (b) 12   (d) 60
4. (a) 36   (c) 84
  (b) 60   (d) 96
5. (a) 36   (c) 60
  (b) 84
6. 12, 36, 60, 72, 96, 108
7. (a) 2   (c) 6
  (b) 10
8. (a) 84   (c) 60
  (b) 108
9. (a) ✔   (f) ✔
  (b) ✗   (g) ✔
  (c) ✔   (h) ✗
  (d) ✗   (i) ✔
  (e) ✗   (j) ✔
10. Teacher check

Set B
1. (a) 24   (c) 60
  (b) 96   (d) 120
2. (a) 5   (c) 3
  (b) 10   (d) 4
3. (a) 48   (c) 108
  (b) 72   (d) 24
4. (a) 96   (c) 24
  (b) 48, 36   (d) 60
5. (a) 48   (c) 108
  (b) 72
6. 108, 96, 72, 48, 36, 24, 0
7. (a) 9   (c) 8
  (b) 0
8. (a) 96   (c) 84
  (b) 48
9. (a) ✔   (f) ✔
  (b) ✗   (g) ✗
  (c) ✔   (h) ✔
  (d) ✗   (i) ✔
  (e) ✔   (j) ✗
10. Teacher check

.... page 29
1. (a) 87   (b) 89
2. (a) 120   (c) 72
  (b) 96   (d) 48
3. (a) 12   (c) 54
  (b) 60   (d) 30
4. (a) 5   (c) 8
  (b) 10
5. (a) 3   (c) 10
  (b) 5
6. (a) 4 r2   (c) 2 r3
  (b) 3 r5
7. (a) 24   (d) 120
  (b) 60   (e) 84
  (c) 48   (f) 96
8. (a) 360   (c) 1080
  (b) 840
9. (a) £1.20   (d) £3.80
  (b) 60p   (e) £4.40
  (c) 60p
10. Teacher check

.... page 30

Set A

1. 36	21. 48
2. 72	22. 24
3. 3	23. 4
4. 12	24. 72
5. 60	25. 84
6. 36	26. 60
7. 7	27. 6
8. 48	28. 0
9. 72	29. 108
10. 0	30. 36
11. 2	31. 10
12. 24	32. 96
13. 96	33. 12
14. 84	34. 120
15. 5	35. 1
16. 108	36. 60
17. 132	37. 120

Answers

18. 12
19. 9
20. 36
38. 48
39. 8
40. 0

Set B

1. 48	21. 36
2. 120	22. 120
3. 8	23. 1
4. 96	24. 108
5. 84	25. 60
6. 48	26. 108
7. 6	27. 7
8. 60	28. 24
9. 108	29. 72
10. 0	30. 84
11. 2	31. 3
12. 0	32. 48
13. 24	33. 96
14. 60	34. 36
15. 4	35. 5
16. 72	36. 12
17. 120	37. 132
18. 24	38. 72
19. 9	39. 0
20. 36	40. 84

·············· page 31

Set A

1. (a) 90 (c) 120
   (b) 60 (d) 135
2. (a) 8 (c) 1
   (b) 5 (d) 7
3. (a) 135 (c) 30
   (b) 105 (d) 45
4. (a) 150 (c) 90
   (b) 30 (d) 15
5. (a) 45 (c) 120
   (b) 75
6. 30, 45, 75, 90, 120, 135
7. (a) 3 (c) 6
   (b) 4
8. (a) 60 (c) 75
   (b) 120
9. (a) ✗ (f) ✔
   (b) ✔ (g) ✔
   (c) ✔ (h) ✗
   (d) ✗ (i) ✔
   (e) ✔ (j) ✔
10. Teacher check

Set B

1. (a) 150 (c) 105
   (b) 75 (d) 30
2. (a) 10 (c) 2
   (b) 6 (d) 3
3. (a) 60 (c) 75
   (b) 120 (d) 15
4. (a) 105 (c) 30
   (b) 45 (d) 135
5. (a) 60 (c) 135
   (b) 90
6. 135, 120, 90, 60, 45, 30, 0
7. (a) 10 (c) 2
   (b) 5
8. (a) 90 (c) 105
   (b) 45
9. (a) ✔ (f) ✔
   (b) ✔ (g) ✔
   (c) ✔ (h) ✔
   (d) ✗ (i) ✗
   (e) ✗ (j) ✔
10. Teacher check

·············· page 32

1. (a) 108 (b) 110
2. (a) 120 (c) 30
   (b) 90 (d) 150
3. (a) 60 (c) 30
   (b) 75 (d) 15
4. (a) 3 (c) 9
   (b) 8 (d) 10
5. (a) 4 (c) 7
   (b) 10
6. (a) 3 r3 (c) 9 r5
   (b) 7 r2
7. (a) 60 (d) 105
   (b) 75 (e) 45
   (c) 30 (f) 135
8. (a) 450 (c) 1350
   (b) 900
9. (a) £4.50 (d) £5.50
   (b) £10.50 (e) £9.50
   (c) £15.00
10. Teacher check

·············· page 33

Set A

1. 45	21. 135
2. 90	22. 75
3. 3	23. 4
4. 15	24. 90
5. 75	25. 105
6. 45	26. 120
7. 7	27. 6
8. 60	28. 75
9. 90	29. 0
10. 150	30. 135
11. 2	31. 1
12. 30	32. 135
13. 60	33. 150
14. 30	34. 15
15. 5	35. 8
16. 0	36. 105
17. 30	37. 120
18. 60	38. 105
19. 9	39. 10
20. 45	40. 120

Set B

1. 135	21. 30
2. 15	22. 60
3. 4	23. 9
4. 45	24. 60
5. 105	25. 45
6. 105	26. 30
7. 6	27. 5
8. 30	28. 105
9. 0	29. 75
10. 75	30. 150
11. 1	31. 2
12. 0	32. 135
13. 150	33. 60
14. 135	34. 45
15. 8	35. 7
16. 15	36. 120
17. 120	37. 90
18. 120	38. 90
19. 10	39. 3
20. 75	40. 90

·············· page 34

Set A

1. (a) 100 (c) 140
   (b) 180 (d) 80
2. (a) 3 (c) 5
   (b) 8 (d) 6
3. (a) 20 (c) 160
   (b) 80 (d) 60
4. (a) 40 (c) 140
   (b) 60 (d) 20
5. (a) 80 (c) 160
   (b) 100
6. 40, 60, 100, 120, 160, 180
7. (a) 5 (c) 0
   (b) 9
8. (a) 160 (c) 180
   (b) 100
9. (a) ✔ (f) ✔
   (b) ✔ (g) ✗
   (c) ✔ (h) ✗
   (d) ✗ (i) ✔
   (e) ✔ (j) ✔
10. Teacher check

Set B

1. (a) 60 (c) 160
   (b) 40 (d) 200
2. (a) 4 (c) 10
   (b) 9 (d) 2
3. (a) 120 (c) 180
   (b) 40 (d) 140
4. (a) 120 (c) 160
   (b) 100 (d) 200
5. (a) 140 (c) 180
   (b) 60
6. 180, 160, 120, 80, 60, 40, 0
7. (a) 6 (c) 3
   (b) 10
8. (a) 200 (c) 140
   (b) 80
9. (a) ✔ (f) ✗
   (b) ✔ (g) ✔
   (c) ✗ (h) ✔
   (d) ✔ (i) ✔
   (e) ✔ (j) ✔
10. Teacher check

·············· page 35

1. (a) 145 (b) 142
2. (a) 160 (c) 40
   (b) 120 (d) 200
3. (a) 300 (c) 40
   (b) 80 (d) 20
4. (a) 5 (c) 10
   (b) 3 (d) 7
5. (a) 4 (c) 10
   (b) 7
6. (a) 3 r8 (c) 8 r15
   (b) 5 r5
7. (a) 40 (d) 160
   (b) 140 (e) 200
   (c) 100 (f) 400
8. (a) 600 (c) 2000
   (b) 1400
9. (a) £12.00 (d) £8.00
   (b) £18.00 (e) £2.00
   (c) £6.00
10. Teacher check

·············· page 36

Set A

1. 100	21. 140
2. 60	22. 40
3. 5	23. 4
4. 60	24. 140
5. 120	25. 240
6. 200	26. 100
7. 3	27. 6
8. 120	28. 40
9. 180	29. 200
10. 80	30. 160
11. 8	31. 9
12. 80	32. 20
13. 80	33. 0
14. 180	34. 120
15. 10	35. 7
16. 100	36. 160
17. 60	37. 160
18. 140	38. 0
19. 2	39. 1
20. 180	40. 200

Set B

1. 200	21. 160
2. 120	22. 60
3. 7	23. 8
4. 40	24. 80
5. 140	25. 180
6. 80	26. 100
7. 5	27. 3
8. 100	28. 60
9. 200	29. 120
10. 40	30. 160
11. 20	31. 9
12. 220	32. 140
13. 100	33. 60
14. 140	34. 200
15. 4	35. 6
16. 160	36. 120
17. 80	37. 220
18. 180	38. 0
19. 10	39. 1
20. 20	40. 180

·············· page 37

Set A

1. (a) 150 (c) 100
   (b) 250 (d) 125
2. (a) 4 (c) 10
   (b) 3 (d) 7
3. (a) 150 (c) 75
   (b) 225 (d) 125
4. (a) 175 (c) 200
   (b) 75 (d) 25
5. (a) 100 (c) 200
   (b) 125
6. 25, 75, 125, 150, 200, 225
7. (a) 8 (c) 9
   (b) 6
8. (a) 200 (c) 50
   (b) 125
9. (a) ✔ (f) ✗
   (b) ✗ (g) ✔
   (c) ✔ (h) ✔
   (d) ✔ (i) ✗
   (e) ✔ (j) ✔
10. Teacher check

Set B

1. (a) 175 (c) 75
   (b) 200 (d) 225
2. (a) 8 (c) 6
   (b) 9 (d) 2
3. (a) 25 (c) 175
   (b) 50 (d) 100
4. (a) 75 (c) 150
   (b) 250 (d) 100
5. (a) 175 (c) 225
   (b) 150
6. 225, 200, 150, 100, 75, 50, 0
7. (a) 4 (c) 7
   (b) 10
8. (a) 75 (c) 175
   (b) 100
9. (a) ✗ (f) ✔
   (b) ✔ (g) ✗
   (c) ✔ (h) ✔
   (d) ✔ (i) ✔
   (e) ✗ (j) ✔
10. Teacher check

·············· page 38

1. (a) 178 (b) 180
2. (a) 250 (c) 100
   (b) 150 (d) 50
3. (a) 75 (c) 100
   (b) 25 (d) 50
4. (a) 5 (c) 4
   (b) 9 (d) 6
5. (a) 10 (c) 5
   (b) 7
6. (a) 3 r4 (c) 8 r15
   (b) 5 r5
7. (a) 75 (d) 175
   (b) 100 (e) 125
   (c) 225 (f) 200
8. (a) 1000 (c) 2500
   (b) 1500
9. (a) £7.50 (d) £2.50
   (b) £17.50 (e) £2.50
   (c) £25.00
10. Teacher check

·············· page 39

Set A

1. 75	21. 150
2. 150	22. 200
3. 4	23. 2
4. 225	24. 50
5. 125	25. 200
6. 250	26. 50
7. 8	27. 5
8. 175	28. 0
9. 175	29. 250
10. 75	30. 125
11. 1	31. 7
12. 200	32. 125
13. 50	33. 225
14. 100	34. 225
15. 3	35. 10
16. 150	36. 75
17. 100	37. 500
18. 175	38. 0
19. 6	39. 9
20. 100	40. 25

Set B

1. 1000	21. 150
2. 0	22. 175
3. 2	23. 4
4. 75	24. 100
5. 75	25. 100
6. 225	26. 100
7. 5	27. 8
8. 25	28. 150
9. 225	29. 50
10. 125	30. 75
11. 7	31. 1
12. 125	32. 200
13. 250	33. 175
14. 50	34. 250
15. 10	35. 3
16. 0	36. 175
17. 200	37. 125
18. 200	38. 150
19. 9	39. 6
20. 50	40. 225

Answers

.... page 40

Set A

1. (a) 200 (c) 400
   (b) 100 (d) 150
2. (a) 4 (c) 7
   (b) 2 (d) 8
3. (a) 450 (c) 100
   (b) 200 (d) 150
4. (a) 100 (c) 350
   (b) 500 (d) 150
5. (a) 200 (c) 400
   (b) 250
6. 100, 150, 250, 300, 400, 450
7. (a) 7 (c) 9
   (b) 5
8. (a) 350 (c) 100
   (b) 500
9. (a) ✔ (f) ✔
   (b) ✗ (g) ✗
   (c) ✔ (h) ✔
   (d) ✔ (i) ✗
   (e) ✔ (j) ✔
10. Teacher check

Set B

1. (a) 500 (c) 350
   (b) 300 (d) 250
2. (a) 6 (c) 9
   (b) 10 (d) 5
3. (a) 400 (c) 50
   (b) 250 (d) 500
4. (a) 400 (c) 150
   (b) 300 (d) 500
5. (a) 350 (c) 450
   (b) 300
6. 500, 400, 350, 250, 200, 150, 50, 0
7. (a) 10 (c) 8
   (b) 4
8. (a) 250 (c) 300
   (b) 450
9. (a) ✔ (f) ✗
   (b) ✔ (g) ✔
   (c) ✗ (h) ✗
   (d) ✗ (i) ✔
   (e) ✔ (j) ✔
10. Teacher check

.... page 41

1. (a) 354 (b) 351
2. (a) 300 (c) 100
   (b) 400 (d) 800
3. (a) 250 (c) 50
   (b) 150 (d) 100
4. (a) 5 (c) 3
   (b) 9 (d) 6
5. (a) 3 (c) 9
   (b) 6
6. (a) 2 r20 (c) 9 r10
   (b) 7 r30
7. (a) 150 (d) 250
   (b) 400 (e) 350
   (c) 500 (f) 450
8. (a) 3000 (c) 3500
   (b) 5000
9. (a) £25.00 (d) £25.00
   (b) £45.00 (e) £5.00
   (c) £20.00
10. Teacher check

.... page 42

Set A

1. 150   21. 300
2. 300   22. 400
3. 4   23. 2
4. 450   24. 100
5. 250   25. 400
6. 500   26. 0
7. 8   27. 5
8. 350   28. 0
9. 350   29. 500
10. 150   30. 250
11. 1   31. 7
12. 400   32. 250
13. 100   33. 450
14. 200   34. 450
15. 3   35. 10
16. 300   36. 150
17. 200   37. 0
18. 350   38. 400
19. 6   39. 9
20. 200   40. 50

Set B

1. 500   21. 2000
2. 0   22. 350
3. 2   23. 4
4. 150   24. 200
5. 150   25. 200
6. 450   26. 200
7. 5   27. 8
8. 50   28. 300
9. 450   29. 100
10. 250   30. 250
11. 7   31. 1
12. 250   32. 400
13. 500   33. 350
14. 100   34. 500
15. 10   35. 3
16. 0   36. 350
17. 400   37. 250
18. 400   38. 300
19. 9   39. 6
20. 100   40. 450

Review answers

.... page 43

Set A

1. 14   21. 16
2. 0   22. 9
3. 8   23. 4 r1
4. 7   24. 5 r2
5. 6   25. 80
6. 12   26. 180
7. 8   27. 8
8. 12   28. 7
9. 120   29. 10
10. 120   30. 0
11. 40   31. 5
12. 60   32. 3
13. 6   33. 9
14. 6   34. 4
15. 12   35. 12
16. 30   36. 15
17. 22   37. 10
18. 27   38. 10
19. 12   39. 40
20. 15   40. 90

Set B

1. 8   21. 18
2. 27   22. 27
3. 9   23. 3 r1
4. 9   24. 7 r1
5. 8   25. 100
6. 9   26. 210
7. 16   27. 10
8. 9   28. 8
9. 80   29. 9
10. 210   30. 9
11. 80   31. 4
12. 120   32. 15
13. 8   33. 10
14. 8   34. 6
15. 16   35. 8
16. 15   36. 21
17. 20   37. 7
18. 21   38. 1
19. 8   39. 140
20. 21   40. 180

.... page 44

Set A

1. 0   21. 8
2. 25   22. 40
3. 4   23. 3 r1
4. 6   24. 7 r2
5. 12   25. 160
6. 20   26. 250
7. 8   27. 6
8. 35   28. 30
9. 280   29. 9
10. 400   30. 10
11. 16   31. 4
12. 20   32. 5
13. 3   33. 5
14. 10   34. 7
15. 12   35. 16
16. 35   36. 45
17. 36   37. 10
18. 50   38. 4
19. 0   39. 280
20. 30   40. 300

Set B

1. 36   21. 24
2. 0   22. 10
3. 4 r2   23. 5 r3
4. 5 r2   24. 8 r2
5. 16   25. 200
6. 15   26. 350
7. 24   27. 7
8. 5   28. 45
9. 240   29. 4
10. 300   30. 0
11. 80   31. 20
12. 100   32. 25
13. 5   33. 7
14. 7   34. 4
15. 16   35. 12
16. 40   36. 25
17. 40   37. 10
18. 55   38. 5
19. 0   39. 400
20. 20   40. 150

.... page 45

Set A

1. 18   21. 6
2. 56   22. 63
3. 6   23. 2 r2
4. 6   24. 4 r2
5. 18   25. 420
6. 28   26. 630
7. 12   27. 4
8. 42   28. 5
9. 360   29. 0
10. 210   30. 2
11. 12   31. 30
12. 14   32. 35
13. 5   33. 4
14. 9   34. 7
15. 18   35. 30
16. 56   36. 49
17. 54   37. 2
18. 21   38. 10
19. 24   39. 480
20. 21   40. 350

Set B

1. 30   21. 0
2. 0   22. 49
3. 7   23. 3 r2
4. 8   24. 7 r2
5. 24   25. 300
6. 21   26. 490
7. 42   27. 10
8. 7   28. 0
9. 180   29. 6
10. 560   30. 9
11. 120   31. 6
12. 140   32. 14
13. 3   33. 3
14. 4   34. 4
15. 24   35. 6
16. 42   36. 63
17. 30   37. 8
18. 28   38. 1
19. 12   39. 240
20. 28   40. 420

.... page 46

Set A

1. 40   21. 72
2. 81   22. 81
3. 4   23. 2 r3
4. 2   24. 3 r4
5. 32   25. 640
6. 36   26. 810
7. 16   27. 4
8. 63   28. 5
9. 560   29. 7
10. 270   30. 8
11. 16   31. 40
12. 18   32. 45
13. 5   33. 5
14. 1   34. 7
15. 32   35. 8
16. 27   36. 36
17. 56   37. 3
18. 54   38. 4
19. 8   39. 320
20. 27   40. 900

Set B

1. 48   21. 56
2. 0   22. 9
3. 2   23. 5 r4
4. 10   24. 9 r5
5. 24   25. 800
6. 27   26. 540
7. 24   27. 10
8. 72   28. 7
9. 480   29. 2
10. 450   30. 10
11. 160   31. 20
12. 180   32. 9
13. 3   33. 1
14. 9   34. 8
15. 72   35. 32
16. 90   36. 81
17. 24   37. 4
18. 18   38. 5
19. 72   39. 800
20. 45   40. 630

.... page 47

Set A

1. 70   21. 10
2. 0   22. 60
3. 8   23. 8 r7
4. 6   24. 3 r3
5. 30   25. 1000
6. 36   26. 360
7. 50   27. 5
8. 12   28. 4
9. 400   29. 0
10. 240   30. 8
11. 20   31. 5
12. 24   32. 6
13. 3   33. 9
14. 9   34. 2
15. 30   35. 90
16. 48   36. 48
17. 60   37. 4
18. 36   38. 10
19. 60   39. 600
20. 36   40. 1200

Set B

1. 0   21. 80
2. 96   22. 48
3. 10   23. 9 r4
4. 7   24. 4 r2
5. 10   25. 200
6. 36   26. 600
7. 10   27. 7
8. 24   28. 0
9. 500   29. 10
10. 0   30. 10
11. 200   31. 50
12. 240   32. 60
13. 6   33. 4
14. 5   34. 4
15. 50   35. 60
16. 84   36. 60
17. 90   37. 6
18. 72   38. 4
19. 90   39. 500
20. 0   40. 480

FUNGI
FORAYS

First published in 2012 by New Holland Publishers (UK) Ltd
London • Cape Town • Sydney • Auckland

www.newhollandpublishers.com

Garfield House, 86–88 Edgware Road, London W2 2EA, UK
Wembly Square, First Floor, Solan Street Gardens, Cape Town 8000
Unit 1, 66 Gibbes Street, Chatswood, New South Wales 2067, Australia
218 Lake Road, Northcote, Auckland, New Zealand

10 9 8 7 6 5 4 3 2 1

ISBN 978 1 84773 938 4

Senior Editor Krystyna Mayer
Designer Nicola Liddiard
Production Melanie Dowland
Publisher Simon Papps
Printer Toppan Leefung Printing Ltd (China)

All photographs by Daniel Butler except Horn of Plenty (p. 6) by
Dr Andrew Tutt; Brown Roll Rim (p. 9) by Jon Bemrose; Chanterelle
by Dietmar Nill/naturepl.com; Horn of Plenty (p. 28) by Wild Foragers;
Horn of Plenty (p. 29) by Jade Pothecary; Yellow Stainer (p. 69) by
Dr Barthó Loránd; Field Blewit (p. 87) by Michael Webber and Morel
(pp. 98 and 99) by Peregrine Crewe.

FUNGI FORAYS

DANIEL BUTLER

NEW HOLLAND

Contents

Introduction

MUCH OF THE NORTHERN HEMISPHERE PROVIDES THE IDEAL GROWING CONDITIONS FOR SOME OF THE MOST DELICIOUS MUSHROOMS, YET VERY FEW OF US NOTICE THE WILD BOUNTY THAT SURROUNDS US. EVEN THOUGH EDIBLE MUSHROOMS ARE WITHIN EASY REACH OF VIRTUALLY EVERYONE, MOST PEOPLE SIMPLY DO NOT KNOW WHERE TO START LOOKING, LET ALONE HAVE THE CONFIDENCE TO EAT THEIR FINDS. THIS IS NOT HELPED BY THE MAJORITY OF FIELD GUIDES, WHICH SIMPLY SHOW THE MUSHROOMS IN CLOSE-UP PICTURES.

As anyone who has attempted to find mushrooms will know, in practice the first step is to recognize where to look. Even then many mushrooms can be very difficult to spot, because they tend to be superbly camouflaged against their surroundings. It is only when you know the best places to look that you can begin the process of making a preliminary identification, with the final confirmation occurring back home.

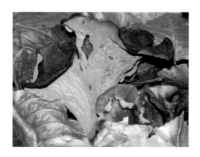

This book focuses on the first two stages of mushroom hunting – the habitats of the fungi and what they look like in their natural surroundings. Some of the best locations, of course, are in remote woods and ancient pastures, but there are plenty of opportunities to find choice fungi in even the busiest city. Superbly edible species lurk in back gardens, urban parks and churchyards, on golf courses, disused railway lines and waste ground, and along roadsides.

The following chapters focus on six distinct locations. Each begins with a brief description of the habitat and where to look within it. This is followed by a photographic guide to a variety of the best species found within the habitat, with notes on where to find them and how to identify them with total confidence.

Fears, myth and reality

Most city dwellers seem convinced that all wild mushrooms are lethal: that death lurks beneath every cap. If you suggest an interest in fungi, let alone confess to gathering and eating mushrooms collected from the wild, you are bombarded with ghoulish tales of families found dead around a pot of 'toadstools'.

In actual fact, the increasingly fashionable pastime of 'foraging' is remarkably free from risk. To start with, most participants are sensible

OPPOSITE The Horn of Plenty: one of many superbly camouflaged fungi.

ABOVE Deciduous woodland is one of the richest fungus habitats.

to the point of paranoia – they simply will not risk making a mistake. In addition, the overwhelming majority of the world's thousands of fungus species are harmless. Most are extremely small and spend their lives buried out of sight beneath the ground or in the roots or bark of a plant. Of those that are easily seen, only a couple of hundred are edible. Even within this category many fungi are not brilliant, and only a score or so are really excellent. It is this group that sensible foragers target, while steering well clear of the couple of dozen seriously poisonous species.

To put things in context, the overwhelming majority (literally 99 per cent) of the world's fungi are simply not gastronomically interesting: they will neither delight the taste buds nor hospitalize you.

They are simply 'inedible', and indigestion after eating them is the likeliest result of experimentation.

That said, the fungi that are nasty can be very nasty indeed. Eating just one Deathcap (*Amanita phalloides*) not only may, but probably will kill you. Worse, it does so in a very unpleasant way, slowly destroying the liver until eventually the victim dies from a massive body shutdown. Other species, such as the Deadly Webcap (*Cortinarius rubellus*), attack the

kidneys. This is probably a slightly less unpleasant way to go, but no one wants to put it to the test.

It is also worth noting that some species that until recently were regarded as harmless are now known to cause serious adverse reactions in susceptible individuals. The Purple-staining Bolete (*Boletus erythropus*) is often described as 'edible but not worthwhile'. Despite this, it is widely eaten in some places, although it is now thought that consuming it in quantity over a long period may be linked to kidney damage. Similarly, the Brown Rollrim (*Paxillus involutus*) was regarded as edible until 1944, when a German mycologist who had eaten the mushroom for many years suddenly died from acute kidney failure.

The majority of mushroom hunters are aware of the possible dangers of the most deadly species and adopt an ultra-cautious approach to all wild fungi. As a result, deaths are very rare, particularly in Britain. The number rises if one takes into account Europe as a whole, and rises again if North America is included. Even so, each year there are probably less than a score fatalities from cases of mistaken identity across the developed world.

OPPOSITE The Deathcap is one of the most poisonous of fungi.

TOP Eating the Purple-staining Bolete has been linked to kidney damage.

ABOVE Consumption of the Brown Rollrim may cause kidney failure.

Ironically, this same caution leads to the most common cause of mushroom poisoning. Immured in the traditional distrust of toadstools, many people ignore the most exotic-looking species, heading instead for the familiar Field Mushroom (*Agaricus campestris*). As an *Agaricus*, this species is closely related to the cultivated mushroom that accounts for the vast majority of fungi consumed in the West. However, its reassuring exterior can be the hunter's undoing.

While the Field Mushroom is still locally common in pastoral areas, it has a close relative that favours exactly the same sites. This is the Yellow Stainer (*A. xanthodermus*), which can be extremely unpleasant in its effects, producing a strong allergic reaction in about half of those who eat it. It never kills or causes lasting damage, but the acute burst of vomiting and diarrhoea it produces is horrible.

The mistake in identification is actually very easy to avoid. Yellow Stainers live up to their name by

TOP The Destroying Angel is deadly poisonous even in a minute quantity.
BELOW The Sulphur Tuft is a common poisonous woodland species.

discolouring: if a thumb is run firmly across the cap this will bruise yellow and give off a distinct whiff of carbolic (see also page 69).

This is also interesting because it demonstrates another aspect of the widespread cultural ignorance of mushrooms that exaggerates the toxicity of even the most poisonous of species. No one denies that a Destroying Angel (*Amanita virosa*) is a killer (just half a mature specimen can see off an adult). Even so, the advice in some source books to discard an entire haul if, by chance, it has come into contact with one seems excessive. The idea that a few micrograms of spores can taint the others sufficiently to produce poisoning symptoms does not seem very credible, although this is not a theory many people would want to put to the test.

It is also worth noting that even the most edible of mushrooms occasionally provoke an allergic reaction in a rare individual. The first time you try a new mushroom, therefore, always cook it to make it a little more digestible, and eat it in moderation – if you enjoy the experience, you can always eat more a day or two later.

It is important to keep a sense of perspective with regard to poisonous mushrooms. Many poisonous species are not only completely distinctive in appearance, but both beautiful and very useful to edible mushroom hunters. The classic toadstool Fly Agaric (*Amanita muscaria*), for example, is stunningly beautiful and very obvious with its white-flecked red cap. Just as importantly, however, it loves exactly the same conditions as the edible but less conspicuous Porcini (*Boletus edulis*) – so if you happen on the distinctive Fly Agaric during your forays, always check the vicinity for the delectable Porcini.

The naming of mushrooms

Mycology is a relatively new science and is still in a state of flux. Bear in mind that a number of edible species have recently been reclassified by taxonomists, and can thus occur in field guides under more than one scientific name – something that may be confusing to a novice.

The situation is even more tangled when it comes to common names. In this book the most frequent English name, backed up by the latest scientific name, is used for each species. Even this can be confusing – and nowhere more so than in the case of that 'king of mushrooms' *Boletus edulis*. This was once commonly known in Britain as the Penny Bun, but today very few people use this name, relying instead on the French or Italian names (Cep and Porcini respectively). The latter has been used in this book since it is probably in slightly wider usage across the English-speaking world. The variations in a mushroom's name make no difference to its edibility, of course, but they provide an extra layer of potential confusion for the beginner.

Common alternate names are also given in this book where these exist. French names are generally provided, because the catering and wholesale trades often use them rather than the English names.

Harvesting mushrooms

It goes without saying that you should never eat any fungus without being absolutely confident of its identity. How do you ensure this? Well, start by ignoring old wives' tales about edible species smelling 'good', being easy to

RIGHT The beautiful though poisonous Fly Agaric is unmistakable.

peel or not reacting to the touch of a penny. The only way to tell the edible from the poisonous is by positive identification. In practice, the real reason for correct identification is to save yourself not from death by poisoning, but from extreme frustration. It takes years of experience to be able to identify every one of the thousands of fungus species with confidence – and the vast majority are not edible or poisonous anyway.

This means that if, as a beginner, you fill your basket with dozens of samples, you are likely to do no more than discourage yourself. Once home it

ABOVE Experienced hunters can find a variety of fungi on a single foray.

will take an age to put a name to each specimen – and once you have done so, it will probably only be to discover that most are of no gastronomic interest. In other words, they will neither delight your taste buds nor poison you – and just suppose some are indeed edible, by the time you have identified them you will probably have forgotten exactly where you found them.

As a result, it makes sense to set out on every foray with a single target in mind – preferably something that is easy to identify in the field with reasonable certainty. Having decided on a suitable species, familiarize yourself with its appearance and set out to find it in the appropriate habitat, preferably armed with this guide to confirm or refute your preliminary identification in the field.

Harvest promising fungi with a sharp knife or scissors. Many sources suggest this is to avoid damaging the invisible mycelium (the extensive network of fine threads that join, branch and weave beneath the surface and are attached to the fruit body of a fungus that you see on the surface). In actual fact, the main reason for using a knife or scissors is to minimize the amount of dirt that invariably clings to every fruiting body. If this goes into the basket it works its way into the pores and gills of a haul, leading to additional work in the kitchen.

Ideally, use a wicker basket for holding the harvest. In theory this helps to spread spores for the future (although spore reproduction is so inefficient that this is actually unlikely). Much more importantly, it keeps the fungi in prime condition. Many begin to decay the second they are picked (Shaggy Inkcaps melt almost as you watch, for example). If at all possible, avoid putting fungi in plastic bags. These are certainly easy to scrunch up in a pocket for an unexpected find, but fungi have such a high water content that they sweat after harvesting and the deterioration process accelerates as the water condenses inside the bag. If you want to be forearmed for the unexpected, but do not want to be encumbered by a basket, a cotton bag or – better still – an onion net is a far better option.

When you stumble on a big haul – many fungi grow communally and can occur in huge quantities – practise self-restraint. There is no point in gathering several kilos if these end up wasted. This deprives wildlife of food, is wasteful and gives fungi hunters a bad name. That said, many fungi store well in various forms, so there is nothing wrong with gathering large quantities if you are set on stashing away the bounty for times of famine (see also preserving, pages 124–7).

Once home, go straight to the kitchen to process the harvest. Most importantly, go through the basket, cleaning out any dirt and insects, while cross-checking your field identification with a second source – preferably a good fungus encylopaedia. Having done this, process the fungi as quickly as possible, whether by cooking or preserving. It is all too easy to leave a basket on the side overnight, only to find that the mushrooms have decayed or become riddled with insect life to the point of uselessness by the next morning.

Understanding mushrooms

There is a common misconception that fungi only fruit in autumn. In truth they are there throughout the year, with edible varieties usually being available from spring to late winter.

The mushroom picker's season kicks off with Morels and St George's Mushrooms (spring), and develops with Chicken of the Woods and Fairy Ring Champignons (summer), Chanterelles (summer to autumn) and Porcini (autumn). The first frost stubs out the majority of fruiting, but it actually stimulates blewits, and fungi such as Jew's Ear and Oyster Mushrooms grow around the year when weather conditions are favourable. In other words, it is quite possible to locate a mushroom feast in any season, provided you know where to look.

Until recently there was no suggestion that there was anything wrong with harvesting food from the wild. Indeed, the early settlers and pioneers who tamed America relied heavily on berries and game as they plodded westwards. As recently as the Second World War, British hedgerows formed a valuable source of vitamin C in the form of blackberries and rose-hips, while nettles were turned into camouflage netting. Pendulums have a habit of swinging back and we are now in danger of going too far in the opposite direction. Where there was once a total lack of protection, this is now often replaced by a knee-jerk desire to wrap the countryside in cotton wool – to insist that on no account should humans remove anything from the wild. The underlying assumption is that wild plants and fungi can be wiped out by indiscriminate harvesting.

This is fair enough in theory when gathering food 'in the wild' is taken to an extreme, but it does need to be put in context. Humans have been harvesting wild-grown food since the dawn of time. Certainly, when it comes to plants it is possible to over-collect and wipe out populations, but with fungi there is no reason to hold back. Mushrooms are really just fruiting bodies that burst out of the mycelium at the appropriate time of year. Picking one no more harms the invisible body that lies hidden beneath the soil or bark, than picking a blackberry damages the parent bramble.

It is also worth remembering that each mycelium can live for scores or even hundreds of years. Over that time, all it needs to achieve to maintain the health of the species is for just two spores from one of the hundreds of mushrooms it produces to succeed. It must be borne in mind that each of these fruiting bodies produces literally tens of millions of spores. This is actually a fantastically inefficient method of reproduction, but just in case any doubt remains, by the time

a mushroom is big enough to be worth picking, the cap will have opened and the majority of the spores will already have dispersed.

There is therefore no reason to feel guilty or tentative when harvesting mushrooms. Your efforts will have no impact on organisms that have existed on Earth since long before the dinosaurs, and that are certainly going to be around many millennia after humans have vanished. There is one final note of warning, however: fungi hunting is seriously addictive. The discovery of that first Porcini, followed by its rich scent filling the kitchen, could change the way you view the countryside forever.

BELOW The exquisite Porcini: king of edible mushrooms.

Broadleaved woodland

MATURE BROADLEAVED WOODLAND IS PROBABLY THE RICHEST
FUNGUS HABITAT. SCORES OF EDIBLE SPECIES GROW HERE, BREAKING
DOWN THE FALLEN FOLIAGE AND, IN THE PROCESS, RELEASING SOLUBLE
NUTRIENTS FOR THE SURROUNDING TREE ROOTS TO ABSORB FROM
THE GROUND WATER. MANY ALSO HAVE COMPLICATED SYMBIOTIC
RELATIONSHIPS WITH THE TREES, TAPPING INTO THE XYLEM AND
PHLOEM 'PLUMBING' WITHIN THE BARK, WHICH MOVES ESSENTIAL
CHEMICALS AND WATER AROUND THE HOST AND IN RETURN RELEASES
NUTRIENTS FROM THE LEAF MOULD DIRECTLY INTO THE TREE.

While studying the rotting forest floor, also bear in mind that this is a three-dimensional habitat. Bracket fungi grow on trunks and branches, often far above the ground, while the more familiar Oyster Mushrooms sprout on dead timber.

Much more difficult to find, but most rewarding of all, are the truffles that grow beneath the surface. Some writers suggest that these can be found by looking for small 'inverted cones' of hovering flies, but in reality a trained dog or pig, with its superior sense of smell, is much better at finding these gems than any human.

Oak may be the most famous fungus host, but it is by no means the only – or necessarily the best – deciduous species. Beech, birch, chestnut and ash woods can also prove rich hunting grounds.

Leaf mould

The moist soil that forms as leaves break down is one of the richest fungus growing media, particularly in oak and beech woodlands. The Trumpet Chanterelle is just one of the species found here.

Trunks and branches

Fungi grow at all levels. The Beefsteak Fungus tends to grow beneath head height, often in a hollow trunk or where a tree limb has been lost.

Dead and dying wood

Fungi are agents of decay and many species, including Oyster Mushrooms, work to break down fallen branches and ancient stumps.

Streams and ditches

Many fungi love the damp conditions of streams and ditches – look for Chanterelles along their banks among the roots of birch and oak.

Chanterelle

This is one of the greatest of all wild fungi. For centuries it has delighted gastronomes with its fusion of great taste, texture and aroma. The scientific name, *Cantharellus cibarius*, comes from the Greek *kantharos* (goblet) and the latin *cibus* (food). Ironically, its English common name is a case of mistaken identity. This name is taken directly from the French, but in fact in France it is known as the Girolle and it is the Trumpet or Winter version (*C. tubaeformis*, page 26) that is known as the Chanterelle.

The delicately fluted golden trumpets vary widely in shape, size and colour, depending on age, soil and weather conditions. The usually golden, convex tiny fungi slowly enlarge and invert to create rough goblets with deeply ridged, gill-like structures running down the stem. Most specimens stand less than 6cm tall, but some can reach 15cm across and weigh over 100g. In addition, Chanterelles often grow in quantity. Despite this and their apparently

FACT FILE

SCIENTIFIC NAME
Cantharellus cibarius

OTHER NAMES Girolle (France)

CAP Up to 15cm across. Pale or bright yellow, fading with age.

STEM Up to 8cm tall. Yellow, slowly turning orange with age, before fading to white.

FLESH Firm, meat-like texture.

SPORES White, cream or pale yellow.

SEASON Late spring to autumn.

garish hue, they are well camouflaged, disappearing into the leaf mould and dead grass backdrop of their woodland habitat. Nonetheless, they are quite common, thriving in woods, hedge bottoms and ditches from Scandinavia to the Apennines in Italy, and from the Urals of Kazakhstan and Russia to the North American Rockies.

Chanterelles are distinctly bitter when raw, and for this reason should always be cooked. Heat transforms them into the marvellously aromatic fungi that are so highly prized by gastronomes. So much so that in the early 1990s, the woods of Oregon in the United States rang with gunfire in what became commonly known as the 'Chanterelle wars', during which rival gangs of commercial pickers battled over prime patches. Two pickers lost their lives before a licensing system restored some semblance of calm. Why the frenzy? Because this delicate little fungus has one of the most exquisite flavours of any wild mushroom.

Key identifiers

Distinct apricot aroma.

Grows in association with broadleaved trees.

Favours damp soil along ditches and streams.

Usually golden-yellow, but may sometimes be almost white.

Ridges that run down the stem from the underside to the cap.

Quick tips

Look for it along mossy banks.

Grows from late summer onwards.

Distinct apricot smell.

Once you have found one, keep looking because they rarely grow alone.

Taste

Distinctly bitter when raw, but sweetening with cooking to produce a delicate, slightly peppery taste. It blends particularly effectively with white meats and dairy products. It can be dried, but is probably best converted into Chanterelle butter.

The lookalike

The False Chanterelle (*Hygrophoropsis aurantiaca*) is annoyingly common. It is not deadly poisonous, but some people react badly to it, and prolonged consumption of large quantities may lead to kidney damage. At best it is tasteless and at worst bitter. Luckily, there are foolproof ways of telling the two species apart. On a true

Chanterelle the ridges under the cap resemble an aerial photograph of a river delta where the water channels snaking through the mud sometimes rejoin each other. Those on the False Chanterelle resemble tree branches – once they form they never rejoin. Its colour is also vivid orange, while the Chanterelle is a subtler shade of yellow and in quantity has an apricot aroma.

Trumpet Chanterelle

Although fairly abundant, if patchily distributed, this is a spectacularly well-camouflaged fungus, so it is extremely difficult to spot. Finding a patch is a red-letter day and a tribute to a hunter's eyesight and fieldcraft. Fortunately, once the first one is found, vast troupes usually slowly come into focus across the surrounding woodland floor.

Commercial pickers sometimes use rakes to harvest large numbers of the fungi quickly, but such an invasive harvesting technique seems likely to damage the delicate mycelia. They are thus best gathered using scissors. This method also has the advantage of minimizing the amount of dirt joining the fungi in the basket.

In common with other members of the chanterelle genus, Trumpet Chanterelles are very variable in shape, particularly when young. The caps are initially convex with a small depression in the centre. The edges slowly turn up and acquire wavy margins, creating a rough cup or funnel. The colour is similarly variable, but usually comprises a brown cap with a hollow yellowish stem. Narrow irregular gills initially run down the top of the stem, but they quickly peter out. Seen side-on, the whole fungus looks like a tiny, wind-inverted

FACT FILE

SCIENTIFIC NAME
Cantharellus tubaeformis

OTHER NAMES Winter Chanterelle, Yellow Leg, Chanterelle (France)

CAP Up to 5cm across. Brown or grey cap that inverts to a rough funnel as it ages.

STEM Up to 8cm tall. Yellow.

FLESH Yellow and brown, fibrous.

SPORES White, cream or pale yellow.

SEASON Late summer to late autumn.

umbrella. The Trumpet Chanterelle's growing season starts slightly later than that of its better known relative, the Chanterelle (page 22), commencing in late summer and continuing into late autumn. This accounts for one of its other common names, the Winter Chanterelle.

Key identifiers

Brilliantly camouflaged, but it is prolific where it occurs.

Grows beneath conifers and in broadleaved woods, but has a marked preference for beech and chestnut.

Grows later than its better known golden relative, the Chanterelle.

Found most commonly on acid soils.

Taste

Excellent, if a little more chewy than that of the true Chanterelle. It is distinctly bitter when raw, but becomes sweet once it has been cooked. It can be dried, although it is probably better flash fried and frozen, or best of all potted with melted butter.

Horn of Plenty

The Horn of Plenty is usually found in deciduous leaf litter, and occasionally in grass near trees. It is another funnel-shaped fungus, and although it is fairly uncommon it can be locally abundant. Unfortunately, due to its superb camouflage it can be difficult to find – the first discovery should be a matter for major celebration, not least because where it does occur it usually does so in large numbers. One tip is to search areas where its close and marginally more visible relatives, the Chanterelle and Trumpet Chanterelle (pages 22 and 26), occur.

Despite the Horn of Plenty's unprepossessing appearance it has

FACT FILE

SCIENTIFIC NAME
Craterellus cornucopioides

OTHER NAMES Black Trumpets, Trompette des morts (France)

CAP Up to 10cm across. Grey or black cap that inverts to a rough funnel with age.

STEM Up to 15cm tall. Black or grey.

FLESH Black or grey, and fibrous.

SPORES White, cream or pale yellow.

SEASON Late summer to late autumn.

a superb flavour, which explains its common English name. This is much nicer than the French common name, *trompette des morts* (trumpets of the dead), which clearly derives from its funereal looks, but hardly helps with marketing. As a result, it is sometimes

Key identifiers

Brilliantly camouflaged (very difficult to find).

Prolific where it occurs.

Grows in broadleaved woods, with a marked preference for beech and chestnut.

Can sometimes emerge in grass near to trees and shrubs.

Taste

Although no beauty, this drab fungus has an excellent flavour. Its black flesh can look particularly good set against white fish. It dries moderately well, but is perhaps best stored in butter.

packaged as *trompette des maures* (trumpet of the Moors). It is delicious served in a white sauce with fish or spread thinly on toast, but it can be a little chewy and the dark colour can be off-putting, so it is perhaps best shredded.

Oyster Mushroom

This common mushroom grows in tight clusters of flat caps that fan out from dead trees and fallen branches

FACT FILE

SCIENTIFIC NAME
Pleurotus ostreatus

OTHER NAMES Branching Oyster,
Pleurote (French)

APPEARANCE Cap up to 20cm across.
Flat, growing from the sides of
dead wood. Varies between white,
cream, yellow, brown and grey.

FLESH White to cream.

SPORES White.

SEASON All year.

(particularly those of beech). There are four closely related species, all edible, with caps that vary from slate-blue, through browns and yellows, to near white. Older mushrooms can be tough and infested with insects, so it is best to target younger specimens and to discard the stems.

The Oyster Mushroom is one of the few fungi that is commercially grown on a large scale, and most people would rate its taste as superior to that of conventional cultivated mushrooms. As is the case with domesticated Field Blewits (page 86), the fungus seems to lose something with taming and genuinely wild Oyster Mushrooms are clearly superior in taste. On the other hand, the cultivated fungi dry well and can be added to better flavoured dried wild mushrooms in order to bulk them out.

Key identifiers

Always found on dead or dying deciduous trees.

Grows most commonly on oak, chestnut, birch and beech.

Taste

Excellent. Similar to conventional cultivated mushrooms, but more delicate in flavour and texture. Dries well and may be used for bulking up wild mushroom mixtures.

Beefsteak Fungus

This is surely one of the most recognizable fungi, and the most timid of beginners can instantly identify the brick-red slabs with pale undersides that emerge from broadleaved trees. These do indeed look very similar to prime cuts of red meat, even to the point of 'bleeding' a crimson sap when cut. The same sap stains the timber on which the fungus grows, and in the past this striking wood was in enormous demand by cabinet makers, who used it to produce superb veneers (some prime examples of which are on display in the great palace of Versailles, in France).

There is no serious possibility of confusing the Beefsteak Fungus with any other species, which is the main reason for it so often being branded as 'delicious'. Unfortunately, it often grows on oak and is therefore full of tannins, which can make it very bitter. Some commentators suggest that soaking it in milk before cooking counters this, while others value it for its firm texture, which allows it to be cooked like its namesake. As is the case with other bracket fungi, older specimens can be tough and powdery.

Key identifiers

Red and meaty.

Grows on deciduous trees, usually oak, willow or beech.

Generally grows on a trunk, particularly where this has been damaged.

Tends to occur at head height or above.

Taste

Variable, depending on the taster's palate and the host tree. It can be bitter, but this flavour can be reduced by soaking it in milk. It is best preserved in frozen finished dishes.

Amethyst Deceiver

Despite living up to its name, with a vivid purple cap and stem, this delicate little fungus can be difficult to spot against the muted browns and blacks of a forest floor. It grows in both broadleaved and conifer woods, but is most common among the fallen leaves beneath beech trees. It stands only a few centimetres high, but makes up for this with its colour, according to which even beginners can identify it with certainty. Like so many small fungi, it is a social beast; after spotting the first, scores more usually slowly come into focus in the general area. Its close relative, the Deceiver (page 106),

emerges in a bewildering array of shapes and sizes, but the Amethyst Deceiver is more regular in appearance and its colour clinches any problems with identification.

FACT FILE

SCIENTIFIC NAME
Laccaria amethystina

CAP Less than 5cm across (usually smaller). Lilac to imperial purple in shade. Initially domed, sometimes with a dimple in the centre, and flattening out with age.

STEM Up to 10cm tall. Thin and uniform in shape.

FLESH Purple when fresh, drying after picking to dusty grey-brown.

SPORES White, cream or yellow.

SEASON Summer and autumn.

Key identifiers

Striking purple colour.

Grows in woodland,
often in association
with beech.

Gills have a regular
long-short-long pattern.

Fairly common
throughout Europe.

Uncommon in North
America, where it is
largely restricted to
New England.

Taste

Excellent flavour, but
the striking colour fades
fast after picking and
vanishes completely
with cooking. Very good
eaten fresh, but also
dries well.

Summer Truffle

The **truffle** is a much-misunderstood fungus – not least because it grows out of sight below ground and is therefore very difficult to find. On top of this, there are several truffle species – two of which, the Black or Perigord Truffle (*Tuber melanosporum*) and the White or Alba Truffle (*T. magnatum*) – are extremely valuable. These species are largely confined to northern Italy and the Mediterranean respectively, but the Summer Truffle is considerably more widespread.

All truffles have symbiotic relationships with deciduous trees – usually beech, chestnut or oak – and prefer impoverished chalky soils. They grow just under the surface alongside the trees' lateral roots. Once found,

the warty, pitted black spheres are instantly recognizable, but their scent is even more distinctive. As a result they are traditionally located with the aid of a dog or pig due to the superior sense of smell of these animals. Indeed,

FACT FILE

SCIENTIFIC NAME
Tuber aestivum

OTHER NAMES Tartuffe (Italy), Truffe (France)

APPEARANCE Black sphere covered in black pyramidal warts.

SIZE Up to 14cm in diameter.

FLESH Off-white, becoming mottled.

SPORES White, cream or yellow.

SEASON Summer to autumn.

even a sharp-nosed human can sometimes detect the rich, heady scent, but the unaided hunter is left to hope that the fungi are sufficiently close to the surface to produce small but visible lumps on the surface of the soil.

Key identifiers

Warty black sphere.

Grows underground in woodland.

Usually found near beech or oak.

Favours poor chalky soil.

Extremely difficult to find without a trained dog or pig.

Taste

Excellent. These pungent fungi are so aromatic that just one tuber placed in a bowl of eggs will flavour them overnight. They also store well in oil, turning it into an aromatic flavouring in its own right.

Velvet Shank

The Velvet Shank often grows in large clusters of orange fungi on the dead and dying wood of deciduous trees. The cap is darker than the yellow gills, while the velvety stem darkens

FACT FILE

SCIENTIFIC NAME
Flammulina velutipes

OTHER NAMES Enoki, Enotake

CAP Up to 10cm across. Yellow.

STEM Up to 10cm tall. Orange, sometimes rather blackened at the base.

FLESH Orange-brown.

SPORES White.

SEASON Late autumn and winter.

towards the base. The stem is very tough so is best discarded. Although the Velvet Shank cannot be described as a particularly tasty fungus, it makes up for it by growing through the winter. Indeed, unlike almost any other fungi, it seems completely undaunted by hard frost and can easily survive being frozen solid. It is thus at its most visible when poking up through the snow or dusted with hoar frost. It more than makes up for its lack of gastronomic excitement by being virtually the only edible fungus it is possible to find in mid-winter.

This is one of the handful of edible wild fungi that can be cultivated. The Japanese have been growing it for centuries, and it can appear in Asian shops as Enoki – although when sold in this way the fungi are generally thin, tightly bunched together and alabaster white in colour because they have been grown in the dark.

Key identifiers

Yellow, almost translucent cap and stem.

Grows on dead and dying trees, usually elm.

Decidedly velvety feel to the stem.

Can survive frost and even snow.

Very common.

Taste

Reasonable, but this winter fungus can be distinctly chewy. A good way to use it is to dry it and process it into a powder that can be used as a condiment.

Hen of the Woods

At first glance this green-grey fungus, which parasitizes deciduous trees (usually oak), looks less than appealing. It also can blend in with the base of a tree's trunk, making it easy to miss. In fact, this large bracket fungus is well worth searching out, although it is often compared unfavourably with its close relative, the Chicken of the Woods (page 116). This has soft, tender flesh, while the Hen is slightly stronger in flavour. Both fungi are excellent meat substitutes in risottos and casseroles. As is the case with other bracket fungi, it should be harvested when young. It turns woody with age and the surface becomes dry and powdery. Its condition is easy to tell: if a knife slides easily through the flesh it is edible, but if you have to saw it, it is too old to eat.

FACT FILE

SCIENTIFIC NAME
Grifola frondosa

CAP Tightly packed, wrinkled 'leaves' up to 40cm across. Green, brown and yellow.

FLESH Firm and succulent when young, toughening when older.

SPORES White, cream or yellow.

SEASON Summer and autumn.

Key identifiers

Forms a grey-green-brown wrinkled mass of 'leaves'.

Grows on deciduous trees, usually oak.

Normally found where the trunk meets the ground, but sometimes on lateral roots.

Up to 40cm across.

Taste

Excellent. Stronger tasting than the Chicken of the Woods, but sharing the same meaty texture. Toughens with age, so it is not suitable for drying. Freezes relatively well.

Conifer woodland

MOST EARLY FIELD GUIDES SUGGEST THAT BROADLEAVED WOODLAND IS THE RICHEST FUNGUS HABITAT. THIS IS BECAUSE ENGLISH-SPEAKING CULTURES ARE GENERALLY VERY WEAK ON MUSHROOM LORE, AND AS A CONSEQUENCE EARLY BOOKS ABOUT FUNGI WERE WRITTEN BY AUTHORS WHO TURNED TO FRENCH AND ITALIAN EXPERTS FOR ADVICE. BECAUSE OAK AND BEECH WOODLANDS PREDOMINATE IN BOTH COUNTRIES, NOT SURPRISINGLY THESE AUTHORS WERE STEERED TOWARDS BROADLEAVED WOODLAND.

While it is certainly true that there is a greater range of edible fungi associated with deciduous trees, it is by no means the case that conifer plantations are fungal deserts. Mature pine trees readily form symbiotic relationships with several of the most delicious species. In autumn, commercial pine plantations along Europe's western fringe, for example, are often full of Porcini, Bay Boletes and Wood Hedgehogs. As a rough rule of thumb, the most promising conifer in terms of its association with fungi is the Scots Pine, but Larch, Norway Spruce and even that suburban curse, the Leylandii, can play host to many edible fungi.

What you can find, and where

On the trees

There are not many species that grow on pine, but one of the prized fungi to look for is the Cauliflower Fungus (also found on golf courses, page 92), which favours Scots Pine. Search around the bases of trees in late summer, when the young fungi are at their best.

Woodland edge

Trees that get most light grow best here, which benefits the fungi – like the Shaggy Parasol – associated with them. The richest hunting grounds are often along rides and paths.

Mossy banks

Moss is a favourite haunt of many a fungus, but if it is late summer look for the likes of the Porcini, Chanterelle or Bay Bolete during mid- to late autumn.

Forest floor

Many mushrooms, edible, inedible and poisonous, favour the acid-rich soil of coniferous woodland. While some, like the Porcini, blewits and deceivers, are equally at home in deciduous forests, others are pure pine-only species. The *Suillus* genus is particularly common here, and Larch and Pine Boletes can be found glistening among the needles, as can the distinctive Wood Hedgehog.

Porcini

The British once usually called this the Penny Bun or King Bolete, but due to the recent culinary globalization most people now know it by its Italian or French epithets (Porcini and Cep respectively). Because it is arguably slightly better known in its Italian guise across the western world, the name Porcini is used in this book. No slight is intended towards followers of cordon bleu, and Italian speakers are asked to forgive the constant use of the plural (as any purist would point out, one mushroom should be a Porcino). Whatever name is used, however, this is undoubtedly the world's most commercially important wild fungus.

Many other fungus species, such as White Truffles and Morels, are much more expensive by weight, but Porcini are harvested and exported by the tonne from forests around the northern hemisphere. This is because

FACT FILE

SCIENTIFIC NAME
Boletus edulis

OTHER NAMES Penny Bun, King Bolete, Cep, Cèpe de Bordeaux (French)

CAP Up to 30cm across. Light to dark brown, often with a white bloom when just emerging.

STEM Up to 25cm tall. Generally bulbous, and white to cream with beige streaks.

FLESH Cream or yellow.

SPORES Green-brown.

SEASON Summer and autumn.

Conifer woodland

they are large and meaty fungi that dry extremely well. Although the fresh mushroom makes excellent eating, drying makes it truly three-dimensional. It not only preserves the autumn haul indefinitely, but also transforms what is normally a very good meaty fungus into a distinctive

rich, nutty taste sensation that can perk up a wealth of lesser ingredients. As a result, Porcini are in great demand with gastronomes – so much so that many developing countries harness the natural wealth of the forests and export them in huge quantities to richer countries on the other side of the globe. Indeed, although most of the little packages now on sale in delicatessens and supermarkets suggest that the fungi they contain originate in Italy or France, in fact they were probably grown in western China or the former Soviet Bloc. This seems

ridiculous to amateur mushroom hunters, for despite its well-deserved culinary reputation this is far from a rare jewel. Unlike the subterranean truffles or fantastically camouflaged Morel, Porcini are common in temperate forests around the globe, and comparatively conspicuous.

The Porcini's superb eating qualities and the ease of identification make it the perfect beginner's mushroom. Its spongy gills and brown cap, and the thick beige and cream stem, can only really be mistaken for the almost equally edible Bay and Orange Birch Boletes (pages 50 and 102), or for the decidedly inferior, but also edible Brown Birch Bolete (page 84). Unlike the flesh of the Bay and Orange Birch Boletes, however, that of the Porcini is always white and does not discolour. The cap can measure up to 30cm across, and individual specimens may weigh 2kg. Unfortunately, older examples usually fall prey to tiny insect larvae that burrow into the base of the stem and tunnel up into the cap. Lightly infested mushrooms can still be dried. The larvae shrivel up and fall out as a mushroom dries – and it is in any case later soaked in boiling water and strained.

Key identifiers

Domed rusty-brown cap.

Thick, usually bulbous or tapering stem.

Stem white or cream, and often streaked with beige.

Pores very small at first, growing larger.

Sponge white at first, then turning yellow, green and dark brown.

Quick tips

Look for it on mossy banks situated along woodland edges.

Grows from summer to autumn.

Thick, generally bulbous, creamy-beige stem.

Often found near the more visible Fly Agaric (page 12).

Taste

Excellent. Probably the most commercially important wild fungus. Good fresh, but drying intensifies the flavour.

The lookalike

Fortunately, the Porcini is difficult to mistake. It is closest in appearance to the Bay, Orange Birch and Brown Birch Boletes, all of which are edible. There are one or two spongy-gilled poisonous mushrooms, Satan's Bolete (*B. satanus*) and *B. satinoides*, but both of these species are extremely rare. They also have white caps and very red pores, so are quite different from the Porcini.

There is one suspect bolete that is relatively common – the Purple-staining Bolete (*B. erythropus*), which is found in deciduous and coniferous woodland in northern Europe and North America, often in the same places as the Porcini. However, apart from having a bulbous stem and spongy gills, it bears very little resemblance to a Porcini. A large and solid mushroom, it has a cap that grows to about 20cm across. It has a reddish sponge, and when a fresh specimen is bruised, broken or cut the yellow flesh immediately turns indigo, then black.

Bay Bolete

This common bolete grows from late summer to the first frost, usually emerging slightly ahead of its bigger relative, the Porcini (page 46). It is slightly smaller, with a cap rarely exceeding 15cm, but every bit as good to eat, not least because it is less prone to insect attack.

The Bay Bolete has a thinner, darker stem than the Porcini, with spongy gills that vary from cream to yellow. When pushed lightly with a finger the sponge bruises blue-green, slowly darkening to near black. As a result, the fungus is easy to distinguish from similar species such as the Porcini,

and Brown and Orange Birch Boletes (pages 84 and 102).

The blue tint of the Bay Bolete's flesh can make it appear unappetizing raw, but this colouration disappears

FACT FILE

SCIENTIFIC NAME
Boletus badius

OTHER NAME Cèpe des châtaigniers (French)

CAP Up to 16cm across. Rusty-brown, white or yellow sponge bruising blue.

STEM Up to 10cm tall. Fairly even in width and a uniform brown.

FLESH Cream or yellow, oxidizing to dark grey.

SPORES Green-brown.

SEASON Summer and autumn.

Key identifiers

Domed rusty-brown cap.

Sponge turns blue when it is pressed lightly with a thumb.

Pores small and tightly packed.

Always grows in proximity to trees.

Favours mossy banks.

Fairly common.

Taste

Excellent. Every bit as good as the Porcini. Very good fresh. The Italians are particularly fond of it bottled in oil as an antipasti, but drying it intensifies its flavour.

when the fungus is cooked. It can be used in any recipe that calls for Porcini, and is also a useful addition to wild fungus mixes, beefing up the taste of other species with its superior flavour.

Wood Hedgehog

The Wood Hedgehog is well worth finding, for it can grow in large numbers. All the same, this low-growing, irregularly shaped, pale-capped fungus can be very difficult to spot, particularly when the caps are obscured by tussocky grass, leaf mould or undergrowth. Normally the fruiting bodies are fairly small and – despite their colour – easily overlooked. Occasionally they swell significantly, reaching 20cm across, when they can reveal the mycelium's characteristic 'spider's web' subterranean structure, with the fruiting bodies emerging in rough circles through the leaf mould. The unfailing identifying trait is

FACT FILE

SCIENTIFIC NAME
Hydnum repandum

OTHER NAMES Hedgehog Fungus, Pied de mouton (French)

CAP Up to 20cm across. White or cream, sometimes mottled with grey spots. Spines underneath instead of gills.

STEM Very short and solid.

FLESH White and firm.

SPORES White, cream or yellow.

SEASON Summer and autumn.

evident when the fungus is overturned. Rather than conventional gills it has tiny spines. These provide it with its common English name, but the French *pied de mouton* (sheep's foot) seems more accurate, for they closely resemble the wet wool on a sheep's lower leg.

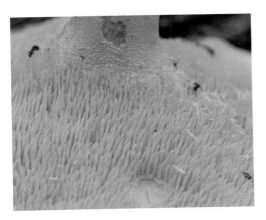

Key identifiers

Convex at first, later inverting to a rough funnel shape.

Very small at first, but can grow to up to 20cm across.

Grows in deciduous and conifer woodland.

Fairly common, but locally abundant.

Often grows in large partial rings.

Taste

Excellent. Its creamy, firm flesh is delicious. The taste is vaguely reminiscent of that of the Chanterelle (page 22), to which it is distantly related. it is. however, arguably superior, with a crunchy texture that combines particularly well with cheese or cream on fresh pasta. Delicious fresh, but preserves well in butter or flash fried and frozen.

Shaggy Parasol

This is the woodland version of its close relative, the Parasol (page 82). It is shorter and more thickset, getting its name from the rough scales that form on the cap. It emerges from the soil as a tight dark sphere topping a stem that is significantly thicker and shorter than that of the true Parasol. The ball then rapidly opens out to form a flat cap some 10–15cm off the ground. The white gills and flesh have a tendency to turn reddish-brown with age or bruising. As in the case of its relative, the stem is tough and fibrous, so it should be discarded. The cap, on the other hand, tastes superb, having a distinctly nutty flavour. Because of this, the Shaggy Parasol is particularly useful for improving the quality of a fresh mushroom mixture.

Due no doubt to their strong flavour, Shaggy Parasols can occasionally cause mild indigestion, so treat them with a little caution

FACT FILE

SCIENTIFIC NAME
Chlorophyllum rhacodes

CAP Up to 15cm across. Scaly cream-beige cap surface.

STEM Up to 15cm tall. Appears relatively thick and hollow.

FLESH White.

SPORES White, cream or yellow.

SEASON Summer and autumn.

when first sampling them. Most people, however, find them absolutely delicious, and they are definitely worth adding to the basket.

Key identifiers

Characteristic umbrella shape.

Grows under conifers (Leylandii are particular favourites).

Very scaly cap surface.

Taste

Excellent. Nutty, slightly sweet flesh. Some individuals find it indigestible, so it should be eaten in moderation on the first occasion. It can be dried, but is best eaten fresh.

Yellow Swamp & Common Yellow Russulas

These two yellow russula species are superficially difficult to tell apart, but they are equally edible and each is common and prolific, growing under birch and pine respectively. They are also useful 'indicator' species, because they grow in the same habitats though slightly earlier than other fine edible species like the Porcini (page 46). Their colour makes them easy to spot, and a productive walk in late summer can yield exciting hints of things to come.

Many russulas are difficult to identify with total certainty without a mycology degree and the use of a microscope to inspect the spores. Fortunately, these two particular species are both common, and their bright yellow colour is distinctive. In contrast, the two toxic russulas,

the Sickener (*R. emetica*), shown left, and Beechwood Sickener (*R. nobilis*), both have red caps. There are scores of other drab russulas, some of which are edible, but even more are extremely bitter and the accidental inclusion of even a single specimen can spoil an entire dish. Luckily, all fungi of the *Russula* genus are safe to test for edibility by nibbling a tiny portion of the cap for taste.

FACT FILE

SCIENTIFIC NAMES
Russula claroflava & *R. ochroleuca*

CAP Up to 10cm across. Yellow.

STEM Up to 6cm tall. White or cream, with an even diameter throughout.

GILLS White or cream, curling up into the cap without touching the stem. Break easily when brushed lightly with a finger.

FLESH White, sometimes pinkish after cutting.

SPORES White, cream or yellow.

SEASON Late summer and autumn.

Key identifiers

Yellow cap with a lightly furrowed edge.

Grows in large numbers.

White gills break easily when brushed with a finger.

Grows in damp woods.

Very common.

Taste

Moderate to good, particularly when mixed with other species to give a range of tastes, textures and colours. Best preserved by cooking and freezing.

Pine Bolete

The Pine Bolete bears a superficial resemblance to the boletes, although it is smaller than most Porcini (page 46). Like its close relative, the Larch Bolete (page 60), its has a cap that is 5–10cm across, but in both species the spongy gills have larger tubes that are less densely packed than those of a true bolete. The slightest hint of moisture turns the cap into a slimy miniature skating rink. This gooey covering is unpalatable, so most guides recommend peeling the fungus. It remains unexciting even after peeling, however, so it is best used in mixed mushroom dishes – preferably dried – and to bulk out casseroles and soups.

Key identifiers

Domed dark brown cap that flattens out with age.

Cream to yellow 'sponge' instead of gills.

Spongy pores more open than those of true boletes.

Grows beneath pines and spruce.

Very common.

Taste

Good, but a bit watery. The slimy cap surface can be indigestible, so peel the mushrooms before cooking or preserving. Probably best used after drying, which intensifies the flavour.

Larch Bolete

This yellow mushroom stands up to 12cm tall, but generally grows fairly close to the ground and is often almost obscured by grass. The cap is usually 5–12cm across and, as in the case of its close relative, the Pine Bolete (page 58), the pores in the spongy gills are larger and less densely packed than those of the true boletes.

The surface of this mushroom's cap becomes extremely slimy when even remotely wet, and this covering is generally regarded as too indigestible to eat. Most sources thus recommend peeling the mushroom. The underlying flesh is perfectly acceptable in flavour (if not very exciting).

As their scientific names denote, the Larch and Pine Boletes do not belong in the *Boletus* genus, although they are members of the same family, the Boletaceae. Although the Larch Bolete is not in the same league as the Porcini (page 46), it is still useful. It begins to emerge a fortnight or so before more exciting species, and is also relatively visible.

Conifer woodland

Key identifiers

Domed yellow cap that flattens out with age.

Cream to yellow 'sponge' instead of gills.

Sponge pores more open than in *Boletus* fungi.

Always grows underneath Larch.

Very common.

Taste

Good, but a bit watery. The slimy cap surface is indigestible, so peel the fungus before cooking or preserving it. Works very well fried and served with crispy lardons of bacon, but is probably best dried to intensify its flavour.

Pasture

THERE ARE PLENTY OF EDIBLE MUSHROOMS THAT GROW IN GRASS, WELL AWAY FROM THE NEAREST TREE, BUT FINDING THEM IS NOW OFTEN DIFFICULT. MOST PASTURELAND MYCELIA ARE RELATIVELY DELICATE – ALTHOUGH THOSE OF SOME FUNGI, SUCH AS ST GEORGE'S MUSHROOM, ARE KNOWN TO DATE BACK TO MORE THAN 500 YEARS, THEY STILL DEPEND ON COMPLEX INTER-RELATIONSHIPS WITH NATIVE GRASSES. THESE ARE THREATENED BY OUR INCREASINGLY EFFICIENT FARMING METHODS.

Many ancient fields have been ploughed up. Those that remain as grass are often reseeded with faster growing hybrid strains, while others are treated with herbicides and fertilizers. These factors are anathema for most pastureland species. As a result waxcaps, Field Mushrooms and Horse Mushrooms are increasingly rare, and to find them in any numbers hunters need to acquire fieldcraft and often some historical knowledge. Look for old commons, heaths and other public land that may not have been ploughed by a landowner looking for profit. Poor soils in mountains or near the sea can be fertile hunting grounds.

Distinctive islands of dark green Common Nettles can pepper farmland. They often mark the site of a long-abandoned haystack or midden, and the protection of the prickly foliage and nutrient-rich soil provides the perfect habitat for Giant Puffballs.

What you can find, and where

Stinging nettles
Giant Puffballs love the shade and
protection of the barbed leaves of
the Common Nettle.

Improved pasture

Many fields are now regularly replanted with fast-growing hybrid grasses. These can still be home to numerous fungi, such as *Agaricus macrosporus*, especially when they are grazed by livestock (horses are a particular favourite).

Short-cropped grass

In autumn, damp rough pasture is the perfect habitat for Meadow Waxcaps.

Ancient pasture

The most ancient flower-rich meadows are favourite haunts of particularly long-lived fungi such as St George's Mushroom.

What you can find, and where

Field Mushroom

The Field Mushroom has declined sharply in recent times due to the intensification of agriculture, as well as the loss of grassland and grazing livestock (particularly horses). Nonetheless, this wild ancestor of the cultivated mushroom is still common.

As in the domesticated version, its gills begin pink. They gradually darken as the cap matures, and end up brown or even black. Because the Field Mushroom so closely resembles its cultivated cousin, it can instantly be identified by even the most confirmed city dweller. As a result, it is the only mushroom that most people will pick and therefore apparently needs very little by way of a description. However,

as previously mentioned (page 11), the general familiarity of this mushroom can lead to mistakes in identification. A close relative of the Field Mushroom,

FACT FILE

SCIENTIFIC NAME
Agaricus campestris

OTHER NAME Pink Bottom

CAP Up to 10cm across. White to beige with pink gills that age to dark brown or black.

STEM Rarely more than 3–5cm tall. Up to 1cm thick.

FLESH Firm and creamy white.

SPORES Purple to black.

SEASON Summer to autumn.

the Yellow Stainer (*A. xanthodermus*) looks very similar, but this species provokes a violent allergic reaction in about half of the people who eat it.

Although never fatal, the symptoms generally involve vomiting and diarrhoea for up to 24 hours (see also page 69).

Key identifiers

Young buttons have
pink gills.

As the cap opens and
flattens, the gills
turn brown.

Prefers unimproved
grassland, particularly
that grazed by livestock.

Smells 'mushroomy'.

Make sure it does not
bruise yellow or smell
of carbolic.

Quick tips

Closely resembles a
cultivated mushroom.

Often clusters near
old horse and cattle
droppings.

Grows from summer
to autumn.

Taste

Better than any
cultivated mushroom,
but not in the premier
league. It can be dried
or salted to produce
a mushroom sauce
or flavouring.

The lookalike

The Yellow Stainer (*A. xanthodermus*) is similar in shape to the Field
Mushroom and closely related to it, but it provokes violent stomach
upsets in many people. Fortunately, the two species are easy to tell

apart because the former lives up to
its name by bruising bright yellow.
The sure rule of thumb is to avoid
any *Agaricus* whose stem or cap
turns yellow when cut or bruised.
Another test is smell – the Yellow
Stainer smells unpleasant (some
source books compare its odour to
that of carbolic), while the Field
Mushroom smells like a normal
mushroom, possibly with a hint
of aniseed.

Agaricus macrosporus

Unlike its well-known relatives, the Field and Horse Mushrooms (for which it is often mistaken), this common mushroom has no English name. In practice all three species are very similar in appearance and flavour. That said, *A. macrosporus* is usually larger than the other two species and as it ages, its cap frequently cracks.

Due to the cap's large size (up to 25cm across), it can be visible for hundreds of metres, particularly when it is growing in its usual clusters of rough rings. In common with the better known *Agaricus* species, young specimens have pink gills that darken to near black in mature examples. Its flesh sometimes turns red where it is damaged. Its cap can turn a faint yellow when bruised, leading to potential confusion with the unpleasant Yellow Stainer (page 69). This species is much more vivid in colour when bruised, however, and also has an aroma of carbolic, while *A. macrosporus* has a distinct whiff of almonds or possibly aniseed.

FACT FILE

SCIENTIFIC NAME
Agaricus macrosporus

CAP Up to 25cm across. Like a large Field Mushroom.

STEM White, up to 5cm thick.

FLESH Firm and creamy white, sometimes turning red where it is damaged.

SPORES Purple to black.

SEASON Summer to autumn.

Key identifiers

Young buttons have pink gills.

As the cap opens and flattens, the gills turn brown-black.

Caps can be up to 25cm across.

Surface of older caps often cracks.

Favours unimproved grassland, particularly that grazed by livestock.

Smells mildly of almonds when young; later faintly reminiscent of ammonia.

Taste

Good, but not in the premier league. Very useful for mixing with other, stronger tasting mushrooms. It can be dried or salted to produce a seasoning powder or sauce.

Meadow Waxcap

This orange-brown mushroom grows in unimproved pasture from early to mid-autumn. Unfortunately, as is the case with so many grassland species, it struggles with artificial fertilizers and herbicides, as well as ploughing and reseeding with fast-growing grass hybrids. It is still relatively common, but is most usually found in poorer upland areas where it tends to emerge following rain, often growing in rough rings. Its cap lives up to its name, having a waxy texture, particularly when damp. Its creamy gills run down the stem, and it is more substantial and less garishly coloured than many other waxcaps, such as the equally edible Scarlet Waxcap.

FACT FILE

SCIENTIFIC NAME
Hygrocybe pratensis

OTHER NAME Buffcap

CAP SIZE AND COLOUR Up to 8cm across. Surface orange-brown, fading with age. Gills creamy, curling down the stem.

STEM Up to 5cm tall. Cream.

FLESH Firm.

SPORES White to cream.

SEASON Autumn.

Key identifiers

Orange to buff cap.

Pale gills curling down thick creamy stem.

Tends to emerge after damp periods.

Favours unimproved grassland.

Taste

Good texture and flavour. These make it welcome in the kitchen, particularly as part of a mixed mushroom dish, where its thick flesh complements more fragile species. It is probably best eaten fresh, or else cooked and frozen in finished dishes.

St George's Mushroom

Although this fungus is shaped roughly like a cultivated mushroom, its gills are pale cream and it has a strong mealy smell. There are other pale mushrooms that are potentially dangerous, but these grow later in the season, so positive identification is easy. One point to note is that the species used to be classified as a member of the *Tricholoma* genus, so it appears in older guides as *T. gambosa*.

The species' common English name stems from its traditional emergence on St George's Day (23 April). In reality it tends to be a few days late, and continues to crop throughout May. On the other hand, its Italian name is *marzolino* ('the March one'), while in Germany it is known as *maipilz* because it emerges in May.

This is one of the first and most delicious of the spring mushrooms. It grows in rough rings that start very

FACT FILE

SCIENTIFIC NAME
Calocybe gambosa

OTHER NAME Mousseron vrai
(French)

CAP Up to 12cm across. White or
beige, darkening with age and
sometimes cracking.

STEM Up to 8cm tall. Solid, cream
or white.

FLESH Creamy.

SPORES White, cream or pale yellow.

SEASON Spring.

small with the parent spores and slowly enlarge over time, the diameter of a ring giving an indication of the age of the fungus. Some rings on the South Downs in England are thought to date back to at least the Middle Ages.

Key identifiers

All white (gills included).

Grows in rough rings in unimproved pasture.

Mealy aroma.

Emerges in early to mid-spring before most other pastoral species.

Most commonly grows on chalky soils.

Taste

Excellent. A great early-season mushroom that perfectly complements white meat and fish and is particularly highly prized in Italy. It can be dried, but is probably best flash fried and frozen.

Giant Puffball

Even though the Giant Puffball is widely distributed and locally common, due to its habit of growing among stinging camouflage many people have never seen one. A way to find it is to look for old middens and rotten haystacks covered with nettles, then wade in with a walking stick to part the foliage. Once found it is unmistakable: at up to 80cm in diameter and weighing several kilos, it can be nothing else.

When young the puffball cuts open to reveal firm white flesh. Most sources usually recommend slicing and frying it in high-quality bacon fat, butter or olive oil. The taste is mild and the texture is not unlike that of marshmallows, so it is probably best to combine it with other ingredients. It makes a memorable dish when baked and stuffed with a mixture of nuts, tomatoes, garlic and herbs, before being stuffed back into its leathery outer skin. Alternatively and perhaps best of all, it can be used as a pasta substitute in a lasagne.

FACT FILE

SCIENTIFIC NAME
Calvatia gigantea

APPEARANCE An unmistakable large white sphere.

SIZE Up to 80cm in diameter.

FLESH Creamy white and firm when edible, later turning into an inedible black powder.

SPORES Purple to black.

SEASON Summer to autumn.

Key identifiers

Grows on rich soil, particularly in old middens.

Very often found in nettle patches.

Uncommon, although locally abundant.

Often fruits in hot weather after rain.

Taste

Moderately good, but probably highly rated more for its sheer size than its quality. It does not preserve well, so is best eaten fresh.

Golf courses

AT FIRST GLANCE THESE MAN-MADE HABITATS WOULD SEEM STRANGE PLACES TO FIND FUNGI, BUT IN CREATING MIXTURES OF ROUGHS AND FAIRWAYS, GOLF-COURSE DESIGNERS HAVE INADVERTENTLY PROVIDED A GOOD MIX OF HABITATS IN SMALL AREAS. MANY GOLF COURSES ARE BUILT ON THE SANDY ALKALINE SOILS OF FORMER HEATHS OR DUNES. ROUGHS PROVIDE THE RICHEST PICKINGS, PARTICULARLY WHEN THEY ARE EXTENSIVELY PLANTED WITH SILVER BIRCH. CHANTERELLES (PAGE 22), FOR EXAMPLE, ARE COMMON HERE, ALONG WITH BROWN AND ORANGE BIRCH BOLETES (PAGES 84 AND 102).

Scots Pine is slower growing than birch, but only just, and is popular on golf courses because as one of the most attractive conifers it provides visual variety and year-round foliage. More importantly for golf players, it has no low-growing side branches to get in the way of play. Much more significant for the mushroom hunter, however, is that it is closely linked to two or three excellent fungus species. It is, for example, one of the prime hosts of the Cauliflower Fungus. Look, too, among the needles for the Yellow Swamp Russula (page 56).

Naturally, a great advantage of a golf course is that a leisurely round provides the perfect opportunity to closely scour a large area of varied habitats for fungi (particularly for less-skilled players, who spend more than their share of time in the roughs).

What you can find, and where

Fairways

Although regular mowing and the use of fertilizers often inhibits traditional pastureland species, fast-growing woodland fungi such as Saffron Milkcaps frequently snake out into the open from their host trees.

Trees

Scots Pines are very common on many courses, and they are the perfect host for the delicious Cauliflower Fungus and several edible russulas.

Links

The well-drained, sandy, chalky soil of a golf course can provide the perfect conditions for Field Blewits.

Roughs

Fast-growing birch trees are a favourite with golf-course designers – fortunately these trees have a rich relationship with many edible fungi, such as the Brown Birch Bolete.

What you can find, and where

Parasol

The Parasol is a perfect beginner's mushroom. Not only is it one of the most immediately identifiable fungi, but it is also very visible, standing out high above the surrounding grass. Better still, when large it has no dangerous lookalikes – although some small (2–5cm tall) woodland relatives can cause gastric upsets so are best avoided.

The young fungus emerges like a drumstick – a rounded head on a tall stem. As it grows, the 'ball' unfurls until it resembles a Victorian lady's frilly umbrella, standing up to 30cm tall with the cap up to 25cm across (the unfurling continues after picking, in the basket). This leaves a little 'ruff' around the stem where the cap was once attached, although this usually falls off by the time the cap is fully extended. The stem is fibrous and woody, so is best discarded, while old caps can suffer from insect attack.

FACT FILE

SCIENTIFIC NAME
Macrolepiota procera

CAP Up to 25cm across. A mixture of cream, beige and brown, with a flaky texture.

STEM Up to 30cm tall. Thin and fibrous, often with a loose 'ruff' near the cap.

FLESH Delicate, and prone to insect attack when old.

SPORES White, cream or yellow.

SEASON Summer and autumn.

Key identifiers

Unmistakable umbrella shape when mature.

Large – up to 30cm tall and 25cm across.

Occurs in rough pasture and woodland edges.

Uncommon, although locally abundant.

Often fruits for several years in one place before disappearing.

Taste

Excellent. Nutty and slightly sweet flesh. It is arguably at its best for breakfast following an early morning walk, fried quickly in butter and served on toast with a dash of lemon and black pepper. It can be dried, but is better eaten fresh.

Brown Birch Bolete

This **brown-capped bolete** generally grows on poor ground, but always in close proximity to birch, so golf courses, railway lines, canals and waste ground are promising prospects for finding it. It can grow to up to 20cm tall and is the species most easily mistaken for a Porcini (page 46). From afar – and particularly to a beginner – it closely resembles this fungus, causing the heart to race only for hopes to be dashed when it is upturned, for it has a thinner stem than its superior lookalike, and this is always marked with flecks of black. Unlike its close relative, the Orange Birch Bolete (page 102), its flavour is insipid and in good years it is not worth collecting. It does, however, come into its own in poor years for fungi. It is common, growing wherever there are plenty of birch trees, and when there is not much else around it is certainly worth gathering.

FACT FILE

SCIENTIFIC NAME
Leccinum scabrum

OTHER NAME Bolet rude (France)

CAP Up to 15cm across. Brown, with a white or yellow sponge, gradually darkening to brown or near black.

STEM Up to 10cm tall. White or cream, and flecked with tiny black scales.

FLESH White. Sometimes pinkish after cutting.

SPORES Brown.

SEASON Late summer and autumn.

Key identifiers

Domed brown cap.

Sponge instead of gills.

Thin stem covered with tiny black flecks.

Always grows near to birch.

Very common.

Taste

Moderate. Decidedly watery, and young specimens are best, particularly when dried to intensify the flavour and mixed with more strongly flavoured mushroom species.

Field Blewit

This **mushroom** is very closely related to the Wood Blewit (page 118). It has a pale cap that is at first convex, but later flattens and can even become concave. Its stem is streaked bluish-purple. The species is notable for being one of the few wild fungi that is regularly gathered and sold openly on British market stalls. It is one of the rare wild mushrooms that can be cultivated, and in France it is grown in caves located along the Loire Valley. It does seem to lose most of its superb flavour under cultivated conditions, so it is well worth looking for it in the wild. Like the Wood Blewit, the Field Blewit is relatively widespread and common. Due to its powerful flavour it can cause digestive upsets in some individuals, so it should always be cooked, and used in moderation (particularly in early experiments). It is best treated more as a flavouring than as a conventional ingredient.

FACT FILE

SCIENTIFIC NAME
Lepista saeva

OTHER NAMES Blue Leg,
Pied violet (French)

CAP Up to 10cm across. Off-white to light brown. At first convex, then flattening or even inverting slightly and acquiring wavy edges. White or slightly pink gills.

STEM Up to 10cm tall. Streaked with blue and purple. Usually slightly more bulbous at the base.

FLESH White to pinkish.

SPORES Pink.

SEASON Late autumn to winter.

Key identifiers

White to dirty
brown cap.

Grows in unimproved
pasture.

Triggered into fruiting
by the first frosts.

Stalk streaked with blue
and purple.

Often appears in
rough rings.

Fairly common.

Taste

Excellent. Perfumed and
powerful. A strongly
flavoured mushroom
that must always be
cooked. Treat it more
as a flavouring than
as a bulk ingredient,
and combine it with
other strong-tasting
ingredients such as
red meats or leeks. It
dries well.

Saffron Milkcap

The caps of this species vary in colour, usually containing a mixture of orange, brown and green. Its name comes from the light orange milky sap that exudes from the gills when they are damaged. The cap is usually pale cream to bright orange, and is marked with concentric darker bands. To the uninitiated, this mushroom's habit of bruising a rather unappetizing shade of green when damaged is off-putting, but in fact this trait provides one of the most distinctive forms of recognition – apart from the characteristic orange 'milk' that oozes from the gills.

FACT FILE

SCIENTIFIC NAME
Lactarius deliciosus

OTHER NAME Vache rouge (France)

CAP Up to 15cm across. Yellow, orange and brown, often with green-blue bruising. Gills ooze yellow-orange milk.

STEM Up to 6cm tall. Thick walls with a hollow centre. Stains carrot, then blue when cut.

FLESH Brittle and crunchy.

SPORES White, cream or yellow.

SEASON Summer and autumn.

The biggest risk of making an error in identification relates to very young specimens, which can just about be confused with the very poisonous

Woolly Milkcap (*L. torminosus*). Small specimens should be cut in half and examined closely, and any dubious examples discarded. In general,

however, the lack of fibres and distinctively coloured sap make identification of the mature Saffron Milkcap a simple matter.

Key identifiers

A very distinctive orange milk oozes from the gills of young and fresh specimens.

Milk may be absent from old or dry specimens.

Cap and stem often have some green-blue discolouration.

Grows near pines, especially Scots Pine.

Quick tips

Look for dark rings in short grass, which are visible even when no mushrooms are present.

Usually found on sandy soil.

Uncommon, although locally abundant.

Grows from late summer to autumn.

Check the rim under the cap for 'cotton wool' (discard if present).

Taste

Excellent flavour with a slightly crunchy texture that is among the best of the autumn fungi. It can be dried, although it is much better eaten fresh or frozen in finished dishes.

The lookalike

The highly poisonous Woolly Milkcap (*L. torminosus*) bears only a superficial resemblance to its edible relative and lives up to its name, having a cotton wool-like web around the inside of the cap

rim. Its milk is also white rather than yellow, so mistakes in identification are easy to avoid. The biggest risk of confusion between the two species lies with young specimens of the Saffron Milkcap – always cut these in half and examine them closely.

Cauliflower Fungus

The Cauliflower Fungus is one of the easiest fungi to recognize with total certainty, although it looks much more like a marine sponge than its vegetable namesake. It attacks mature conifers, feeding off a tree's resinous sap and slowly killing the host in the process (as a result it is hated by foresters). Harvesting has no impact on the long-term prognosis for the tree.

The Cauliflower Fungus comes up year after year, so if you find one make a note of its location – it will almost certainly fruit in the near vicinity the following season. Large specimens can reach 50cm across and weigh more than 2kg. The fungus lives up to the second part of its scientific name with its wonderful crunchy texture, and is good both raw and cooked. Its main drawback is that pine needles and insects readily collect in its network of cavities, so it requires careful brushing before cooking (as in the case of all mushrooms, avoid washing, which dilutes the flavour).

FACT FILE

SCIENTIFIC NAME
Sparassis crispa

OTHER NAMES Wood Cauliflower, Crépu (French)

CAP Up to 50cm in diameter. Off-white and formless.

STEM Even brown, with the remains of a ring near the top.

FLESH Cream, turning brown with age.

SPORES White, cream or yellow.

SEASON Summer and autumn.

Key identifiers

Always grows at the bases of or on the lateral roots of conifers, usually Scots Pine.

Resembles a marine sponge in appearance.

Fruits at the same spot year after year.

Parasite that slowly kills its host.

Taste

Excellent taste and even better texture. Dries well, but is superb when fresh and keeps well in a refrigerator, so it is perhaps best eaten fresh over a period of several days. Try frying it in batter to create a tempura-style nibble.

Brownfield sites

THE TERM 'BROWNFIELD SITES' REFERS TO LAND THAT WAS ONCE
DEVELOPED (FOR EXAMPLE FOR INDUSTRY, WASTE DISPOSAL OR
TRANSPORT), BUT WHICH HAS NOW BEEN ABANDONED. UNLIKE THE
OBVIOUSLY RICH CONVENTIONAL FUNGI HABITATS OF WOODS AND
FIELDS, THESE WASTELANDS CAN FEEL BLEAK AND DESOLATE, YET
IN REALITY THE DEPLETED SOILS OFTEN PROVE RICH IN FUNGI.

Abandoned railway lines are one particularly fruitful area. In the days before the car, our ancestors built millions of kilometres of train tracks across the northern hemisphere. Over the past half century, a large proportion have been dismantled and left to encroaching scrub and slow decay. The invasive birch and willows that rapidly take over cuttings and embankments create a prime habitat for many woodland species. Likewise, as old factories and mills slowly decay and nature begins to reclaim the land, a handful of opportunistic fungi are among the first to move in.

In Europe, perhaps the most extreme examples of land that was once developed are the urban bombsites of the Second World War. The devastated ruins of Europe's great cities were covered in ash-, lime- and cement-enriched waste, creating the perfect conditions for Morels. Even today, seekers of this delicious lover of scorched earth conditions flock to the sites of forest fires in search of the Morel's elusive presence.

What you can find, and where

Sites of fires

When woods are felled foresters often burn off the brush, which creates the perfect conditions for ash-loving species such as Morels.

Industrial sites

Shaggy Inkcaps seem to love the compacted ground on waste ground in the vicinity of abandoned factories, and can even force their way through tarmac and old concrete.

Paths

Some mushrooms revel in compacted ground – Deceivers are particularly common along rough paths and tracks through waste ground.

Railway embankments

Many fungi, like the Orange Birch Bolete, thrive on steep, well-drained wooded slopes, and these are plentiful along abandoned railway lines.

Morel

This is a **deceptively** well-camouflaged mushroom. It has a strangely shaped, deeply pitted, yellow-brown to near-black cap. This grows on a thick white stem that emerges from sandy soil beneath trees or even amid short-cropped grass. The Morel is usually only 5–10cm tall, although bigger specimens up to 20cm in height can be found. As it ages, the cap tends to fade and becomes even more deeply pitted, allowing insects and woodlice to take shelter. These also like to hide in the hollow stem.

Great care should be taken not to confuse the Morel with the poisonous False Morel (*Gyromitra esculenta*),

which has a multi-chambered stem (page 101). It can be eaten when cooked, but is very poisonous when raw and there is evidence that even when cooked the toxins can be cumulative, so it should be avoided altogether. Even the true Morel can be indigestible raw, so should always be

cooked. The flavour is superb, however, combining very well with white meats such as chicken. Being hollow, the fungus is excellent stuffed, and it can be dried and powdered for use as a flavouring. Its timing is also welcome, for its arrival in spring heralds the start of the new mushroom season.

Brownfield sites

Key identifiers

Well camouflaged.

Favours alkaline soils.

Has a preference for scorched areas, for example the sites of bonfires, waste ground and the aftermaths of forest fires.

Cap very distinctive, but can be confused with the False Morel.

Quick tips

Look for pitted beige, grey or black cones on short white stems growing through needles, leaf mould or bark mulch on chalky soil.

Grows in early to mid-spring.

Taste

One of the world's greatest edible fungi, with a strong aromatic flavour. It should always be cooked, and it is a good idea to halve each specimen to ensure that it is free from insects. Check also that it is not a False Morel (see below). The Morel dries well.

The lookalike

The False Morel (*Gyromitra esculenta*) can look similar to its edible counterpart, but when raw it is deadly poisonous. It is illegal to sell it in many countries, but in others it can be sold as edible with a warning. Research suggests that even after cooking it can cause damage if eaten often, so it is best avoided. Fortunately, its

resemblance to the Morel is superficial. The False Morel's surface looks 'folded', rather like that of a brain; the pits on the true Morel's surface are sharply ridged. When sliced in half, the False Morel's stem and cap contain several thick-walled chambers, while the Morel has thinner walls and just one large cavity.

Orange Birch Bolete

This mushroom emerges slightly earlier than some of the other spongy-gilled autumn fungi, frequently appearing in high summer. It can be relatively large, standing up to 20cm tall. As its common name suggests, its domed cap has a distinctly orange hue. The spongy white gills slowly darken with age, and the white stem is always marked with a black lattice – almost as if a passing car has sprayed it with dirty water.

The Orange Birch Bolete can be confused with the closely related Brown Birch Bolete (page 84), not least because both fungi grow in

exactly the same habitats and often side by side. The brown version is also edible, but far less good to eat, with a thin, watery texture and flavour. Orange Birch Boletes, however, make excellent eating: they are just as good

FACT FILE

SCIENTIFIC NAME
Leccinum versipelle

OTHER NAME Bolete changeant (French)

CAP Up to 20cm across. Orange to brown.

STEM Up to 20cm tall. Fairly even in width, but flecked with brown and blue-black stains when cut or bruised.

FLESH White, oxidizing to dark grey.

SPORES Brown.

SEASON Summer and autumn.

as Porcini and, importantly, less
prone to insect attack. Apart from
the differences in cap colour between
the two bolete species, the Orange's
flesh slowly turns first blue, then
black when cut or bruised.

Key identifiers

Dome-shaped orange-brown cap.

Tall, relatively thin white stem, flecked with black.

Slowly oxidizes to blue-black when damaged.

Always grows in close proximity to birch.

Common.

Taste

Excellent. Every bit as good as the Porcini. Good fresh; try studding the caps with garlic, brushing them with oil and grilling them. Their flavour does, however, improve with drying.

Shaggy Inkcap

To find Shaggy Inkcaps, look out for troupes of thin white spikes poking up like miniature rockets through grass and gravel; these can be very visible on roadside verges. The fungus is surprisingly powerful and can force its way through tarmac. It grows quickly, and within a day or two the long white spikes open out to produce a flaking white cap, from which it derives one of its alternate common names of Lawyer's Wig.

After harvesting the white flesh and pink gills rapidly turn black and begin to dissolve into a thick ink. Medieval monks used the ink to illustrate manuscripts, and you can still entertain children by leaving a few caps in a glass overnight and drawing mushroom pictures with the resulting liquid. Because the fungus continues to ripen rapidly after picking, you should hurry home with your haul and cook it immediately, discarding the fibrous stem. The only slight danger of mistaken identity is

FACT FILE

SCIENTIFIC NAME
Coprinus comatus

OTHER NAMES Lawyer's Wig, Grey Shaggy Mane, Coprin chevalu (French)

CAP Up to 12cm across. Flaky surfaced, torpedo-shaped white cap that slowly curls up from the lower edge.

STEM Up to 30cm tall. White and fibrous.

FLESH White, dissolving into black ink.

SPORES Black.

SEASON Summer and autumn.

with the Common Inkcap (*Coprinopsis atramentaria*). This has a much smoother cap, which is usually slightly ridged and distinctly grey. It is just as edible unless it is consumed with alcohol, when it produces a non-fatal although extremely unpleasant reaction.

Key identifiers

Flaky white caps are unmistakable.

Often grows in extensive troupes.

Cap shortens, curls up at the edges and begins to melt into black ink with age.

Avoid confusion with the closely related Common Inkcap.

Taste

Excellent. Very good flavour, but the texture can be too slimy for some, so avoid problems by liquidizing the fungus into soups and casseroles. Begins to turn to ink very quickly, so eat it immediately after harvesting it. Preserve it by freezing it in finished dishes.

The Deceiver

Beginners can be forgiven for assuming from the common name that this denotes a suspect mushroom, but this common woodland fungus gets its name from its very variable appearance. It generally emerges as a small domed cap ranging in shade from almost orange to tawny-pink, and when old or dry it can fade to near white. The cap often slowly enlarges and involutes to create a rough goblet up to 10cm across.

Due to the huge variety of shapes and forms this fungus can take, it can be difficult for beginners to identify it with certainty, but help comes in the form of its sociability. It tends to emerge in huge numbers from the straggling subterranean mycelium. This trait and its variability are very helpful to the mushroom hunter, pointing to just one species – it is particularly apparent where it forces its way through the densely packed soil along forest paths and tracks.

FACT FILE

SCIENTIFIC NAME
Laccaria laccata

OTHER NAME Clitocybe laqué (French)

CAP Up to 10cm across. Extremely variable: brick-red, orange and brown, to pinkish-white.

STEM Up to 10cm tall. Thin and uniform.

FLESH Orange, fading after picking.

SPORES White, cream or yellow.

SEASON Summer and autumn.

Key identifiers

Very variable in colour and shape.

Grows in extensive troupes, often along woodland rides.

When present in numbers, the varied shapes make it easy to identify.

Gills have a regular long-short-long pattern.

Very common.

Taste

Excellent, although sometimes played down by authors of guidebooks worried by its extremely variable appearance. It is wonderful fresh, but dries well too.

Jew's Ear

This fungus gets its most common name from its supposed resemblance to a human ear and because, according to folklore, Judas hanged himself on an elder. This must be a myth (elders do not grow in Palestine and are too fragile to make a credible gallows), but the species is almost always found on this tree.

The flesh of this fungus is rubbery and chewy, and perhaps because of this most books on edible fungi do not rate it highly. It is, however, worth adding to the repertoire, not least because it is common on wasteland and in neglected hedgerows. It also grows virtually all year round, and its flavour is good even if its texture is slightly gelatinous. Indeed, a close relative is used extensively in Chinese

cooking, and can be found dried in many ethnic shops. The way to deal with the problem with the texture is to shred the fungus finely before cooking it. When frying it in hot oil, watch out for spitting due to the evaporation of pockets of water in the fungus.

FACT FILE

SCIENTIFIC NAME
Auricularia auricula-judae

OTHER NAME Jelly Ear

APPEARANCE Rough brown-purple hemispheres each measuring up to 10cm in diameter.

FLESH Leathery.

SPORES White, cream or yellow.

SEASON All year.

Key identifiers

Grows on trees, most commonly on elder.

Fruits following damp mild weather.

Can appear in quite considerable quantities.

Very common in scrub and in hedgerows that have been neglected.

Taste

Better than its appearance. It has a good mushroom flavour, but is leathery in texture so is best finely shredded.

City parks

THE MANICURED LAWNS AND FLOWER BEDS OF A PARK IN THE CENTRE
OF A CITY MIGHT SEEM UNLIKELY PLACES TO FIND EDIBLE FUNGI, BUT
IN HABITAT TERMS THEY RESEMBLE OUR RICHEST LAND HABITATS –
THE WOODLAND EDGE. AS SUCH, THEY PROVIDE PERFECT CONDITIONS
FOR A WIDE RANGE OF PASTORAL AND WOODLAND FUNGI.

Several fungus species love neatly manicured lawns. These include the Fairy Ring Champignon, which flushes several times over the course of the summer and early autumn following rainfall, although the characteristic green rings that so obviously mark the subterranean mycelia show up darker against the grass throughout the growing season.

Older parks are often rich in mature or even veteran trees. These are a prime target for opportunistic bracket and parasitic fungi such as the Chicken of the Woods, Beefsteak Fungus (page 32) and Cauliflower Fungus (page 92). Beneath the trees, flower beds provide surprisingly fertile hunting grounds for unlikely species. The main reason for this lies in the increasing use of mulches to reduce labour-intensive and costly weeding. Bark is particularly popular as a mulch, and this forest-based material is steeped in a huge variety of spores. As a consequence, woodland mushrooms frequently crop up in and around flower borders, which would otherwise be the last place to look for species such as Wood Blewits.

What you can find, and where

Borders
Bark mulches mimic the rich humus of the forest floor, providing ideal conditions for fungi such as Wood Blewits, which often spread to the neighbouring grass.

Trees

Many older parks contain mature trees. As these age, they become hosts to opportunistic invaders such as the Chicken of the Woods.

Lawns

Short-mown grass provides the perfect conditions for the Fairy Ring Champignon.

Shrubs

A rich mix of small trees provides the perfect conditions for the parasitic Honey Fungus.

Honey Fungus

This **parasitic and destructive** fungus is ubiquitous. Indeed, if anything it is more frequent in suburbia than it is in the wild. Gardeners hate it as a destructive parasite of trees and shrubs. It typically appears in clusters on stumps, but can also fruit from invisible lateral roots that snake out underground and may appear many metres away from the nearest potential host. The fruiting bodies are variable in colour and appearance, and tend to grow in clumps, which are usually yellow, orange or brown in colour with black flecking around the centres of the caps.

FACT FILE

SCIENTIFIC NAME
Armillaria mellea

OTHER NAMES Boot Lace Fungus, Enoki, Enotake

CAP Up to 12cm across. Yellow to brown, usually flecked with black.

STEM Hollow and fibrous, usually with the remains of a ring just below the cap. Similar in colour to the cap.

FLESH White.

SPORES White.

SEASON Late autumn and winter.

Horticulturalists and foresters have good reason to loathe this mushroom, for it invariably kills its host. While eating the fruiting bodies will not save a tree or shrub that is being parasitized by the Honey Fungus, at least it acts as some consolation for the loss. In its raw state the fungus is mildly poisonous, so it should be blanched in boiling water before cooking.

Key identifiers

Grows on dead and dying shrubs and trees.

Often appears in substantial clumps.

Caps very variable in colour.

Cap surface often flecked with tiny black spots.

Top of the stem usually has the remains of a cottony white-to-yellow ring below the cap.

Very common.

Taste

Fair to good. It must always be cooked, and eaten in moderation, because it is mildly toxic when raw.

Chicken of the Woods

With its bright egg-yolk yellow colour and lumpy appearance, the Chicken of the Woods is one of the most easily recognizable edible species. Indeed, there really is nothing that it can be mistaken for. Pale sulphurous buboes emerge from its host's trunk in early summer, swelling out from the bark of a mature tree to resemble a stack of yellow dinner plates. As this bracket fungus ages it generally turns from very light yellow to orange, before fading again to powdery white. The margin remains bright yellow as the fungus matures.

Harvest the Chicken of the Woods while it is still young and tender. One way to test its condition with ease is to note the texture as it is cut from the tree. When in prime condition this should be like chilled butter: the knife should almost slide through the flesh with moderate pressure. If a vigorous sawing action is required, the fungus will be as tough in a cooked dish.

FACT FILE

SCIENTIFIC NAME
Laetiporus sulphureus

OTHER NAME Sulphur Shelf

APPEARANCE Fruit body up to 40cm. Initially bulbous lumps, later turning into stacks of shelves.

STEM Yellow, slowly turning orange with age, before fading to white.

FLESH Firm, meat-like texture.

SPORES White, cream or pale yellow.

SEASON Late spring to autumn.

Key identifiers

Yellow colour and structure make it impossible to mistake.

Grows on deciduous trees, usually oak, willow and beech.

Avoid if Yew is the host, since every part of this tree is poisonous apart from the red flesh of its berries, or arils.

Can appear anywhere from ground level to high in the tree canopy.

Best when young and firm, becoming tough and powdery with age.

Taste

Although it does not taste like chicken, it has a great taste in its own right. While young and tender its firm texture, which it retains even when cooked slowly in a casserole, makes it a perfect meat substitute. It freezes fairly well due to its meaty structure.

Species profile   Chicken of the Woods   117

Wood Blewit

This striking mushroom has a brown-purple cap with lilac gills. The cap is domed at first, gradually flattening and losing some of its vivid colour. The Wood Blewitt is relatively common, often growing in large numbers in association with all types of tree, but confusingly it also grows in the open, well away from the nearest tree or shrub – perhaps pointing to a long-gone wood. Most autumn fungi are harmed by frost, but sub-zero temperatures actually trigger the mycelia of Wood Blewits into fruiting.

The fungi generally emerge with the first frosts, and in mild winters can grow well into the New Year.

This species has a powerful flavour that can upset some stomachs, so it should always be cooked, which breaks down the most indigestible proteins. Because of its strong flavour, it should be treated as a flavouring rather than as an ingredient in its own right.

FACT FILE

SCIENTIFIC NAME
Lepista nuda

OTHER NAME Pied bleu (French)

CAP Up to 12cm across. Blue to purple, fading to brown. At first domed, then flattening or even inverting slightly and acquiring wavy edges.

STEM Up to 10cm tall. Purple underside. Fairly uniform stem, sometimes slightly more bulbous at the base.

FLESH Purple to grey-brown.

SPORES Pink.

SEASON Late autumn to winter.

Key identifiers

Blue-purple cap, fading to brown.

Gills and stem keep their bright shade longer than the cap.

Grows in all types of woods, but also found in open fields.

Very common.

Taste

Excellent. Perfumed and powerful, and at its best when young and purple. A strongly flavoured mushroom that must always be cooked, it is generally best combined with red meats and powerful vegetables. It dries well.

Fairy Ring Champignon

Troupes of **Fairy Ring Champignons** love short-cropped grass. In the past this fungus was usually found on old and unimproved pasture, but nowadays it is most likely to be spotted on neatly mown suburban lawns, in city parks, and on golf courses and sports grounds. Due to this mushroom's beneficial release of nutrients to the surrounding grass, the rings are often clearly visible, even when no mushrooms are present. These characteristic rough circles slowly increase in diameter as the mycelium matures.

Fairy Ring Champignons flush throughout early and high summer,

but can also continue to crop into early autumn, particularly after rain (they rapidly dry out in hot weather). They are best harvested with scissors; the tough stems should be discarded. Care needs to be taken not to confuse the species with the potentially deadly False Fairy Ring (page 123).

FACT FILE

SCIENTIFIC NAME
Marasmius oreades

OTHER NAMES Fairy Ring Mushroom, Mousseron (French)

CAP Up to 5cm across. Tan, appearing in distinct rings in short grass.

STEM Up to 9cm tall. Thin and fibrous.

FLESH Delicate.

SPORES White, cream or pale yellow.

SEASON Late spring to autumn.

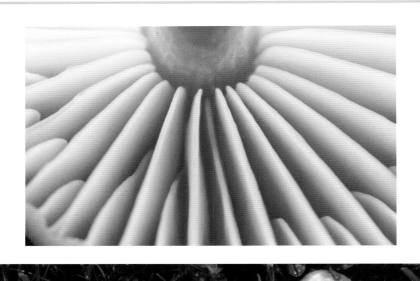

Key identifiers

Grows in rings.

Usually found in short grass (lawns and playing fields are favourites).

Always check the gill structure – the gills should curl up into the cap without touching the stem.

The gills of the deadly poisonous False Fairy Ring curl down and are attached to the stem.

Quick tips

Look for dark rings in short grass that are visible even when no mushrooms are present.

Grows from summer to autumn.

Taste

Excellent. The delicate flavour superbly complements lighter flavours such as those of white fish and meat. The fungus can be dried, bottled or frozen, but it is definitely best eaten fresh.

The lookalike

The poisonous False Fairy Ring (*Clitocybe rivulosa*) can look very similar to the Fairy Ring Champignon. In addition, rather alarmingly it grows in rings in close proximity to or even overlapping those of the edible species. The poisonous version is normally paler – almost waxlike in shade – and tends to have a flatter cap, but there is still a significant overlap in appearance between the two species.

Fortunately it is very easy to tell the two species apart by looking at the gills. Those of the edible species have a distinctive pattern of varying lengths, with shorter and mid-length ones alternating between the longest structures. More importantly, they always curl up into the cap and never quite meet the stem. By contrast, the gills of the False Fairy Ring curve down towards the ground and are firmly attached to the stem.

Preserving mushrooms

ONE OF THE DRAWBACKS OF THE MUSHROOM YEAR IS THAT IT IS
MARKED BY SUDDEN GLUTS FOLLOWED BY LONG FAMINES. ONE
MOMENT THE WOODS AND FIELDS ARE FILLED WITH MORE
MUSHROOMS THAN YOU CAN POSSIBLY CONSUME, THE NEXT THEY
ARE COMPLETELY DEVOID OF ANYTHING. THERE IS MUCH TO BE SAID
FOR ADOPTING THE SEASONAL EATING HABITS OF OUR ANCESTORS
AND GLUTTING ON THE FRESH BOUNTY UNTIL YOU ARE BORED
SENSELESS, THEN WAITING FOR THE NEXT HARVEST THE FOLLOWING
YEAR. THIS IS PARTICULARLY TRUE WHEN IT COMES TO SOME
FLAVOURSOME BUT VERY PERISHABLE OR DELICATE FUNGI SUCH AS
INKCAPS, PUFFBALLS AND PARASOLS. MANY OTHER FUNGI PRESERVE
WELL, HOWEVER, ALTHOUGH THE PRESERVATION METHOD AND
LEVEL OF SUCCESS VARY WIDELY BETWEEN SPECIES.

Drying

This works particularly well with fungi
such as the boletes (like the Porcini
shown on the right), where the process
not only prolongs the mushrooms
almost indefinitely, but also positively
improves their flavour. Drying is a
well-established food-preservation
technique in hot and dry climates,
but for obvious reasons it is less
culturally established in many cooler
and damper parts throughout the
northern hemisphere.

In reality drying is easy to carry out
virtually anywhere, providing you
follow the basic rules of circulating as

much dry air as possible around the fungi when drying them. It is possible to dry small specimens whole, but speed is of the essence (microscopic fungi in the form of moulds start to attack bigger specimens as soon as they are harvested), so large fungi should be thinly sliced. The slices need to be spread out across a wire rack or threaded on to cotton, making sure they do not touch. They should then be placed above a very gentle heat source – suspended above a stove or radiator, for example, or placed in an airing cupboard.

There is a considerable number of drying machines on the market, but many of these tend to be geared towards drying more challenging produce such as meat, fruits and vegetables. Because of this, they can be too hot for drying fungi, even at their lowest settings, and end up toasting them. Some sources suggest drying mushrooms in an oven on its lowest heat with the door open, but this technique also tends to be too fierce. Keen woodworkers can try sun-drying mushrooms in a miniature greenhouse that incorporates plenty of ventilation to ensure a good airflow around the fungi.

Preserving in butter

Many of the more delicate mushrooms, such as the Chanterelle (above) and Wood Hedgehog, lose their aromatic qualities when dried. Potting in butter is therefore a better way to keep them fresh for up to a month or two. Clean the mushrooms, chop them finely and weigh them before melting an equal weight of unsalted butter in a pan. Fry the mushrooms in the butter with a little garlic for 3–4 minutes. Stir in a small pinch of paprika and perhaps some tomato purée, before tipping while still hot into sterile jars and sealing tightly. The mushrooms should keep for several weeks in a refrigerator and may be used either as a flavouring or as a spread on toast.

Preserving in oil

Italians are particularly fond of preserving bolete mixtures in olive oil for use as antipasti, although the texture of such preserves can be rather too slimy for some tastes. Wipe clean the fungi and dunk them briefly in vinegar before carefully packing them in jars. Add olive oil to cover and tap the jars repeatedly to lose any air bubbles. Place the jars in a very low oven with the lids loosely in place. After 30 minutes, remove the jars from the oven and tighten the lids. The fungi should keep for several months.

Pickling

Many people feel that vinegar overpowers the delicate flavour of most fungi, but pickling is a favourite in much of central Europe. Boil up sufficient cider vinegar to cover the fungi, together with bay leaves, spices and salt. Pour over cleaned and roughly chopped fungi that have been layered in jars. Place in an oven on its lowest setting for 30 minutes, then remove and tighten the lids to seal the jars.

Ketchup (katsup)

The essence of a wild harvest can be stored as a liquor. This method works particularly well with prolific species such as members of the *Suillus* genus (like the Larch Bolete pictured above, right). Layer sliced mushrooms in a

crock with a thin covering of salt between each layer. After three days, press the pile lightly. Strain the resulting liquid through cheesecloth, bring it to a boil and bottle it.

Freezing

Most fungi have a high water content, so that sub-zero temperatures make them soggy. However, this is not a concern in many recipes, and fungi can be flash fried with a few chopped shallots and garlic, then frozen in small containers. For use in cooking, they can be defrosted and tipped into casseroles, omelettes and risottos.

Preserving mushrooms